REVISE PEARSON EDEXCEL A LEVEL
Mathematics
REVISION WORKBOOK

Series Consultant: Harry Smith

Author: Glyn Payne

Notes from the publisher

While the publishers have made every attempt to ensure that advice on the qualification and its assessment is accurate, the official specification and associated assessment guidance materials are the only authoritative source of information and should always be referred to for definitive guidance.

Pearson examiners have not contributed to any sections in this resource relevant to examination papers for which they have responsibility.

Also available to support your revision:

Revise A Level Revision Planner   9781292191546

The **Revise A Level Revision Planner** helps you to plan and organise your time, step-by-step, throughout your A level revision. Use this book and wall chart to mastermind your revision.

For the full range of Pearson revision titles across KS2, KS3, GCSE, Functional Skills, AS/A Level and BTEC visit: www.pearsonschools.co.uk/revise

Contents

A small bit of small print

Pearson Edexcel publishes Sample Assessment Material and the Specification on its website. This is the official content and this book should be used in conjunction with it. The questions in this book have been written to help you practise every topic in the book. Remember: the real exam questions may not look like this.

Index laws

1 Express $25^{-\frac{3}{2}}$ in the form 5^n (2)

....

Guided **2** Express $\sqrt{3}\left(27^{\frac{2}{3}}\right)$ in the form 3^x (2)

$\sqrt{3}\left(27^{\frac{2}{3}}\right) = 3^{\cdots} \times \left(27^{\cdots}\right)^2 =$ .... = ...

3 Simplify $3x\left(2x^{-\frac{3}{4}}\right)$ (2)

....

4 Simplify $\dfrac{20x^{\frac{5}{3}}}{4x}$ (2)

....

Guided **5** Simplify fully $\dfrac{\left(3x^{\frac{1}{2}}\right)^3}{9x^3}$ (3)

$\dfrac{\left(3x^{\frac{1}{2}}\right)^3}{9x^3} = \dfrac{\cdots\cdots\cdots}{9x^3} =$ .... = ...

> First simplify the numerator.

6 Write $\dfrac{3 - x^{\frac{3}{2}}}{\sqrt{x}}$ in the form $3x^p - x^q$ where p and q are constants. (2)

....

....

....

7 Solve $3^{2x+1} \times 9^x = 27$ (2)

....

....

....

> Write both sides of the equation as powers of 3 to find x.

8 Solve $2^{2x-3} \times 4^{x+2} = 8$ (4)

....

....

....

9 Write $\dfrac{6\sqrt{x} + 4x^{-\frac{3}{2}}}{2x^3}$ in the form $3x^p + 2x^q$ where p and q are constants. (2)

....

....

....

....

Expanding and factorising

> **Guided** 1 Expand $(x - 1)(x + 2)^2$ **(2)**

$(x - 1)(x + 2)^2 = (x - 1)(x^2 \dots\dots\dots\dots\dots\dots)$

....

....

> First expand $(x + 2)^2$.

> Multiply out and collect like terms, then multiply by $(x - 1)$.

> **Guided** 2 Factorise completely $x^3 - 9x$ **(2)**

$x^3 - 9x = x(x^2 \dots\dots\dots)$

....

....

> First take out the common factor. Then factorise the expression inside the brackets.

3 Expand $(x - 4)(x + 2)(x - 1)$ **(2)**

....

....

....

4 Factorise completely $x^3 + 4x^2 - 5x$ **(3)**

....

....

....

5 Show that $(2 - 3\sqrt{x})^2$ can be written as $4 - k\sqrt{x} + 9x$ where k is a constant. **(2)**

....

....

....

6 Given that $f(x) = (x^2 - 4x)(x + 3) + 6x$

(a) express $f(x)$ in the form $x(ax^2 + bx + c)$ where a, b and c are constants. **(3)**

....

....

....

(b) Hence factorise $f(x)$ completely. **(2)**

....

....

Surds

1 Write $\sqrt{72}$ in the form $a\sqrt{2}$ where a is an integer. **(2)**

....

Guided

2 Simplify $\sqrt{18} + \sqrt{50}$, giving your answer in the form $a\sqrt{b}$ where a and b are integers. **(2)**

$$\sqrt{18} + \sqrt{50} = \sqrt{9 \times 2} + \sqrt{25 \times 2}$$

$$= 3 \times \sqrt{2} + \text{.........................}$$

....

Guided

3 Express $\dfrac{\sqrt{5} + 3}{\sqrt{5} - 2}$ in the form $a + b\sqrt{5}$

where a and b are integers. **(4)**

> Insert brackets and rationalise the denominator.

> Multiply out the brackets in the numerator and the denominator.

$$\frac{\sqrt{5} + 3}{\sqrt{5} - 2} = \frac{(\sqrt{5} + 3)(\sqrt{5} \text{ ....})}{(\sqrt{5} - 2)(\sqrt{5} \text{ ....})}$$

....

....

....

....

4 Express $\sqrt{75} + \dfrac{21}{\sqrt{3}}$ in the form $a\sqrt{3}$ where a is an integer. **(3)**

....

....

> Rationalise the denominator in the second term.

....

5 $(9 + a\sqrt{2})(3 - \sqrt{2}) = 23 - b\sqrt{2}$ where a and b are integers.

Find the values of a and b. **(4)**

....

....

6 $(c - \sqrt{3})^2 = d - 14\sqrt{3}$ where c and d are integers.

Find the values of c and d. **(3)**

....

....

7 Write $\dfrac{3(2 - \sqrt{5})}{2 + \sqrt{5}}$ in the form $a\sqrt{5} + b$ where a and b are integers. **(4)**

....

....

....

Quadratic equations

1　Solve $3(x-1)^2 + 8x - 11 = 0$　　　　　　　　　　　　　　　　　　(3)

....

....

....

....

> **Guided**

2　Given that $f(x) = x^2 - 10x + 15$

(a) express $f(x)$ in the form $(x+a)^2 + b$ where a and b are integers.　(3)

$x^2 - 10x + 15 = (x\,..............)^2 - ....\ + 15$ 　　　　　　| $2a = -10$ |

$= ....$ 　　　　　　| Subtract a^2. |

....

(b) Hence, or otherwise, show that the roots of $x^2 - 10x + 15 = 0$ are $c \pm d\sqrt{10}$,
where c and d are integers to be found.　　　　　　　　　　(3)

$(x\,..............)^2 - ....\ = 0$ 　　　　| Rearrange into completed square form, then square root both sides. |

$(x\,..............)^2 = ...$

$x\,.............. = ...$ 　　　　| Any positive number has two square roots. |

....

....

....

3　$8x - 6 - x^2 = q - (x+p)^2$ where p and q are integers. Find the values of p and q.　(3)

....

....　　| **Problem solving** Complete the square on the LHS or expand the RHS and equate coefficients. |

....

....

....

....

4　$3x^2 + 6x + 5 = a(x+b)^2 + c$ where a, b and c are integers. Find the values of a, b and c.　(3)

....

....　　| **Problem solving** Complete the square on the LHS or expand the RHS and equate coefficients. |

....

....

....

....

Functions and roots

Guided 1   Solve $2x^4 - x^2 - 28 = 0$ (4)

Let $u = x^2$, then $2u^2 - \text{..........} - \text{..........} = 0$, $(2u \text{..........})(u \text{..........}) = 0$

so $2u \text{..........} = 0$ or $u \text{..........} = 0$, giving $u = \text{..........}$ or $u = \text{..........}$

So, using $u = x^2$, $x^2 = -\text{..........}$ but x^2 cannot be negative

so $x^2 = \text{..........}$, giving $x = \text{..........}$ or $x = \text{..........}$

> Solve for u.

2   Solve $63x^3 = 8 - 8x^6$ (4)

> Use $u = x^3$

3   Solve $2x - 13\sqrt{x} + 15 = 0$ (4)

> Use $u = \sqrt{x}$

4   Solve $x - 5\sqrt{x} = 24$ (4)

5   $f(x) = 4x^4 + 5x^2 - 6$ $x \in \mathbb{R}, x < 0$

Show that $f(x) = 0$ has only one root and determine its exact value.   (4)

6   Solve $x + 2\sqrt{x} = 7$, giving your answer in the form $a - b\sqrt{2}$ where a and b are integers to be found.   (5)

Sketching quadratics

Guided 1 Sketch the curve with equation $y = (x - 3)(x + 2)$, showing clearly the coordinates of any points where the curve crosses the coordinate axes. **(3)**

When $x = 0$, $y = (0 - 3)(0 + 2)$

$= \ldots\ldots\ldots$

When $y = 0$, $0 = (x - 3)(x + 2)$

so $x = \ldots\ldots\ldots$ or $x = \ldots\ldots\ldots$

Guided 2 Sketch the curve with equation $y = (x + 3)^2 + 4$, showing clearly the coordinates of any points where the curve crosses the coordinate axes. **(3)**

The coordinates of the vertex

are ($\ldots\ldots\ldots$, $\ldots\ldots\ldots$)

When $x = 0$, $y = (0 + 3)^2 + 4$

$= \ldots\ldots\ldots$

> The curve with equation $y = (x + a)^2 + b$ has a **vertex** at $(-a, b)$.

3 Sketch the curve with equation $y = x(5 - x)$, showing clearly the coordinates of any points where the curve crosses the coordinate axes. **(3)**

$\ldots\ldots\ldots\ldots\ldots\ldots\ldots\ldots\ldots\ldots\ldots\ldots\ldots\ldots\ldots\ldots\ldots\ldots\ldots$

$\ldots\ldots\ldots\ldots\ldots\ldots\ldots\ldots\ldots\ldots\ldots\ldots\ldots\ldots\ldots\ldots\ldots\ldots\ldots$

$\ldots\ldots\ldots\ldots\ldots\ldots\ldots\ldots\ldots\ldots\ldots\ldots\ldots\ldots\ldots\ldots\ldots\ldots\ldots$

$\ldots\ldots\ldots\ldots\ldots\ldots\ldots\ldots\ldots\ldots\ldots\ldots\ldots\ldots\ldots\ldots\ldots\ldots\ldots$

$\ldots\ldots\ldots\ldots\ldots\ldots\ldots\ldots\ldots\ldots\ldots\ldots\ldots\ldots\ldots\ldots\ldots\ldots\ldots$

4 $f(x) = 3x^2 - 12x + 17$

(a) Write $f(x)$ in the form $3(x - a)^2 + b$ where a and b are integers to be determined. **(3)**

$\ldots\ldots\ldots\ldots\ldots\ldots\ldots\ldots\ldots\ldots\ldots\ldots\ldots\ldots\ldots\ldots\ldots\ldots\ldots\ldots\ldots\ldots\ldots\ldots\ldots\ldots\ldots\ldots\ldots\ldots\ldots\ldots\ldots\ldots\ldots\ldots$

$\ldots\ldots\ldots\ldots\ldots\ldots\ldots\ldots\ldots\ldots\ldots\ldots\ldots\ldots\ldots\ldots\ldots\ldots\ldots\ldots\ldots\ldots\ldots\ldots\ldots\ldots\ldots\ldots\ldots\ldots\ldots\ldots\ldots\ldots\ldots\ldots$

(b) Sketch the graph of $y = f(x)$, labelling the minimum point and any points of intersection with the axes. **(3)**

$\ldots\ldots\ldots\ldots\ldots\ldots\ldots\ldots\ldots\ldots\ldots\ldots\ldots\ldots\ldots\ldots\ldots\ldots\ldots$

$\ldots\ldots\ldots\ldots\ldots\ldots\ldots\ldots\ldots\ldots\ldots\ldots\ldots\ldots\ldots\ldots\ldots\ldots\ldots$

$\ldots\ldots\ldots\ldots\ldots\ldots\ldots\ldots\ldots\ldots\ldots\ldots\ldots\ldots\ldots\ldots\ldots\ldots\ldots$

$\ldots\ldots\ldots\ldots\ldots\ldots\ldots\ldots\ldots\ldots\ldots\ldots\ldots\ldots\ldots\ldots\ldots\ldots\ldots$

$\ldots\ldots\ldots\ldots\ldots\ldots\ldots\ldots\ldots\ldots\ldots\ldots\ldots\ldots\ldots\ldots\ldots\ldots\ldots$

(c) Use your graph to explain why the equation $3x^2 - 12x + 17 = 0$ has no real solutions. **(1)**

$\ldots\ldots\ldots\ldots\ldots\ldots\ldots\ldots\ldots\ldots\ldots\ldots\ldots\ldots\ldots\ldots\ldots\ldots\ldots\ldots\ldots\ldots\ldots\ldots\ldots\ldots\ldots\ldots\ldots\ldots\ldots\ldots\ldots\ldots\ldots\ldots$

The discriminant

Guided **1** The equation $x^2 - 2px + p = 0$, where p is a non-zero constant, has equal roots.
Find the value of p. **(4)**

$a = 1, b = -2p, c = $ ....

> Identify the values of a, b and c.

$b^2 - 4ac = (-2p)^2 - 4 \times 1 \times$ ....

....

> **Problem solving** For equal roots, $b^2 - 4ac = 0$. Then solve to find p.

....

....

....

Guided **2** The equation $3x^2 + kx - 5 = k$ has no real solutions for x. Show that $k^2 + 12k + 60 < 0$ **(3)**

$3x^2 + kx - 5$ .... $= 0$

> Write in the form $ax^2 + bx + c = 0$ before identifying the values of a, b and c.

$a = 3, b = k, c = $ ....

$b^2 - 4ac = (k)^2 - 4 \times 3 \times$ ....

> **Problem solving** For no real roots, $b^2 - 4ac < 0$.

....

....

....

3 Find the value of the discriminant of $3x - 7 - x^2$ **(2)**

....

....

....

4 $f(x) = x^2 + (p - 4)x - 3p$ where p is a constant.

(a) Find the discriminant of $f(x)$ in terms of p. **(2)**

....

....

....

(b) Show that the discriminant can be written in the form $(p + a)^2 + b$ where a and b are integers to be found. **(2)**

....

....

....

(c) Show that, for all values of p, the equation $f(x) = 0$ has distinct real roots. **(2)**

> **Problem solving** Complete the square of the expression for the discriminant. Show this will always be ≥ 0.

....

....

....

Modelling with quadratics

Guided   **1**   A river cruise boat is sailing on a 60 km round trip.

It leaves the pier and sails 30 km upstream (against the current) before sailing back downstream (with the current) to the pier.

The total time for the trip is 3 hours.

The river flows at a speed of 5.5 km/h.

(a) Given that the speed of the boat in still water is u km/h, write down two expressions, in terms of u, for the times t_1 and t_2 of the journeys upstream and downstream respectively. **(3)**

Relative speed upstream = speed of boat − speed of current = ... km/h

Time to travel upstream, $t_1 = \dfrac{\text{distance}}{\text{relative speed}} = \dfrac{30}{............}$ hours

Relative speed downstream = ... km/h

so $t_2 = \dfrac{\text{distance}}{\text{relative speed}} = \dfrac{30}{............}$ hours

(b) Form an equation in u and rearrange it into the form $au^2 + bu + c = 0$ where a, b and c are numbers to be determined. **(3)**

$\dfrac{30}{............} + \dfrac{30}{............} = 3$

.... = ...

.... = ... so .... = 0

(c) By completing the square, or otherwise, determine the value of u.
Hence find the values of t_1 and t_2 to the nearest minute. **(5)**

....

....

....

....

2   A football is kicked from the ground at an angle of 32° above the horizontal and with a speed of 27 m s⁻¹. Its height h above the ground at time t can be modelled by the equation $h = 14.3t - 5t^2$ where t represents the time it is in the air.

(a) For how long is the ball in the air? **(2)**

> **Problem solving** When the ball hits the ground, $h = 0$

....

....

(b) By completing the square, or otherwise, determine the maximum height of the ball above the ground during its flight. **(4)**

> Re-write the equation as $h = -5(t^2 - kt)$, where k is a constant.

....

....

....

....

Simultaneous equations

Guided 1 Solve the simultaneous equations

$$x - y = 3 \qquad ①$$
$$x^2 - 2y = 6 \qquad ② \qquad \textbf{(5)}$$

> Number the equations to keep track of your working.

$$y = \text{.....................} \qquad ③$$

> Rearrange ① to write y in terms of x and substitute in ②.

$$x^2 - 2(\text{.....................}) = 6$$

$$\text{.....................................} = 6$$

$$\text{.....................................} = 0$$

> Solve the quadratic to find the two values of x.
> Substitute into ③ to find the corresponding values of y.

....

2 (a) By eliminating y from the equations $y = x + 8$

$$xy + 3x^2 = 16$$

show that $x^2 + 2x - 4 = 0$ **(2)**

....

....

(b) Hence, or otherwise, solve the simultaneous equations $y = x + 8$

$$xy + 3x^2 = 16$$

giving your answers in the form $a \pm b\sqrt{5}$, where a and b are integers. **(3)**

....

....

....

3 The quadratic curve C has the equation $y = x^2 - 10x + 21$, and the line L has the equation $y = 5 - 2x$.

(a) Find the coordinates of any points of intersection of C and L. **(5)**

....

....

....

....

(b) Sketch the graphs of C and L on the same axes
and explain how the sketch supports your
answer to part (a). **(4)**

....

....

....

....

....

....

Inequalities

Guided **1** Find the set of values of x for which

(a) $2(x - 3) < 4 - 3x$ **(2)**

$2x - 6 < 4 - 3x$

> Expand the brackets and rearrange to make x the subject.

$5x <$ .... so $x <$ ....

(b) $(2x - 5)(2 + x) < 0$ **(3)**

$(2x - 5)(2 + x) = 0$

> Make equal to zero and solve to find where the graph of $y = (2x - 5)(2 + x)$ crosses the x-axis.

So $x =$ .... or $x =$ ....

....

> Identify the range of values of x which makes $y < 0$.

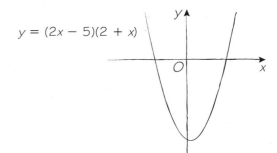

$y = (2x - 5)(2 + x)$

(c) both $2(x - 3) < 4 - 3x$ and $(2x - 5)(2 + x) < 0$

.... $< x <$ .... **(2)**

> The values where the inequalities **overlap** are the values which satisfy them both.

2 (a) Find the set of values of x for which $x^2 - 8x + 15 > 0$ **(3)**

....

....

(b) Sketch the curve with equation $y = x^2 - 8x + 15$. Show on your sketch the coordinates at which the curve meets the x-axis to illustrate your answer to part (a). **(1)**

....

....

3 The equation $x^2 + 2kx + (3 - 2k) = 0$, where k is a constant, has different real roots.

(a) Show that $k^2 + 2k - 3 > 0$ **(2)**

....

....

(b) Find the set of possible values of k. **(3)**

....

....

4 Find the set of values of p for which the equation $x^2 - 2px - (p - 6) = 0$ has no real solutions. **(5)**

....

....

....

Inequalities on graphs

Guided 1 (a) Sketch the graphs of $y = 2x^2 + 3x - 5$ and $y = 2x + 1$ on the same axes, showing any points of intersection with the coordinate axes. **(4)**

$2x^2 + 3x - 5 = 0,$ $(2x\text{.............})(x\text{.............}) = 0$

$x = \text{.............}$ and $x = \text{.............}$

When $x = 0,$ $y = \text{.............}$

For $y = 2x + 1,$

graph crosses y-axis when $x = 0,$ so $y = \text{.............}$

graph crosses x-axis when $y = 0,$ so $x = \text{.............}$

(b) Determine the coordinates of the points of intersection of the two graphs. **(4)**

$2x^2 + 3x - 5 = 2x + 1,$ $2x^2\text{.....................} = 0,$ $(2x\text{.............})(x\text{.............}) = 0$

$x = \text{.............}$ and $x = \text{.............}$

When $x = \text{.............},$ $y = \text{.............}$ and when $x = \text{.............},$ $y = \text{.............}$

(c) Solve the inequality $2x^2 + 3x - 5 \geqslant 2x + 1$ **(1)**

....

2 $f(x) = 6 - 5x - x^2,$ $g(x) = -4 - 2x$

(a) Find the coordinates of the points of intersection of the two functions. **(4)**

....

....

(b) On the grid, draw the graphs of $y = f(x)$ and $y = g(x)$. Show the coordinates of the points at which the graphs meet the axes. **(4)**

....

....

....

....

....

....

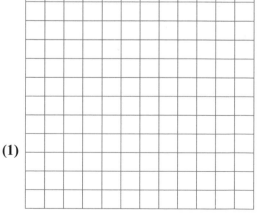

(c) Solve the inequality $f(x) > g(x)$ **(1)**

....

....

(d) Shade the region on the graph that satisfies all of the following inequalities:

$y \leqslant f(x),$ $y \geqslant g(x),$ $x \leqslant -2$ **(2)**

Cubic and quartic graphs

Guided **1** The curve C has the equation $y = x(x + 2)(x - 5)$. Sketch C, showing clearly the coordinates of the points where the curve meets the coordinate axes. **(4)**

When $y = 0$, $0 = x(x + 2)(x - 5)$ so $x = $ .... or $x = $ .... or $x = $ ....

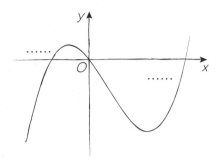

> The curve crosses the x-axis at the values of x which make each factor equal to 0.

> As x is a factor of $x(x + 2)(x - 5)$, the curve C will pass through the origin.

Guided **2** The curve C has the equation $y = (x + 1)^2(3 - x)$. Sketch C, showing clearly the coordinates of the points where the curve meets the coordinate axes. **(4)**

When $y = 0$, $0 = (x + 1)^2(3 - x)$ so $x = $ .... or $x = $ ....

When $x = 0$, $y = (0 + 1)^2(3 - 0) = $ ....

> As the factor $(x + 1)$ is repeated, the curve touches the x-axis at $x = -1$.

> Work out the point where the curve crosses the y-axis by setting $x = 0$.

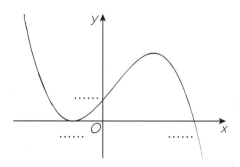

> As the coefficient of x^3 is negative, the shape of the curve will be 'upside down'.

3 The curve C has the equation $y = (x - 1)(x + 2)(x - 4)$. Sketch C, showing clearly the coordinates of the points where the curve meets the coordinate axes. **(4)**

....

....

....

4 Sketch the graph of $y = x(x + 4)(3x^2 - 11x + 6)$
Show clearly the coordinates of any intersections with the axes. **(4)**

....

....

....

Transformations 1

1 The diagram shows a sketch of a curve with equation $y = f(x)$. The curve has a maximum point at $(-2, 4)$ and a minimum point at $(0, 0)$.

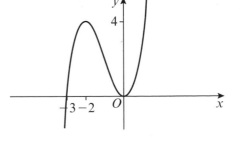

On the same diagram, sketch the curve with equation

(a) $f(x - 2)$ **(3)**

> $f(x + a)$ is a translation of $f(x)$ by $\begin{pmatrix} -a \\ 0 \end{pmatrix}$

(b) $f(-x)$ **(3)**

> $f(-x)$ is a reflection of $f(x)$ in the y-axis.

On each sketch, show clearly the coordinates of the maximum and minimum points and any points of intersection with the axes.

2 The diagram shows a sketch of a curve with equation $y = f(x)$.
The curve has a minimum point at $(4, -16)$.
On separate diagrams, sketch the curve with equation

(a) $y = 3f(x)$ **(3)**

> $af(x)$ is a stretch, scale factor a, of $f(x)$ in the y-direction.

(b) $y = -f(x)$ **(3)**

> $-f(x)$ is a reflection of $f(x)$ in the x-axis.

(c) $y = f(2x)$ **(3)**

> $f(ax)$ is a stretch, scale factor $\frac{1}{a}$, of $f(x)$ in the x-direction.

On each sketch, show clearly the coordinates of the minimum point and any points of intersection with the axes.

The curve with equation $y = f(x + k)$ has a minimum point on the y-axis.

(d) What is the value of k? **(1)**

....

Transformations 2

1 The diagram shows a sketch of part of the curve with equation $y = f(x)$.

The curve has a minimum point at $(2, -5)$ and an asymptote with equation $y = -1$

On separate diagrams, sketch the curve with equation

(a) $y = f(x) + 3$ **(2)**

(b) $y = 3f(x)$ **(2)**

(c) $y = f(x - 1)$ **(3)**

On each diagram, show clearly the coordinates of the minimum point, and the asymptote with its equation.

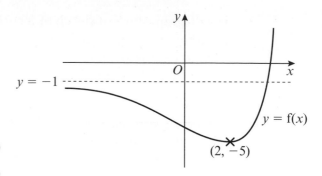

> The asymptote is horizontal so it is only transformed by a transformation in the y-direction.

2 The diagram shows a sketch of the curve with equation $y = f(x)$ where $f(x) = \dfrac{3x}{x - 1}$, $x \neq 1$

The curve has asymptotes with equations $y = 3$ and $x = 1$

(a) Sketch the curve with equation $y = f(x - 3)$ and state the equations of its asymptotes. **(3)**

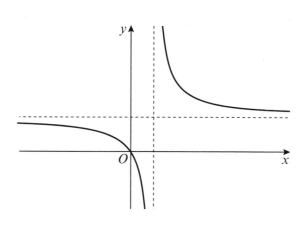

(b) Find the coordinates of the points where the curve with equation $y = f(x - 3)$ crosses the coordinate axes. **(3)**

....

....

....

Reciprocal graphs

1   The diagram shows a sketch of the
    curve with equation $y = \dfrac{4}{x}$, $x \neq 0$

    (a) On a separate diagram, sketch the
        curve with equation $y = \dfrac{4}{x-1}$, $x \neq 1$,
        showing any asymptotes and the coordinates
        of any point at which the curve crosses
        a coordinate axis.   **(3)**

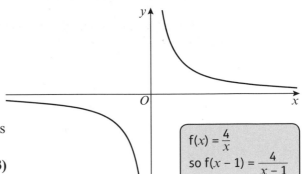

$f(x) = \dfrac{4}{x}$

so $f(x-1) = \dfrac{4}{x-1}$

    (b) Write down the equations of the asymptotes of the curve in part (a).   **(2)**

    ....

2   (a) Sketch the graph of $y = -\dfrac{8}{x^2}$, $x \neq 0$ **(2)**

> Leave your answers
> in surd form where
> appropriate.

    (b) On a separate diagram, sketch the graph of $y = -\dfrac{8}{x^2} + 4$, $x \neq 0$

        Write down the equations of any asymptotes and the coordinates of any intersections of
        the graph with the axes.   **(3)**

    ....

    (c) On a separate diagram, sketch the graph of $y = -\dfrac{8}{(x-2)^2}$, $x \neq 2$

        Write down the equations of any asymptotes and the coordinates of any intersections of
        the graph with the axes.   **(3)**

    ....

Points of intersection

Guided 1 The curve C has equation $y = -\dfrac{3}{x}$ and the line l has equation $x + y + 2 = 0$

(a) On the same axes, sketch the graphs of C and l, indicating clearly the coordinates of any intersections with the axes. **(3)**

....

....

....

....

....

....

(b) Find the coordinates of the points of intersection of C and l. **(6)**

$y = -x - 2$

$-\dfrac{3}{x} = -x - 2$

> Rearrange the linear equation to $y = -x - 2$.
> The x-coordinates at the points of intersection are the solutions to the equation $-\dfrac{3}{x} = -x - 2$.

....

....

....

....

2 (a) On the same axes, sketch the graphs of the curves with equation

(i) $y = x^2(x + 2)$

(ii) $y = x(4 - x)$

and indicate on your sketches the coordinates of all the points where the curves cross the x-axis. **(6)**

....

....

....

....

....

(b) Use algebra to find the coordinates of the points where the graphs intersect. **(7)**

....

....

....

....

....

....

....

Equations of lines

1   The line L has equation $y = 7 - 3x$

Show that the point $(3, -2)$ lies on L.   **(1)**

....

> **Guided**   **2**   The line L has equation $2x + 7y - 3 = 0$

Find the gradient of L.   **(2)**

> Rearrange the equation to make y the subject.

$7y = $ ....

$y = $ ....

Gradient $= $ ....

> The equation of a straight line can be written in the form $y = mx + c$, where m is the gradient of the line, and c is the point where it crosses the y-axis.

> **Guided**   **3**   The line L passes through the point A $(3, -2)$ and has gradient $-\frac{1}{3}$

Find an equation of L, giving your answer in the form $y = mx + c$ **(3)**

> If a straight line has gradient m and passes through the point (x_1, y_1), then you can write its equation as $y - y_1 = m(x - x_1)$.

> Remember to write the answer in the form asked for in the question.

$x_1 = $ .... $y_1 = $ .... $m = $ ....

$y - $ .... $= $ .... $(x - $ ....$)$

....

....

> **Guided**   **4**   The points A $(-2, 1)$ and B $(6, -2)$ lie on the line L.

(a)   Find the gradient of the line L.   **(2)**

> If a straight line has gradient m and passes through the points (x_1, y_1) and (x_2, y_2), then $m = \dfrac{y_2 - y_1}{x_2 - x_1}$

$x_1 = $ .... $y_1 = $ .... $x_2 = $ .... $y_2 = $ ....

$m = \dfrac{y_2 - y_1}{x_2 - x_1} = \dfrac{............}{............} = $ ....

(b)   Find an equation for L in the form $ax + by + c = 0$, where a, b and c are integers.   **(2)**

....

....

....

5   (a)   The line L has equation $3y = 4x + p$. The point A $(2, 3)$ lies on L.

Find the value of the constant p.   **(1)**

....

(b)   Find an equation for the straight line joining the points A $(2, 3)$ and B $(-1, 7)$ in the form $ax + by + c = 0$, where a, b and c are integers.   **(4)**

....

....

....

....

Parallel and perpendicular

Guided 1 The line L has equation $y = 4 - 3x$

(a) Show that the point P (3, −5) lies on L. **(1)**

....

(b) Find an equation of the line perpendicular to L, which passes through P.
Give your answer in the form $ax + by + c = 0$, where a, b and c are integers. **(4)**

> If the gradient of one line is a fraction, the gradient of a perpendicular line is found by turning the fraction upside down and changing the sign.

Gradient of L = ...

Gradient of perpendicular line = ...

Equation of perpendicular line through (3, −5) is ....

....

....

Guided 2 The points P and Q have coordinates (−2, 5) and (6, 3) respectively.

(a) Find the coordinates of the midpoint of PQ. **(1)**

Coordinates of midpoint are

$\left(\dfrac{-2 + 6}{2}, \dfrac{............}{2}\right)$ = ...

> The coordinates of the midpoint of the line segment joining the points (x_1, y_1) and (x_2, y_2) are $\left(\dfrac{x_1 + x_2}{2}, \dfrac{y_1 + y_2}{2}\right)$.

(b) The line l is perpendicular to PQ and passes through the midpoint of PQ.
Find an equation for l, giving your answer in the form $ax + by + c = 0$, where a, b and c are integers. **(4)**

....

....

....

....

3 The line l_1 has equation $3x + 4y - 5 = 0$
The line l_2 is perpendicular to l_1 and passes through the point (1, 3).

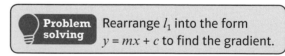

> **Problem solving** Rearrange l_1 into the form $y = mx + c$ to find the gradient.

Find the equation of l_2 in the form $y = mx + c$, where m and c are constants. **(5)**

....

....

....

....

....

Lengths and areas

1 A is the point $(-1, 6)$ and B is the point $(3, -2)$.
The length of AB is $p\sqrt{5}$, where p is an integer.
Find the value of p.   **(3)**

> Draw a sketch showing the positions of points A and B and use Pythagoras' theorem.

....

....

....

....

Guided

2   The line l_1 has equation $y = x + 1$
The line l_2 has equation $x + 3y - 15 = 0$
l_1 and l_2 intersect at the point A.

(a) Find the coordinates of A.   **(3)**

$x + 3(x + 1) - 15 = 0$

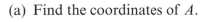
$x + 3x +$ ....

> Start by solving the equations simultaneously.

....

....

l_1 crosses the x-axis at the point B.
l_2 crosses the x-axis at the point C.

(b) Find the area of triangle ABC.   **(3)**

> Substitute $y = 0$ into the equations to find the x-coordinates of B and C, then use Area $= \frac{1}{2} \times$ base $\times$ height.

....

....

3   The line l_1 has equation $3x - 2y + 18 = 0$
The line l_2 is perpendicular to l_1 and passes through the point $(1, 4)$.
Find the area of the triangle formed by the lines l_1, l_2 and the x-axis.   **(9)**

....

....

....

....

....

....

....

....

....

....

....

Equation of a circle

1 A circle C has centre $(4, -1)$ and radius 6.

Write down the equation of the circle in the form $(x - a)^2 + (y - b)^2 = r^2$ **(2)**

....

Guided 2 The circle C has centre $(2, 3)$ and passes through the point $(-1, 7)$.

(a) Find an equation for C. **(4)**

$r = \sqrt{(-1 - 2)^2 + (\underline{} - \underline{})^2} = \underline{}$

$(x\underline{})^2 + (y\underline{})^2 = r^2$

....

> First find r^2 using the formula for the distance between two points.

> Then find an equation for C using $(x - a)^2 + (y - b)^2 = r^2$ where (a, b) are the coordinates of the centre of C.

(b) Verify that the point $(5, 7)$ lies on C. **(1)**

$(5\underline{})^2 + (7\underline{})^2 = \underline{}$

....

....

> Substitute $x = 5$ and $y = 7$ into the left-hand side of the equation of the circle. Show all your working to verify that the value of the expression is equal to $25 = 5^2$.

3 The points A and B have coordinates $(-3, 5)$ and $(5, 11)$ respectively.

Given that AB is a diameter of the circle C, find an equation for C. **(5)**

....

....

....

....

4. The circle C has equation $x^2 + y^2 + 2x - 6y = 6$

(a) Find the centre and the radius of C. **(5)**

....

....

....

....

 Problem solving First rearrange the formula, then complete the square to write it in the form $(x - a)^2 + (y - b)^2 = r^2$.

(b) Find the coordinates of the points where C crosses the coordinate axes, giving your answers as simplified surds. **(6)**

....

....

....

....

....

....

Circle properties

1 The circle C has equation $x^2 + y^2 + 4x - 6y = 12$

The points $P(1, 7)$ and $Q(-5, -1)$ lie on the circle. Show that PQ is a diameter of C. **(2)**

....

....

....

Guided **2** The line $5y = 3x + 32$ is a tangent to the circle C, touching C at the point $P(1, 7)$, as shown in the diagram. The point Q is the centre of C.

(a) Find an equation of the straight line through P and Q in the form $ax + by + c = 0$, where a, b and c are integers. **(3)**

> The line through P and Q is **perpendicular** to the tangent.

Gradient of tangent = ...

Gradient of line through P and Q = ...

Equation of line is $y - y_1 = m(x - x_1)$

....

....

(b) Given that Q lies on the line $y = 2$, find the coordinates of Q. **(1)**

....

3 A circle has equation $(x - 2)^2 + (y + 5)^2 = 180$
The tangent to the circle at the point $(8, 7)$ meets the x-axis at P and the y-axis at Q.

(a) Find the coordinates of P and Q. **(5)**

> **Problem solving** Find the gradient from the centre to $(8, 7)$.
> Use $y - y_1 = m(x - x_1)$ to find the equation of the tangent.

....

....

....

....

....

(b) Find the area of the triangle PQC, where C is the centre of the circle. **(4)**

....

....

....

....

Solving circle problems

> **Guided**

1 A circle has equation $(x + 3)^2 + (y + 2)^2 = 26$

A straight line has equation $y = 2x - 3$

The straight line intersects the circle twice.

Find the coordinates of the two points of intersection. **(6)**

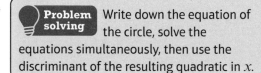

Solve the equations simultaneously.

Substitute $y = 2x - 3$ into the equation of the circle.

$(x + 3)^2 + (2x - 3 + 2)^2 = 26 \implies (x + 3)^2 + (2x\underline{\hspace{1.5cm}})^2 = 26$

$x^2 \underline{\hspace{3cm}} + 4x^2 \underline{\hspace{3cm}} = 26$

$5x^2 \underline{\hspace{3cm}} = 0$

$(5x\underline{\hspace{1cm}})(x\underline{\hspace{1cm}}) = 0$, so $x = \underline{\hspace{1.5cm}}$ and $x = \underline{\hspace{1.5cm}}$

When $x = \underline{\hspace{1cm}}$, $y = 2 \times \underline{\hspace{1.5cm}} - 3 = \underline{\hspace{1cm}}$

and when $x = \underline{\hspace{1cm}}$, $y = 2 \times \underline{\hspace{1.5cm}} - 3 = \underline{\hspace{1cm}}$

Work out y for each of your values of x.

....

2 A circle has its centre at the point $(k, -1)$ and radius 4.

A straight line has equation $y = 2x - 1$

The circle and the straight line have no points of intersection.

Find the range of possible values of k, giving your answer in surd form. **(7)**

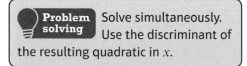

Problem solving Write down the equation of the circle, solve the equations simultaneously, then use the discriminant of the resulting quadratic in x.

....

....

....

....

....

....

3 A circle has equation $x^2 + y^2 = 20$

A straight line has equation $3x - y + k = 0$, where k is a positive constant.

The straight line is a tangent to the circle.

Find the exact value of k. **(7)**

Problem solving Solve simultaneously. Use the discriminant of the resulting quadratic in x.

....

....

....

....

....

....

....

The factor theorem

Guided 1 (a) Use the factor theorem to show that $(x + 2)$ is a factor of $2x^3 - 3x^2 - 11x + 6$ **(2)**

$f(x) = 2x^3 - 3x^2 - 11x + 6$

$f(\_\_\_) = 2(\_\_\_)^3 - 3(\_\_\_)^2 - 11(\_\_\_) + 6$

$= \dots\dots\dots\dots\dots\dots\dots\dots\dots\dots\dots\dots\dots\dots\dots\dots$

$= \dots\dots\dots\dots$

So $(x + 2)$ is a $\dots\dots\dots\dots\dots$

> Remember to write a conclusion or begin by stating, 'If $(x + 2)$ is a factor, then $f(-2) = 0$.'

(b) Factorise $2x^3 - 3x^2 - 11x + 6$ completely. **(4)**

$f(x) = (x + 2)(2x^2 \dots\dots\dots\dots\dots\dots\dots)$

$= (x + 2)(2x \dots\dots\dots\dots)(\dots\dots\dots\dots)$

> $2x^3 - 3x^2 - 11x + 6 = (x + 2)(2x^2 - 7x + 3)$
> Use 'inspection':
> 1st term $2x^2$ to give $2x^3$, last term $+3$ to give $+6$
> A middle term of $-7x$ will give $4x^2 - 7x^2 = -3x^2$ on the RHS, which is what we require.

2 Complete these factorisations.

(a) $2x^3 + 9x^2 - 20x - 12 = (x + 6)(\dots\dots\dots\dots\dots\dots) = (x + 6)(\dots\dots\dots)(\dots\dots\dots)$ **(4)**

(b) $3x^3 - 10x^2 - 16x + 32 = (x - 4)(\dots\dots\dots\dots\dots\dots) = (x - 4)(\dots\dots\dots)(\dots\dots\dots)$ **(4)**

(c) $6x^3 - 29x^2 + 36x - 9 = (x - 3)(\dots\dots\dots\dots\dots\dots) = (x - 3)(\dots\dots\dots)(\dots\dots\dots)$ **(4)**

3 $f(x) = 2x^3 - x^2 - 22x + c,$ where c is a constant.
Given that $f(4) = 0$

(a) find the value of c **(2)**

$\dots\dots\dots\dots\dots\dots\dots\dots\dots\dots\dots\dots\dots\dots\dots\dots\dots\dots\dots\dots\dots\dots\dots\dots\dots\dots\dots\dots\dots\dots\dots\dots\dots\dots$

$\dots\dots\dots\dots\dots\dots\dots\dots\dots\dots\dots\dots\dots\dots\dots\dots\dots\dots\dots\dots\dots\dots\dots\dots\dots\dots\dots\dots\dots\dots\dots\dots\dots\dots$

(b) factorise $f(x)$ completely. **(4)**

$\dots\dots\dots\dots\dots\dots\dots\dots\dots\dots\dots\dots\dots\dots\dots\dots\dots\dots\dots\dots\dots\dots\dots\dots\dots\dots\dots\dots\dots\dots\dots\dots\dots\dots$

$\dots\dots\dots\dots\dots\dots\dots\dots\dots\dots\dots\dots\dots\dots\dots\dots\dots\dots\dots\dots\dots\dots\dots\dots\dots\dots\dots\dots\dots\dots\dots\dots\dots\dots$

$\dots\dots\dots\dots\dots\dots\dots\dots\dots\dots\dots\dots\dots\dots\dots\dots\dots\dots\dots\dots\dots\dots\dots\dots\dots\dots\dots\dots\dots\dots\dots\dots\dots\dots$

4 (a) Use the factor theorem to factorise $f(x) = 3x^3 + 8x^2 - 33x + 10$ **(5)**

$\dots\dots\dots\dots\dots\dots\dots\dots\dots\dots\dots\dots\dots\dots\dots\dots\dots\dots\dots\dots\dots\dots\dots\dots\dots\dots\dots\dots\dots\dots\dots\dots\dots\dots$

$\dots\dots\dots\dots\dots\dots\dots\dots\dots\dots\dots\dots\dots\dots\dots\dots\dots\dots\dots\dots\dots\dots\dots\dots\dots\dots\dots\dots\dots\dots\dots\dots\dots\dots$

$\dots\dots\dots\dots\dots\dots\dots\dots\dots\dots\dots\dots\dots\dots\dots\dots\dots\dots\dots\dots\dots\dots\dots\dots\dots\dots\dots\dots\dots\dots\dots\dots\dots\dots$

$\dots\dots\dots\dots\dots\dots\dots\dots\dots\dots\dots\dots\dots\dots\dots\dots\dots\dots\dots\dots\dots\dots\dots\dots\dots\dots\dots\dots\dots\dots\dots\dots\dots\dots$

> Test $f(1), f(-1), f(2), f(-2)$ and so on, to find a linear factor.

(b) Find all the solutions of $f(x) = 0$ **(2)**

$\dots\dots\dots\dots\dots\dots\dots\dots\dots\dots\dots\dots\dots\dots\dots\dots\dots\dots\dots\dots\dots\dots\dots\dots\dots\dots\dots\dots\dots\dots\dots\dots\dots\dots$

Binomial expansion 1

> **Guided**   **1**   Find the first 3 terms, in ascending powers of x, of the binomial expansion of $(3 - 2x)^5$, giving each term in its simplest form.   **(4)**

> The expansion for $(a + b)^n$ is
> $$a^n + \binom{n}{1}a^{n-1}b + \binom{n}{2}a^{n-2}b^2 + \ldots + b^n$$
> where $\binom{n}{r} = \dfrac{n!}{r!(n-r)!}$

$a = \ldots\ldots\ldots$ $b = \ldots\ldots\ldots$ $n = \ldots\ldots\ldots$

$(3 - 2x)^5 = (3)^5 + \binom{5}{1}(3)^4(\ldots\ldots\ldots) + \ldots\ldots\ldots\ldots\ldots\ldots\ldots$

> Remember to use brackets when substituting and be careful when substituting negative terms.

$\qquad = \ldots\ldots\ldots\ldots\ldots\ldots\ldots\ldots\ldots\ldots\ldots\ldots\ldots\ldots\ldots\ldots\ldots$

$\qquad \approx \ldots\ldots\ldots\ldots\ldots\ldots\ldots\ldots\ldots\ldots\ldots\ldots\ldots\ldots$

> **Guided**   **2**   (a)   Write down the first 3 terms, in ascending powers of x, of the binomial expansion of $(1 + px)^9$, where p is a non-zero constant.   **(2)**

> Remember that $1^n = 1$.

$a = \ldots\ldots\ldots$ $b = \ldots\ldots\ldots$ $n = \ldots\ldots\ldots$

$(1 + px)^9 = 1^9 + \ldots\ldots\ldots\ldots\ldots\ldots\ldots\ldots\ldots\ldots\ldots\ldots\ldots$

$\qquad \approx \ldots\ldots\ldots\ldots\ldots\ldots\ldots\ldots\ldots\ldots\ldots\ldots\ldots\ldots\ldots\ldots\ldots\ldots$

(b)   Given that, in the expansion of $(1 + px)^9$, the coefficient of x is q and the coefficient of x^2 is $20q$, find the value of p and the value of q.   **(4)**

$(1 + px)^9 = \ldots\ldots\ldots\ldots\ldots\ldots\ldots\ldots\ldots\ldots\ldots\ldots\ldots\ldots\ldots$

> Solve the equations simultaneously to find the values of p and q.

$\ldots\ldots\ldots = q \qquad \ldots\ldots\ldots = 20q$

$\ldots\ldots\ldots\ldots\ldots\ldots\ldots\ldots\ldots\ldots\ldots\ldots\ldots\ldots\ldots\ldots\ldots\ldots\ldots\ldots\ldots\ldots$

$\ldots\ldots\ldots\ldots\ldots\ldots\ldots\ldots\ldots\ldots\ldots\ldots\ldots\ldots\ldots\ldots\ldots\ldots\ldots\ldots\ldots\ldots$

3   Find the first 3 terms, in ascending powers of x, of the binomial expansion of $(4 - 3x)^7$ and simplify each term.   **(4)**

$\ldots\ldots\ldots\ldots\ldots\ldots\ldots\ldots\ldots\ldots\ldots\ldots\ldots\ldots\ldots\ldots\ldots\ldots\ldots\ldots\ldots\ldots$

$\ldots\ldots\ldots\ldots\ldots\ldots\ldots\ldots\ldots\ldots\ldots\ldots\ldots\ldots\ldots\ldots\ldots\ldots\ldots\ldots\ldots\ldots$

$\ldots\ldots\ldots\ldots\ldots\ldots\ldots\ldots\ldots\ldots\ldots\ldots\ldots\ldots\ldots\ldots\ldots\ldots\ldots\ldots\ldots\ldots$

4   (a)   Find the first 3 terms, in ascending powers of x, of the binomial expansion of $(2 + 3x)^6$ **(4)**

$\ldots\ldots\ldots\ldots\ldots\ldots\ldots\ldots\ldots\ldots\ldots\ldots\ldots\ldots\ldots\ldots\ldots\ldots\ldots\ldots\ldots\ldots$

$\ldots\ldots\ldots\ldots\ldots\ldots\ldots\ldots\ldots\ldots\ldots\ldots\ldots\ldots\ldots\ldots\ldots\ldots\ldots\ldots\ldots\ldots$

$\ldots\ldots\ldots\ldots\ldots\ldots\ldots\ldots\ldots\ldots\ldots\ldots\ldots\ldots\ldots\ldots\ldots\ldots\ldots\ldots\ldots\ldots$

$\ldots\ldots\ldots\ldots\ldots\ldots\ldots\ldots\ldots\ldots\ldots\ldots\ldots\ldots\ldots\ldots\ldots\ldots\ldots\ldots\ldots\ldots$

(b)   Hence, or otherwise, find the first 3 terms, in ascending powers of x, of the expansion of $\left(1 - \dfrac{x}{4}\right)(2 + 3x)^6$ **(3)**

$\ldots\ldots\ldots\ldots\ldots\ldots\ldots\ldots\ldots\ldots\ldots\ldots\ldots\ldots\ldots\ldots\ldots\ldots\ldots\ldots\ldots\ldots$

$\ldots\ldots\ldots\ldots\ldots\ldots\ldots\ldots\ldots\ldots\ldots\ldots\ldots\ldots\ldots\ldots\ldots\ldots\ldots\ldots\ldots\ldots$

$\ldots\ldots\ldots\ldots\ldots\ldots\ldots\ldots\ldots\ldots\ldots\ldots\ldots\ldots\ldots\ldots\ldots\ldots\ldots\ldots\ldots\ldots$

$\ldots\ldots\ldots\ldots\ldots\ldots\ldots\ldots\ldots\ldots\ldots\ldots\ldots\ldots\ldots\ldots\ldots\ldots\ldots\ldots\ldots\ldots$

Solving binomial problems

1 Find the coefficient of x^7 in the expansion of $\left(4 - \frac{x}{2}\right)^{12}$ **(2)**

> Use the formula for the general term given in the formulae booklet: $\binom{n}{r}a^{n-r}b^r$.

$n =$ .... $r =$ .... $a =$ .... $b =$ ....

$\binom{12}{.....}4^{.....}\left(-\frac{x}{2}\right)^{.....} =$ ....

....

Coefficient = ...

2 The first 4 terms of the expansion of $\left(1 + \frac{x}{2}\right)^8$ are given below:

$$\left(1 + \frac{x}{2}\right)^8 = 1 + 4x + 7x^2 + 7x^3 + \ldots$$

> Find the value of x to substitute in by solving $1 + \frac{x}{2} = 1.005$

Use the expansion to estimate the value of $(1.005)^8$, giving your answer to 5 decimal places.   **(2)**

$1 + \frac{x}{2} = 1.005, \quad \frac{x}{2} =$ ...., $\quad x =$ ....

$(1.005)^8 = 1 + 4(\text{............}) + 7(\text{............})^2 + 7(\text{............})^3 + \text{............} \approx$ ....

3 (a) Find the first 4 terms of the binomial expansion, in ascending powers of x, of $\left(1 + \frac{x}{4}\right)^9$, giving each term in its simplest form.   **(4)**

....

....

....

(b) Use your expansion to estimate the value of $(1.025)^9$, giving your answer to 4 decimal places.   **(3)**

....

....

4 (a) Find the first 4 terms, in ascending powers of x, of the binomial expansion of $(1 - 2x)^7$ Give each term in its simplest form.   **(4)**

....

....

....

(b) Use your expansion to estimate the value of $(0.98)^7$, giving your answer to 4 decimal places.   **(3)**

....

....

(c) If x is small, so that x^3 and higher powers can be ignored, show that
$$\left(1 - \frac{x}{2}\right)(1 - 2x)^7 \approx 1 - \frac{29}{2}x + 91x^2$$ **(2)**

....

....

....

....

Proof

Guided   **1**   The nth term of a sequence is $\dfrac{n}{n+1}$

(a) Write down the $(n+1)$th term.   **(1)**

$(n+1)$th term $= \dfrac{n+1}{\dots\dots\dots}$

(b) Prove that the difference between the $(n+1)$th term and the

     nth term is $\dfrac{1}{(n+1)(n+2)}$ **(3)**

Subtract the algebraic fractions and simplify.

Difference $= \dfrac{n+1}{\dots\dots\dots} - \dfrac{n}{n+1} = \dfrac{\dots\dots\dots\dots\dots}{(\dots\dots\dots)(\dots\dots\dots)} = \dfrac{\dots\dots\dots\dots\dots}{(\dots\dots\dots)(\dots\dots\dots)} = \dfrac{\dots\dots\dots}{(\dots\dots\dots)(\dots\dots\dots)}$

(c) Which two terms have a difference of $\dfrac{1}{156}$?   **(1)**

....

2   Prove that the difference between the cubes of two consecutive odd numbers is 2 greater than 6 times the square of the mean of the two consecutive odd numbers.

Problem solving   Use $(2n+1)$ and $(2n-1)$ as the consecutive odd numbers.

     (6)

....

....

....

....

....

....

3   (a) Prove by exhaustion that $2n^2 - n + 1$ is not divisible by 11 for $1 \leqslant n \leqslant 7$ **(2)**

....

....

(b) By means of a counter example, disprove the statement

     "If n is prime, then $n^2 + 3n + 1$ will always be prime."   **(2)**

....

....

4   Prove that, when n is even, the value of $3n^2 + 6n$ is always divisible by 12.   **(3)**

Problem solving   Factorise, then use the fact that n is even.

....

....

....

....

Cosine rule

Guided **1** In the triangle ABC, $AB = 8\,cm$, $AC = 5\,cm$ and $\angle BAC = 2.1$ radians.
Find the length of BC to 3 significant figures. **(3)**

> Sketch the triangle and label the sides a, b and c. You know two sides and the angle between them, so use the cosine rule.

> The angle is given in radians so make sure your calculator is in radians mode.

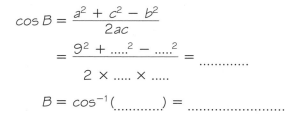

$a^2 = b^2 + c^2 - 2bc\cos A$

$a^2 = 5^2 + \text{...........}^2 - 2 \times \text{...........} \times \text{...........} \times \cos 2.1 = \text{.......................}$

$a = \text{...................}\ cm\ (3\ s.f.)$

Guided **2** In the triangle ABC, $AB = 6\,cm$, $AC = 12\,cm$ and $BC = 9\,cm$. Find the size of angle B, giving your answer in degrees to 3 significant figures. **(3)**

> Sketch the triangle and label the sides a, b and c. You know all three sides so use the cosine rule.

$\cos B = \dfrac{a^2 + c^2 - b^2}{2ac}$

$= \dfrac{9^2 + \text{.....}^2 - \text{.....}^2}{2 \times \text{.....} \times \text{.....}} = \text{.............}$

$B = \cos^{-1}(\text{.............}) = \text{.......................}$

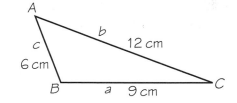

3 A car travels 18 km from P to Q on a bearing of 123°. It then changes direction and travels 26 km from Q to R on a bearing of 345°. Find the distance of R from P, giving your answer to 3 significant figures. **(4)**

....

....

....

....

....

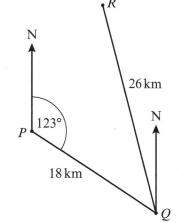

4 The diagram shows a quadrilateral $ABCD$. $AB = 24\,cm$, $BC = 15\,cm$, $CD = 17\,cm$, $DA = 13\,cm$ and angle $ABC = 1.4$ radians. Find the size of the angle ADC in radians to 3 significant figures. **(6)**

....

....

....

....

....

....

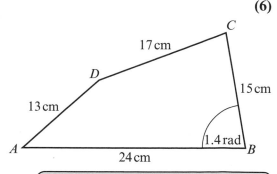

> Draw AC and use the cosine rule twice.

Sine rule

Guided 1 In the triangle ABC, $AC = 9$ cm, $\angle BAC = 0.85$ radians and $\angle ACB = 1.05$ radians.
Find the length of AB to 3 significant figures. **(3)**

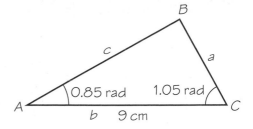
Not SAS or SSS so use the sine rule.

$\angle ABC = \pi - 0.85 - 1.05 =$ .... radians

$\dfrac{b}{\sin B} = \dfrac{c}{\sin C}$, $\dfrac{.....}{\sin ....} = \dfrac{c}{\sin ....}$

so $c = \dfrac{.....\sin ....}{\sin ....} =$ .... cm (3 s.f.)

Guided 2 In the triangle PQR, $PQ = 14$ cm, $PR = 8$ cm, $\angle PQR = 0.3$ radians and $\angle PRQ = x$.

(a) Use the sine rule to find the value of $\sin x$, giving your answer to 3 decimal places. **(3)**

$\dfrac{\sin x}{.....} = \dfrac{\sin 0.3}{.....}$, $\sin x = \dfrac{.....\sin 0.3}{.....} =$ .... (3 d.p.)

Use the alternative form of the sine rule when working out an angle.

(b) Given that there are two possible values of x, find these values of x, giving your answers to 2 decimal places. **(3)**

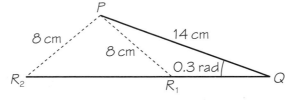

This is known as the ambiguous case of the sine rule.

$x = \sin^{-1}($ .... $) =$ .... (2 d.p.) or $x = \pi - ($ .... $) =$ .... radians (2 d.p.)

3 In the diagram, $AB = 8.3$ cm, $AD = 19.4$ cm
$\angle ABC = 110°$, $\angle ACB = 26°$ and $\angle ADC = 52°$

(a) Find the length of AC. **(3)**

....

....

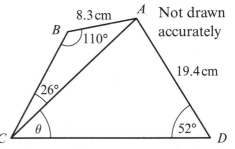
Not drawn accurately

(b) Find the angle ACD, marked θ on the diagram. **(3)**

....

....

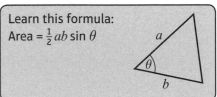
Learn this formula:
Area $= \frac{1}{2}ab\sin\theta$

(c) Work out the area of the quadrilateral $ABCD$.
Give your answer to 3 significant figures. **(6)**

....

....

....

....

Trigonometric graphs

1 (a) Sketch, for $0 \leqslant x \leqslant 360°$, the graph of $y = 3\cos x$ **(2)**

(b) Write down the coordinates of the maximum and minimum points.   **(2)**

....

Guided **2** (a) Sketch, for $0 \leqslant x \leqslant 2\pi$, the graph of $y = \sin\left(x - \dfrac{\pi}{3}\right)$ **(2)**

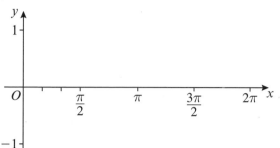

> The graph of $y = \sin\left(x - \dfrac{\pi}{3}\right)$ is a translation of the graph of $y = \sin x$ by $\begin{pmatrix} \dfrac{\pi}{3} \\ 0 \end{pmatrix}$

(b) Write down the exact coordinates of the points where the graph meets the coordinate axes.   **(3)**

> You should know the exact values of sin, cos and tan of $\dfrac{\pi}{6}, \dfrac{\pi}{4}$ and $\dfrac{\pi}{3}$.

When $x = 0$: $y = \sin\left(0 - \dfrac{\pi}{3}\right) = -\sin\left(\dfrac{\pi}{3}\right) =$ ....

Meets y-axis at (0, ...)

When $y = 0$: $x =$ .... and $x =$ ....

Meets x-axis at (............, 0) and (............, 0)

3 The diagram shows part of the curve with equation $y = \cos(ax + b)$, where $a > 0$ and $0 < b < 180°$

The curve cuts the x-axis at the points P and Q.

P is the point $(40°, 0)$ and Q is the point $(160°, 0)$.

Find the values of a and b.   **(4)**

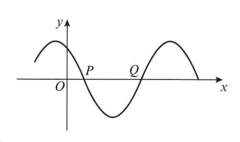

> The graph of $y = \cos x$ crosses the x-axis at 90°, 270°, etc.

....

....

....

....

> **Problem solving** Write down two equations and solve them simultaneously to find a and b.

....

....

....

Trigonometric equations 1

> **Guided**

1 Solve $5\sin x = 2$ in the interval $0 \leqslant x \leqslant 360°$, giving your answers to 1 decimal place. **(3)**

> Draw a sketch of $y = \sin x$ for the range given in the question. This will tell you the number of solutions there are within the range.

> Check your calculator is in degrees mode and work out $\sin^{-1}\left(\frac{2}{5}\right)$ to find the **principal value** of x.

> To find the second value of x, work out $180°$ − (principal value).

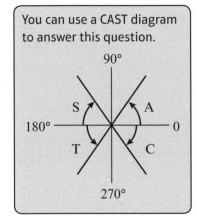

$\sin x = \dfrac{2}{5} = 0.4$

$x = \sin^{-1}(0.4) = $ ....   or $x = 180° − $ .... $= $ ....

> **Guided**

2 Solve $\tan x = 3$ in the interval $0 \leqslant x \leqslant 360°$, giving your answers to 1 decimal place. **(3)**

$\tan x = 3$

$x = \tan^{-1}(3) = $ ....

or $x = 180° + $ .... $= $ ....

3 (a) Sketch the graph of $y = \cos x$ in the interval $0 \leqslant x \leqslant 2\pi$ **(2)**

> You can use a CAST diagram to answer this question.

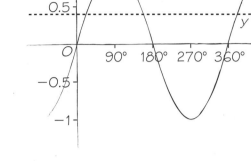

(b) Find the values of x in the interval $0 \leqslant x \leqslant 2\pi$ for which $\cos x = -0.2$, giving your answers correct to 3 decimal places. **(3)**

....

....

4 Solve the following equations in the interval $-\pi \leqslant x \leqslant \pi$, giving your answers to 3 decimal places.

> **Problem solving**   Sketching graphs will help.

(a) $5\sin x + 3 = 0$ **(3)**

....

....

....

(b) $3\cos x = 2$ **(3)**

....

....

....

Trigonometric identities 1

Guided   **1**   (a) Show that the equation $3\sin x = 2\cos^2 x$ can be written in the form $2\sin^2 x + 3\sin x - 2 = 0$ **(2)**

> Write everything in terms of $\sin^2 x$ and $\sin x$ by using $\sin^2 x + \cos^2 x = 1$.

$3\sin x = 2\cos^2 x$ $\sin^2 x + \cos^2 x = 1$ so $\cos^2 x = $ ....

$3\sin x = 2($ .... $)$

....

(b) Hence solve, for $0 \leqslant x < 360°$, $3\sin x = 2\cos^2 x$ **(4)**

$$2\sin^2 x + 3\sin x - 2 = 0$$

$(2\sin x$ ....$)(\sin x$ ....$) = 0$

$\sin x = $ ....

$x = $ ....   or $x = $ ....

> Factorise the quadratic to find solutions for $\sin x$. Remember that $-1 \leqslant \sin x \leqslant 1$, so only one of the factors will give you solutions.

Guided   **2**   (a) Given that $2\cos\theta = 3\sin\theta$, find the value of $\tan\theta$.   **(1)**

> Rearrange the equation to find $\dfrac{\sin\theta}{\cos\theta} = \tan\theta$.

$\dfrac{\sin\theta}{\cos\theta} = \dfrac{............}{............}$ so $\tan\theta = $ ....

(b) Hence, or otherwise, find the values of θ in the interval $0 \leqslant \theta < 360°$ for which $2\cos\theta = 3\sin\theta$, giving your answers to 1 decimal place.   **(3)**

> Find $\tan^{-1}\theta$. Remember that there are two solutions in the range.

$\theta = \tan^{-1}($ ....$)$

$\theta = $ ....   or $\theta = $ ....

3   Find all the solutions, in the interval $0 \leqslant \theta \leqslant 360°$, of the equation $(1 - \tan\theta)(2\sin\theta + 1) = 0$ **(4)**

 Problem solving   Equate each of the factors to zero.

....

....

....

....

4   Find all solutions in the interval $0 \leqslant \theta \leqslant 2\pi$ of the equation $10\sin^2\theta + \cos\theta - 8 = 0$, giving your answers to 3 decimal places.   **(7)**

> **Problem solving**   Write as a quadratic equation in $\cos\theta$.

....

....

....

....

....

....

....

....

Trigonometric equations 2

Guided **1** Solve, for $0 \leqslant x \leqslant 180°$, the equations

(a) $\sin 2x = \frac{1}{2}$　　　　　　　　　　**(4)**

$0 \leqslant 2x \leqslant$ ....° 　Let $Z = 2x$

$\qquad Z = \sin^{-1}\left(\frac{1}{2}\right) =$ ....

or 　$Z = 180° -$ .... $=$ ....

$2x =$ .... 　or 　............

$\quad x =$ .... 　or 　............

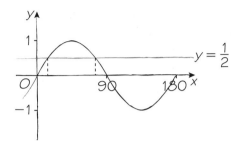

> The range for $2x$ is twice the range for x.

> You should know $\sin 30° = \cos 60° = \frac{1}{2}$

> The sketch shows that there are two solutions of $\sin 2x = \frac{1}{2}$ for $0 \leqslant x \leqslant 180°$.

(b) $\cos (x - 50°) = 0.3$, giving your answers to 1 decimal place.　**(4)**

............° $\leqslant x - 50° \leqslant$ ....° 　Let $Z = x - 50°$

$Z = \cos^{-1}(0.3) =$ .... or $Z = 360° -$ .... $=$ ....

$x - 50° =$ .... or $x =$ ....

> You must work out the range for $(x - 50°)$.

> Check that your solutions for x lie within the given range.

2 Solve, for $-180° \leqslant x < 180°$, $\tan (x + 45°) = 2.5$, giving your answers to 1 decimal place.　**(3)**

....

....

....

....

3 Find all the values of θ, to 1 decimal place, in the interval $0 \leqslant \theta < 360°$ for which
$4 \sin (\theta + 10°) = 3$　　　　　　　　　　**(4)**

....

....

....

4 Find the exact values of θ in the interval $0 \leqslant \theta < 2\pi$
for which $\tan^2 \left(\theta - \frac{5\pi}{12}\right) = 3$　　　**(6)**

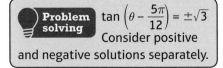

> **Problem solving** $\tan \left(\theta - \frac{5\pi}{12}\right) = \pm\sqrt{3}$
> Consider positive and negative solutions separately.

....

....

....

....

....

....

Vectors

> **Guided**

1 The points P and Q have position vectors $\mathbf{i} + 7\mathbf{j}$ and $3\mathbf{i} + 2\mathbf{j}$ respectively.

(a) Find $\left|\overrightarrow{OP}\right|$ **(1)**

$$\left|\overrightarrow{OP}\right| = \sqrt{1^2 + 7^2} = \sqrt{1 + \text{..............}} = \sqrt{\text{..............}} = \text{..............}$$

(b) Find the vector $\overrightarrow{QP}$. **(2)**

$$\overrightarrow{QP} = \overrightarrow{QO} + \overrightarrow{OP} = \overrightarrow{OP} - \overrightarrow{OQ}$$

$$= \underset{\sim}{\mathbf{i}} + 7\underset{\sim}{\mathbf{j}} - (3\underset{\sim}{\mathbf{i}} + 2\underset{\sim}{\mathbf{j}}) = \text{................}$$

> The position vectors $\overrightarrow{OP}$ and $\overrightarrow{OQ}$ could be written in the forms $\begin{pmatrix} 1 \\ 7 \end{pmatrix}$ and $\begin{pmatrix} 3 \\ 2 \end{pmatrix}$ respectively.

(c) Find the distance QP. **(2)**

....

2 Find unit vectors in the direction of:

(a) $8\mathbf{i} - 6\mathbf{j}$ **(1)**   (b) $8\mathbf{i} + 15\mathbf{j}$ **(1)**

....

....

(c) $16\mathbf{i} - 8\mathbf{j} - 2\mathbf{k}$ **(1)**

....

....

3 For each pair of position vectors $\overrightarrow{OP}$ and $\overrightarrow{OQ}$, find (i) vector $\overrightarrow{PQ}$ and (ii) $\left|\overrightarrow{PQ}\right|$

(a) $\overrightarrow{OP} = 4\mathbf{i} + 3\mathbf{j}$ and $\overrightarrow{OQ} = \mathbf{i} - 2\mathbf{j} + \mathbf{k}$ **(3)**

....

....

(b) $\overrightarrow{OP} = 3\mathbf{i} + \mathbf{j} - \mathbf{k}$ and $\overrightarrow{OQ} = -3\mathbf{i} - \mathbf{j} + 8\mathbf{k}$ **(3)**

....

....

4 $\overrightarrow{OR} = \lambda\mathbf{i} - 2\lambda\mathbf{j}$ where λ is a constant.

Given that $\left|\overrightarrow{OR}\right| = 10$, find the possible values of λ. **(4)**

....

....

5 $\overrightarrow{OP} = \mathbf{i} + \mu\mathbf{j} - 4\mathbf{k}$, $\overrightarrow{OQ} = -3\mu\mathbf{i} + \mathbf{j} + \mathbf{k}$, μ is a constant

Given that $\left|\overrightarrow{QP}\right| = 5\sqrt{3}$, find the possible values of μ. **(7)**

....

....

Solving vector problems

Guided 1 Points A, B and C have position vectors $\begin{pmatrix} -2 \\ 5 \end{pmatrix}$, $\begin{pmatrix} 4 \\ 2 \end{pmatrix}$ and $\begin{pmatrix} 6 \\ 4 \end{pmatrix}$ respectively.

(a) Find the vectors $\overrightarrow{AB}$, $\overrightarrow{BC}$ and $\overrightarrow{AC}$.   **(3)**

$$\overrightarrow{AB} = \overrightarrow{AO} + \overrightarrow{OB} = \overrightarrow{OB} - \overrightarrow{OA} = \begin{pmatrix} 4 \\ 2 \end{pmatrix} - \begin{pmatrix} -2 \\ 5 \end{pmatrix} = \begin{pmatrix} \cdots \\ \cdots \end{pmatrix}$$

$$\overrightarrow{BC} = \overrightarrow{BO} + \overrightarrow{OC} = \overrightarrow{OC} - \overrightarrow{OB} = \begin{pmatrix} \cdots \\ \cdots \end{pmatrix} - \begin{pmatrix} \cdots \\ \cdots \end{pmatrix} = \begin{pmatrix} \cdots \\ \cdots \end{pmatrix}$$

$$\overrightarrow{AC} = \overrightarrow{AO} + \overrightarrow{OC} = \text{.....................} = \text{.....................}$$

(b) Find the area of triangle ABC.   **(4)**

$$\left| \overrightarrow{AB} \right| = \sqrt{6^2 + (-3)^2} = \sqrt{45}$$

....

....

....

....

....

> 1 Use Pythagoras to find the length of all three sides of the triangle.
> 2 Use the cosine rule to find the size of angle C.
> 3 Use area $= \frac{1}{2}ab \sin C$ to find the area of the triangle.

Point D is such that $ABCD$ is a parallelogram.

(c) Write down the area of the parallelogram.   **(1)**

....

(d) Find the position vector of D.   **(2)**

> Sketch a diagram showing the points A, B, C and D and use direction vectors to find the position vector of D.

....

....

....

....

....

2 Here is a sketch of triangle ABC.

Given that $\overrightarrow{AB} = 2\mathbf{i} + 4\mathbf{j} - 5\mathbf{k}$ and $\overrightarrow{BC} = 3\mathbf{i} + 4\mathbf{j} + 2\mathbf{k}$, show that $\angle ABC = 109.4°$ to 1 decimal place.   **(5)**

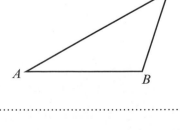

....

....

....

....

....

Differentiating from first principles

Guided **1** Prove, from first principles, that the derivative of $x^3 + 5x^2$ is $3x^2 + 10x$ **(4)**

$f(x) = x^3 + 5x^2$

$f'(x) = \lim_{h \to 0} \dfrac{f(x + h) - f(x)}{h}$

$= \lim_{h \to 0} \dfrac{(x + h)^3 + 5(x + h)^2 - x^3 - 5x^2}{h}$

$= \lim_{h \to 0} \dfrac{x^3 + 3x^2h + \dots\dots + \dots\dots + 5x^2 + \dots\dots + \dots\dots - \dots\dots - 5x^2}{h}$

$= \lim_{h \to 0} \dfrac{3x^2h + \dots\dots\dots\dots\dots\dots\dots}{h}$

$= \lim_{h \to 0} 3x^2 \dots\dots\dots\dots\dots\dots\dots$

As $h \to 0$, $\dots\dots\dots\dots\dots\dots\dots$ so $f'(x) = 3x^2 + 10x$ as required.

2 Points P and Q, with x-coordinates 3 and $3 + h$ respectively, lie on the curve $y = 2x^2 - 7x + 1$

Use differentiation from first principles to find the gradient of the tangent to the curve at point P. **(4)**

....

....

....

....

....

....

....

....

3 $f(x) = ax^2 + 3bx$ where a and b are constants. Prove, from first principles, that $f'(x) = 2ax + 3b$ **(4)**

....

....

....

....

....

....

....

....

Differentiation 1

1 The curve C has equation $y = 5x - 3x^{\frac{3}{2}} + 4x^3$, $x > 0$

Find an expression for $\dfrac{dy}{dx}$ **(3)**

> If $y = ax^n$, then $\dfrac{dy}{dx} = anx^{n-1}$.

....

....

Guided **2** Given that $y = 5x^2 + \dfrac{2}{x} - \dfrac{3}{x^2}$, $x \neq 0$, find $\dfrac{dy}{dx}$ **(3)**

> Write every term in the polynomial in the form ax^n before differentiating.

$y = 5x^2 + 2x^{\cdots\cdots} - 3x^{\cdots\cdots}$

$\dfrac{dy}{dx} = $ ....

Guided **3** Differentiate $\dfrac{3x - 2\sqrt{x}}{x}$, $x \neq 0$, with respect to x. **(3)**

> Divide each term by x and write in the form ax^n before differentiating. Remember that $\sqrt{x} = x^{\frac{1}{2}}$.

$f(x) = \dfrac{3x - 2\sqrt{x}}{x} = \dfrac{3x}{x} - \dfrac{2\sqrt{x}}{x} = $ ....

> Constant terms differentiate to zero.

$f'(x) = $ ....

4 (a) Write $\dfrac{5x^{\frac{1}{3}} - 2}{x}$ in the form $5x^p - 2x^q$, where p and q are constants. **(2)**

....

....

Given that $y = 4x - 9 + \dfrac{5x^{\frac{1}{3}} - 2}{x}$, $x > 0$

(b) find $\dfrac{dy}{dx}$ **(4)**

....

....

....

....

5 Given that $f(x) = \dfrac{(4 + \sqrt{x})^2}{x}$, $x \neq 0$, find $f'(x)$. **(4)**

> Multiply out the brackets, then simplify before differentiating.

....

....

....

....

....

....

....

Differentiation 2

1 Given that $y = 4x^3 - 3x + 5$, find:

(a) $\dfrac{dy}{dx}$ **(3)**

....

(b) $\dfrac{d^2y}{dx^2}$ **(1)**

> Differentiate twice to find the second derivative $\dfrac{d^2y}{dx^2}$ (or $f''(x)$).

....

Guided   **2**   The curve C has equation $y = 5x - \dfrac{2}{x^2}$, $x \neq 0$

The point P has coordinates $(1, 3)$.

(a) Show that P lies on C.   **(1)**

....

(b) Find the gradient of the curve at P.   **(2)**

$y = 5x - \dfrac{2}{x^2} = 5x - 2x^{......}$

$\dfrac{dy}{dx} = $ ....

When $x = 1$, $\dfrac{dy}{dx} = $ ....   Gradient at $P = $ ....

> $\dfrac{dy}{dx}$ represents the gradient of the curve C at any point. To find the gradient at P, substitute $x = 1$.

3 $f(x) = 3x - \dfrac{4}{x}$

(a) Find $f'(x)$.   **(2)**

....

Given that $f'(x) = 12$

(b) find the possible values of x.   **(3)**

....

....

....

4   A curve, C, has equation $y = x^3 + x^2 - 12x$

(a) Find the points where C meets the x-axis, and sketch the curve.   **(5)**

....

....

....

(b) Find $\dfrac{dy}{dx}$ **(2)**

....

(c) Find the gradient of C at each of the points where the curve meets the x-axis.   **(3)**

....

....

Tangents and normals

Guided   **1**   The curve C has equation $y = \frac{1}{3}x^3 + 2x^2 - 8x + 4$

The point P with coordinates $(3, 7)$ lies on C. Find an equation of the tangent to C at P, giving your answer in the form $y = mx + c$, where m and c are constants.   **(5)**

> The gradient of a curve at any point is the same as the gradient of the tangent to the curve at that point.

$y = \frac{1}{3}x^3 + 2x^2 - 8x + 4$

$\frac{dy}{dx} = $ ....

When $x = 3$, $\frac{dy}{dx} = $ ....

> Find the value of $\frac{dy}{dx}$ at P, then use $y - y_1 = m(x - x_1)$ to find the equation of the tangent.

Equation of tangent: $y - $ .... $= $ .... $(x - $ ....$)$

....

Guided   **2**   The curve C has equation $y = 8x + 2x^{\frac{3}{2}} - 3x^2$, $x > 0$

(a) Show that the point $P\,(4, 0)$ lies on C.   **(1)**

....

(b) Find an expression for $\frac{dy}{dx}$ **(3)**

....

(c) Find an equation of the normal to C at the point P, giving your answer in the form $ax + by + c = 0$, where a, b and c are integers.   **(6)**

> The normal to the curve at P is a straight line that is perpendicular to the tangent.

$\frac{dy}{dx} = $ ....

When $x = 4$, $\frac{dy}{dx} = $ ....

Gradient of tangent $= $ .... so gradient of normal $= $ ....

> Write the gradient of the tangent as a fraction. Find the gradient of the normal by turning the fraction upside down and changing the sign.

Equation of normal: $y - $ .... $= $ .... $(x - $ ....$)$

....

3   The curve C has equation $y = (x + 2)(x^2 - 9)$

(a) Show that $\frac{dy}{dx} = 3x^2 + 4x - 9$ **(3)**

....

....

(b) Show that $y = 6x + 18$ is an equation of the tangent to C at the point $(-3, 0)$.   **(2)**

....

....

The tangent to C at the point R is parallel to the tangent at the point $(-3, 0)$.

(c) Find the exact x-coordinate of R.   **(3)**

....

....

....

Stationary points 1

Guided 1 Find the coordinates of the stationary point on the curve
with equation $y = 3x^2 - 18x$ **(4)**

$$\frac{dy}{dx} = \text{........} x - 18$$

$$\text{........} x - 18 = 0$$

$$x = \text{............} \Rightarrow y = \text{........................}$$

> At a **stationary** point or **turning** point, $\frac{dy}{dx} = 0$.

> Solve the equation to find x, then substitute the x-value into the equation for y.

....

Guided 2 The diagram shows part of the curve with equation

$$y = 18 - 5x - \frac{20}{x^2}$$

Use calculus to show that y is decreasing for $x > 2$ **(4)**

$y = 18 - 5x - 20x^{-2}$

$\frac{dy}{dx} = -5 \text{.....................} = -5 \text{.....................}$

If $x > 2$, then $x^3 > \text{............}$ and $\text{............} < 5$

$\text{.............} - 5 < 0$

So $\text{.........................} < 0$ and hence y is decreasing.

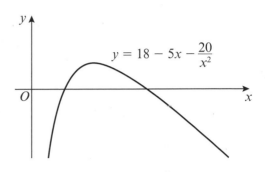

$y = 18 - 5x - \frac{20}{x^2}$

> If y is decreasing, then $\frac{dy}{dx} \leqslant 0$

3 Find the coordinates of the stationary point on the curve with equation $y = 2x^2 - 8x + 5$ **(4)**

....

....

4 Find the coordinates of the turning points on the curve
with equation $y = x^3 - 7x^2 - 5x + 6$ **(6)**

> There are **two** turning points on this curve. Differentiate first, then solve the quadratic equation by factorising.

....

....

....

....

....

5 A curve has equation $f(x) = 27x^2 - \frac{16}{x} - 45$

The function is decreasing for $x < k$, where k is a number to be found.

Use calculus to find the value of k. **(5)**

> Investigate $f'(x) = 0$

....

....

....

....

Stationary points 2

Guided **1** The curve C has equation $y = x^3 + 3x^2 - 24x$

(a) Use calculus to find the coordinates of the stationary points. **(6)**

$\frac{dy}{dx} = 3x^2$ .... , $\frac{dy}{dx} = 0$ when $3x^2$ .... $= 0$

$3(x^2$ .... $) = 0$, $3(x$ .... $)(x$ .... $) = 0$, $x =$ .... and $x =$ ....

When $x =$ .... , $y =$ .... and when $x =$ .... , $y =$ ....

(b) Find $\frac{d^2y}{dx^2}$ and hence verify the nature of the stationary points. **(3)**

$\frac{d^2y}{dx^2} = 6x$ ....   When $x =$ .... , $\frac{d^2y}{dx^2} =$ .... , so we have a ....

When $x =$ .... , $\frac{d^2y}{dx^2} =$ .... , so we have a ....

2 The curve C has equation $y = 8 - 2x - \dfrac{6}{x^3}$, $x \neq 0$

(a) Use calculus to find the exact values of the x-coordinates of the stationary points. **(5)**

....

....

....

....

(b) Find $\frac{d^2y}{dx^2}$ and hence verify the nature of the stationary points. **(3)**

....

....

3 Sketch the graph of $y = f'(x)$ on the axes below each of the curves $y = f(x)$.

(a)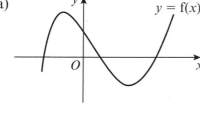

(b)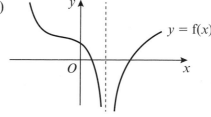

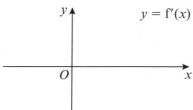

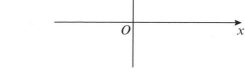

(4)   **(4)**

Modelling with calculus

Guided 1 The diagram shows an open-topped cardboard box, in the shape
of a cuboid. The base of the box is a rectangle x centimetres by
$2x$ centimetres. The height of the box is y centimetres.
The volume of the box is 8000 cm³.

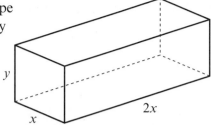

(a) Show that the area, A cm², of the cardboard used to
make the box is given by $A = \dfrac{24\,000}{x} + 2x^2$ **(4)**

Volume = $2x^2y$ = 8000

$y = \dfrac{8000}{\text{..........}} = $ .... $A = $ ....

....

....

> First find an equation connecting x and y using
> the formula for the volume of the cuboid, then
> write y in terms of x. Simplify your answer.

> Work out an expression for A in terms of x,
> remembering that the box is open topped.

(b) Use calculus to find the value of x for which
A is stationary, correct to 3 s.f.   **(4)**

> Differentiate the expression for A and put
> equal to 0, then solve to find the value of x
> which gives a stationary value.

....

....

....

....

(c) Prove that this value of x gives a minimum
value of A.   **(2)**

> Find $\dfrac{d^2A}{dx^2}$ and substitute the value of x.
> Remember to write a statement to say what
> your answer shows.

....

....

(d) Calculate the minimum area of cardboard needed to make the box.   **(2)**

....

....

> Substitute the value of x into the equation for
> A to find the area of cardboard needed.

2 A solid right circular cylinder has radius r cm and height h cm as shown
in the diagram. The total surface area of the cylinder is 900 cm².

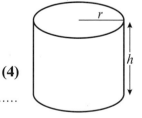

(a) Show that the volume, V cm³, of the cylinder is given by
$V = 450r - \pi r^3$ **(4)**

....

....

....

(b) Given that r varies, use calculus to find the maximum value of V, to the nearest cm³.   **(6)**

....

....

....

(c) Justify that the value of V you have found is a maximum.   **(2)**

....

....

Integration

Guided 1 Given that $y = 4x - \dfrac{3}{x^2}$, $x \neq 0$, find $\int y\,dx$ **(3)**

> Write every term in the polynomial in the form ax^n before integrating.

$y = 4x - 3x^{-2}$

$\int y\,dx = \dfrac{4x^{\cdots}}{\cdots\cdots} \cdots\cdots\cdots\cdots\cdots\cdots\cdots\cdots\cdots\cdots\cdots\cdots\cdots$

> $\int ax^n\,dx = \dfrac{ax^{n+1}}{n+1} + c$ where c is a constant.

$\cdots\cdots\cdots\cdots\cdots\cdots\cdots\cdots\cdots\cdots\cdots\cdots\cdots\cdots\cdots\cdots\cdots\cdots\cdots\cdots\cdots$

Guided 2 Find $\int \left(3x^2 - 5 + x^{-\frac{1}{2}}\right) dx$, giving each term in its simplest form. **(4)**

> Dividing by $\dfrac{a}{b}$ is the same as multiplying by $\dfrac{b}{a}$

$\int \left(3x^2 - 5 + x^{-\frac{1}{2}}\right) dx = \dfrac{3x^3}{\cdots} - \cdots\cdots\cdots\cdots\cdots\cdots\cdots\cdots\cdots\cdots$

$\cdots\cdots\cdots\cdots\cdots\cdots\cdots\cdots\cdots\cdots\cdots\cdots\cdots\cdots\cdots\cdots\cdots\cdots\cdots\cdots\cdots$

3 Find $\int \dfrac{6x - 3}{2x^3}\,dx$ **(4)**

> Write as two separate fractions, then integrate each term.

$\cdots\cdots\cdots\cdots\cdots\cdots\cdots\cdots\cdots\cdots\cdots\cdots\cdots\cdots\cdots\cdots\cdots\cdots\cdots\cdots$

$\cdots\cdots\cdots\cdots\cdots\cdots\cdots\cdots\cdots\cdots\cdots\cdots\cdots\cdots\cdots\cdots\cdots\cdots\cdots\cdots\cdots$

$\cdots\cdots\cdots\cdots\cdots\cdots\cdots\cdots\cdots\cdots\cdots\cdots\cdots\cdots\cdots\cdots\cdots\cdots\cdots\cdots\cdots$

$\cdots\cdots\cdots\cdots\cdots\cdots\cdots\cdots\cdots\cdots\cdots\cdots\cdots\cdots\cdots\cdots\cdots\cdots\cdots\cdots\cdots$

4 (a) Show that $(3 - 2\sqrt{x})^2$ can be written in the form $9 - k\sqrt{x} + 4x$, where k is a constant to be found. **(2)**

$\cdots\cdots\cdots\cdots\cdots\cdots\cdots\cdots\cdots\cdots\cdots\cdots\cdots\cdots\cdots\cdots\cdots\cdots\cdots\cdots\cdots$

$\cdots\cdots\cdots\cdots\cdots\cdots\cdots\cdots\cdots\cdots\cdots\cdots\cdots\cdots\cdots\cdots\cdots\cdots\cdots\cdots\cdots$

(b) Find $\int (3 - 2\sqrt{x})^2\,dx$ **(3)**

$\cdots\cdots\cdots\cdots\cdots\cdots\cdots\cdots\cdots\cdots\cdots\cdots\cdots\cdots\cdots\cdots\cdots\cdots\cdots\cdots\cdots$

$\cdots\cdots\cdots\cdots\cdots\cdots\cdots\cdots\cdots\cdots\cdots\cdots\cdots\cdots\cdots\cdots\cdots\cdots\cdots\cdots\cdots$

$\cdots\cdots\cdots\cdots\cdots\cdots\cdots\cdots\cdots\cdots\cdots\cdots\cdots\cdots\cdots\cdots\cdots\cdots\cdots\cdots\cdots$

5 Given that $\dfrac{4x^2 - 2x^{\frac{5}{2}}}{\sqrt{x}}$ can be written in the form $4x^p - 2x^q$

(a) write down the value of p and the value of q. **(2)**

$\cdots\cdots\cdots\cdots\cdots\cdots\cdots\cdots\cdots\cdots\cdots\cdots\cdots\cdots\cdots\cdots\cdots\cdots\cdots\cdots\cdots$

$\cdots\cdots\cdots\cdots\cdots\cdots\cdots\cdots\cdots\cdots\cdots\cdots\cdots\cdots\cdots\cdots\cdots\cdots\cdots\cdots\cdots$

(b) Find $\int \dfrac{4x^2 - 2x^{\frac{5}{2}}}{\sqrt{x}}\,dx$ **(3)**

$\cdots\cdots\cdots\cdots\cdots\cdots\cdots\cdots\cdots\cdots\cdots\cdots\cdots\cdots\cdots\cdots\cdots\cdots\cdots\cdots\cdots$

$\cdots\cdots\cdots\cdots\cdots\cdots\cdots\cdots\cdots\cdots\cdots\cdots\cdots\cdots\cdots\cdots\cdots\cdots\cdots\cdots\cdots$

$\cdots\cdots\cdots\cdots\cdots\cdots\cdots\cdots\cdots\cdots\cdots\cdots\cdots\cdots\cdots\cdots\cdots\cdots\cdots\cdots\cdots$

$\cdots\cdots\cdots\cdots\cdots\cdots\cdots\cdots\cdots\cdots\cdots\cdots\cdots\cdots\cdots\cdots\cdots\cdots\cdots\cdots\cdots$

Finding the constant

Guided   **1**   The curve C with equation $y = f(x)$, $x \neq 0$, passes through the point (2, 10).

Given that $f'(x) = 3x + \dfrac{2}{x^2}$

(a) find $f(x)$ **(5)**

> To find $f(x)$ you need to integrate $f'(x)$.

> To find the constant of integration, use $f(x) = 10$ when $x = 2$.

$$f(x) = \int \left(3x + \frac{2}{x^2} \right) dx$$

$$= \int (3x + 2x^{\cdots\cdots}) \, dx$$

$$= \dotsb + c$$

$$= \dotsb$$

$$10 = \dotsb + c$$

$$c = \dotsb$$

$$f(x) = \dotsb$$

(b) verify that $f(-1) = 8.5$ **(1)**

> To find $f(-1)$ substitute $x = -1$ into the equation for $f(x)$.

$$f(x) = \dotsb$$

$$f(-1) = \dotsb = \dotsb$$

Guided   **2**   The gradient of a curve C is given by $\dfrac{dy}{dx} = \dfrac{x-3}{\sqrt{x}}$, $x \neq 0$

The point $\left(4, \frac{1}{3}\right)$ lies on C. Find y in terms of x.   **(6)**

> To find y you need to integrate $\dfrac{dy}{dx}$

$$\frac{dy}{dx} = \frac{x-3}{\sqrt{x}} = x^{\cdots\cdots} - 3x^{\cdots\cdots}$$

$$y = \int (x^{\cdots\cdots} - 3x^{\cdots\cdots}) \, dx = \dotsb + c$$

> To find the constant of integration, use $y = \frac{1}{3}$ when $x = 4$.

$$\frac{1}{3} = \dotsb + c$$

$$\frac{1}{3} = \dotsb$$

$$c = \dotsb$$

$$y = \dotsb$$

3   The gradient of a curve C is given by $\dfrac{dy}{dx} = \dfrac{(x^2 - 2)^2}{x^2}$, $x \neq 0$

(a) Show that $\dfrac{dy}{dx} = x^2 - 4 + 4x^{-2}$ **(2)**

....

....

The point $\left(3, \frac{2}{3}\right)$ lies on C.

(b) Find an equation for the curve C in the form $y = f(x)$.   **(6)**

....

....

....

....

....

....

Definite integration

> **Guided**   **1**   Use calculus to find $\int_1^2 (x^3 - 3x^2 + 5x - 7)\,dx$ **(4)**

$$\int_1^2 (x^3 - 3x^2 + 5x - 7)\,dx = \left[\frac{x^{\cdots}}{\cdots} - x^3 + \text{......................................} \right]_1^2$$

$$= (\text{...............................}) - (\text{...............................})$$

$$= \text{...........} - \text{..................} = \text{..................}$$

> **Guided**   **2**   Use calculus to find the exact value of $\int_1^2 \left(2x^2 + 3 - \dfrac{5}{x^2} \right) dx$ **(5)**

$$\int_1^2 \left(2x^2 + 3 - \frac{5}{x^2} \right) dx = \int_1^2 (2x^2 + 3 - 5x^{\cdots})\,dx$$

$$= \left[\frac{2x^{\cdots}}{\cdots} + 3\text{.....................} \right]_1^2 = \left[\text{........................} \right]_1^2$$

$$= (\text{...............................}) - (\text{...............................})$$

$$= \text{...........} - \text{..................} = \text{..................}$$

> Write every term in the polynomial in the form ax^n before integrating.

3   Use calculus to find the value of $\int_1^4 (5x - 3\sqrt{x})\,dx$ **(5)**

....

....

....

....

....

> Dividing by $\dfrac{a}{b}$ is the same as multiplying by $\dfrac{b}{a}$

4   Evaluate $\int_2^8 \left(x + \dfrac{2}{\sqrt{x}} \right) dx$, giving your answer in the form $a + b\sqrt{2}$,

  where a and b are integers.   **(5)**

....

....

....

....

....

5   Use calculus to find the exact value of $\int_1^2 \left(\dfrac{3}{x^4} - \dfrac{2}{x^3} + 5 \right) dx$ **(5)**

....

....

....

....

....

Area under a curve

Guided 1 The diagram shows part of the curve with equation $y = (x + 1)(3 - x)$

Use calculus to find the exact area of the shaded region, R.　**(5)**

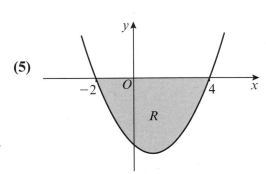

> Expand the brackets, then integrate with limits of −1 and 3.

Graph crosses x-axis at $x = -1$ and $x = 3$

$y = 3 + 2x - x^2$

$$\int_{-1}^{3}\left(3 + 2x - x^2\right) dx = \Big[\dots\dots\dots\dots\dots\dots\Big]_{-1}^{3} = \Big[\dots\dots\dots\dots\dots\dots\Big]_{-1}^{3}$$

$= (\dots\dots\dots\dots) - (\dots\dots\dots\dots) = \dots\dots - \dots\dots = \dots\dots$

Area = $\dots\dots$

Guided 2 The diagram shows part of the curve with equation
$y = (x + 2)(x - 4)$

Find the area of the shaded region, R.　**(5)**

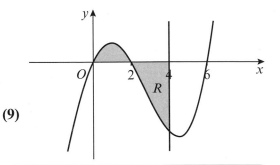

> Remember to write the **positive** value as your answer.

Graph crosses x-axis at $x = \dots\dots$ and $x = \dots\dots$

$y = \dots\dots\dots\dots\dots\dots$

$$\int_{\dots}^{\dots}\left(\dots\dots\dots\dots\dots\right) dx = \Big[\dots\dots\dots\dots\dots\Big]_{\dots}^{\dots} = \Big[\dots\dots\dots\dots\dots\Big]_{\dots}^{\dots}$$

$= (\dots\dots\dots\dots) - (\dots\dots\dots\dots) = \dots\dots\dots\dots\dots\dots = \dots\dots$

Area = $\dots\dots$

3 The diagram shows part of the curve C with
equation　$y = x(x - 2)(x - 6)$

Use calculus to find the total area of the finite
region, shown shaded in the diagram, that is
between $x = 0$ and $x = 4$ and is bounded by C,
the x-axis and the line $x = 4$　**(9)**

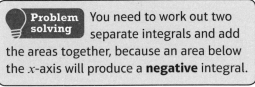

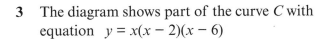

....

....

....

....

....

....

....

....

> **Problem solving**　You need to work out two separate integrals and add the areas together, because an area below the x-axis will produce a **negative** integral.

More areas

> **Guided**

1 The diagram shows part of the curve C with equation $y = x^2 - 6x + 8$

The points L and M have coordinates $(2, 0)$ and $(4, 0)$ respectively. The point N lies on the curve and has x-coordinate 6. The shaded region R is bounded by the curve, the x-axis and the line segment LN. Find the exact area of R.

(7)

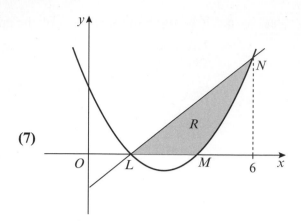

> You need to find the area of the triangle and the area under C between $x = 4$ and $x = 6$ then subtract to find R.

$L\,(2, 0)$; $M\,(4, 0)$ At N: $x = 6$, $y =$ ....

Area of a triangle $= \frac{1}{2} \times$ base $\times$ height $= \frac{1}{2} \times$ .... $\times$ .... $=$ ....

$\displaystyle\int_4^6 \left(x^2 - 6x + 8\right)dx = \left[\dfrac{x^3}{3} - \text{.............} + \text{.............}\right]_4^6 = \left[\text{.............................}\right]_4^6$

$= (\text{.............} - \text{.............} + \text{.............}) - (\text{.............} - \text{.............} + \text{.............})$

$= \text{.............} - \text{.............} = \text{.............}$

Area of $R =$ .... $-$ .... $=$ ....

2 The line with equation $y = 20 - 3x$ cuts the curve with equation $y = x^2 + 2x + 14$ at the points A and B, as shown in the diagram.

  (a) Use algebra to find the coordinates of A and the coordinates of B. **(5)**

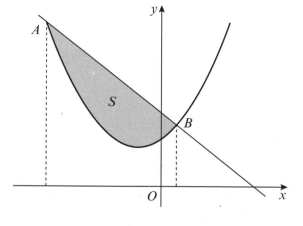

....

....

....

....

The shaded region S is bounded by the line and the curve, as shown in the diagram.

  (b) Use calculus to find the exact area of S. **(7)**

....

....

....

....

> **Problem solving** Find the area of the trapezium and the area under the curve between A and B.
> Area of $S =$ area of trapezium $-$ area under C

....

....

....

....

Exponential functions

1   Match each function to one of the graphs below.

(a) $y = \left(\dfrac{1}{4}\right)^x$ **(1)**   (b) $y = 3^x - 4$ **(1)**   (c) $y = 0.6^x - 1$ **(1)**   (d) $y = -(5^{-x})$ **(1)**

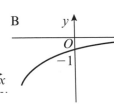

Guided   **2**   Sketch these graphs.

(a) $y = -1 - (0.5)^x$ **(3)**

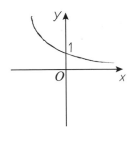
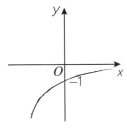
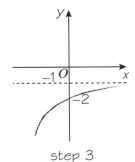

step 1   step 2   step 3

> Step 1: draw $y = 0.5^x$
> Step 2: reflect it in the x-axis.
> Step 3: translate it by $\begin{pmatrix} 0 \\ -1 \end{pmatrix}$

(b) $y = 3^{x+2}$ **(3)**   (c) $y = 4^{x-1} + 2$ **(3)**   (d) $y = 4 - (0.8)^x$ **(3)**

3   Differentiate with respect to x.

(a) $y = e^{6x}$ **(1)**   (b) $y = e^{-3x}$ **(1)**   (c) $y = 4e^{\frac{x}{2}}$ **(1)**   (d) $y = 6e^{0.2x}$ **(1)**

....

(e) $y = 7e^{-x} - 2e^{-4x}$ **(2)**   (f) $y = e^{-2x}(3e^{5x} - 1)$ **(3)**   (g) $y = e^{\frac{x}{4}}(e^x + 2e^{2x})$ **(3)**

....

....

Logarithms

> **Guided**　**1** (a) Write down the value of $\log_8 64$　　(1)

$8^{\cdots} = 64$　so　$\log_8 64 = \ldots\ldots\ldots$

(b) Express $3\log_a 2 + \log_a 7$ as a single logarithm to base a.　　(3)

$3\log_a 2 = \log_a 2^{\cdots} = \log_a \ldots\ldots\ldots$

$\log_a \ldots\ldots\ldots + \log_a 7 = \log_a (\ldots\ldots\ldots \times \ldots\ldots\ldots) = \log_a \ldots\ldots\ldots$

> Use $\log_a (x^n) = n \log_a x$ and $\log_a x + \log_a y = \log_a (xy)$.

2 Find:

(a) the value of p such that $\log_4 p = -2$　　(2)

....

(b) the value of y such that $\log_y 125 = 3$　　(2)

....

3 Express as a single logarithm to base a

(a) $2\log_a 5 + 3\log_a 2$　　(2)

....

....

(b) $4\log_a 3 - \log_a 12$　　(2)

....

....

> **Guided**　**4** Given that $y = 4x^3$, show that $\log_4 y = 1 + 3\log_4 x$　　(3)

$\log_4 y = \log_4 4x^3$

$\qquad = \log_4 \ldots\ldots\ldots + \log_4 \ldots\ldots\ldots$

$\qquad = \ldots\ldots\ldots + \ldots\ldots\ldots \log_4 \ldots\ldots\ldots$

> Take logs on both sides, then use $\log_a m + \log_a n = \log_a (mn)$ to write as the sum of two separate log terms.

> Remember that $\log_a a = 1$.

5 Given that $y^2 = 9x^4$, show that $\log_3 y = 1 + 2\log_3 x$　　(3)

Problem solving Take logs to base 3 on both sides.

....

....

....

....

....

....

6 Write $\log_a\left(\dfrac{x^3\sqrt{y}}{z^4}\right)$ in terms of $\log_a x$, $\log_a y$ and $\log_a z$　　(3)

....

....

Equations with logs

Guided 1 Find the value of x for which $\log_3(2x - 1) - \log_3 x = 1$ **(4)**

$$\log_3\left(\frac{\text{...........................}}{\text{...........................}}\right) = 1$$

> Use $\log_a m - \log_a n = \log_a\left(\frac{m}{n}\right)$ to combine the two log expressions on the left-hand side.

$$\frac{\text{...........................}}{\text{...........................}} = 3^{\cdots}$$

> Use $\log_a b = n \Leftrightarrow a^n = b$, then rearrange the equation to solve for x.

....

2 Solve the equation $\log_2(x + 2) - \log_2 x = \log_2 5$ **(3)**

....

....

Guided 3 Given that a and b are positive constants, solve the simultaneous equations

$$a = 4b \qquad ①$$
$$\log_2 a + \log_2 b = 3 \qquad ②$$

Give your answers as exact numbers.   **(6)**

$\log_2 \text{......} + \log_2 b = 3$

> Substitute ① into ②.

....

....

> Combine the log terms and apply $\log_a b = x \Leftrightarrow a^x = b$.

....

> Remember that a and b are **positive** and give **exact** values.

....

4 (a) Given that $2\log_2(x - 2) - \log_2(6 - x) = 1$, show that $x^2 - 2x - 8 = 0$ **(5)**

....

....

....

....

....

(b) Hence, or otherwise, solve $2\log_2(x - 2) - \log_2(6 - x) = 1$ **(2)**

> Remember that $\log_a b$ is only defined for $b > 0$.

....

....

5 Find the values of x such that $\dfrac{\log_3 81 + \log_3 243}{\log_3 x} = \log_3 x$ **(5)**

....

....

....

....

....

Exponential equations

> **Guided**

1 (a) Find, to 3 significant figures, the value of x for which $3^x = 5$ **(2)**

$3^x = 5$

$\log 3^x = \log 5$

$x \log 3 = \log 5$

> Take logs on both sides or make use of the $\boxed{\log_\blacksquare \square}$ key.

> Rearrange the equation to find x. Then use the $\boxed{\log_\blacksquare \square}$ key.

$x = \dfrac{\cdots\cdots\cdots}{\cdots\cdots} = \cdots\cdots\cdots\cdots$

(b) Solve the equation $3^{2x} - 8(3^x) + 15 = 0$ **(4)**

Let $Y = 3^x$ so $3^{2x} = (3^x)^2 = Y^{\cdots}$

$Y^2 - 8Y + 15 = 0$

> Let $Y = 3^x$, then write as a quadratic in Y and factorise.

$(Y\ldots\ldots)(Y\ldots\ldots) = 0$

$Y = \ldots\ldots$ or $Y = \ldots\ldots$ so $3^x = \ldots\ldots$ or $3^x = \ldots\ldots$

> Use $a^x = b \Leftrightarrow \log_a b = x$ to find the values of x.

$x = \ldots\ldots$ or $x = \ldots\ldots$

2 Solve the equation $5^{2x} + 3(5^x) - 10 = 0$, giving your answer to 2 decimal places. **(6)**

> Remember that $a^x > 0$.

....

....

3 Solve the equation $8^{2x} - 8(8^x) + 7 = 0$ **(6)**

....

....

....

4 Solve, giving answers to 3 decimal places,

(a) $4^x = 3^{x+2}$ **(4)**

> 💡 **Problem solving** Take logs to the same base on both sides, then use the power law. Collect all the x terms on one side of the equation, then factorise to get x on its own.

....

....

(b) $6^{2x-1} = 5^{x+1}$ **(4)**

....

....

5 $f(x) = 3^{0.5x^2}$, $x \in \mathbb{R}$ and $g(x) = 9^{x-1}$, $x \in \mathbb{R}$

Show that the curves $f(x)$ and $g(x)$ meet at exactly one point. **(5)**

> 💡 **Problem solving** Set $f(x) = g(x)$, then take logs of both sides. Use the discriminant of the resulting quadratic in x.

....

....

....

Natural logarithms

Guided 1 Solve $\ln(5x + 24) = 2\ln(x + 2)$ (4)

$\ln(5x + 24) = \ln(x + 2)^2$

$5x + 24 = (x + 2)^2$

Rearrange as a quadratic in
x, factorise and solve. Check
the validity of your answers.

....

....

2 Solve $\ln(x - 3) + \ln(x - 2) = \ln(2x + 24)$ (5)

....

....

3 Find the exact solutions of
$$e^{3x} + 2e^x = 3e^{2x}$$ (5)

Problem solving Write e^{3x} as $(e^x)^3$ and e^{2x}
as $(e^x)^2$. Take all terms
to the LHS, then take out e^x as a
common factor. You will have a
quadratic in e^x as the other factor.

....

....

....

....

4 Solve $3^x e^{2x-1} = 5$

Give your answers in the form $\dfrac{\ln a + b}{\ln c + d}$

where a, b, c and d are integers.   (5)

Problem solving Take logs of both
sides, then use the
laws of logs to simplify the LHS.
Group the x terms together.

....

....

....

5 The function f is defined by
$$f: x \mapsto \frac{5x^2 - 13x - 6}{x^2 - 9}, \qquad x > 3$$

(a) Show that $f(x) = \dfrac{5x + 2}{x + 3}$ (3)

....

....

(b) Hence, or otherwise, solve the equation $\ln(5x^2 - 13x - 6) = 2 + \ln(x^2 - 9)$, $x > 3$,
giving your answer in terms of e.   (4)

....

....

....

....

Exponential modelling

Guided 1 A heated metal bar is put in a liquid. The temperature of the bar, $T°C$, at time t minutes is modelled by the equation

$$T = 350\,e^{-0.08t} + 20, \qquad t \geqslant 0$$

(a) Write down the temperature of the bar as it enters the liquid. **(1)**

....

(b) Find t when $T = 280$, giving your answer to 3 significant figures. **(4)**

$280 = 350\,e^{-0.08t} + 20$ so $\dfrac{260}{350} = e^{-0.08t}$ so $\ln\left(\dfrac{260}{350}\right) = -0.08t$

....

(c) Find the rate at which the temperature is decreasing at time $t = 40$. Give your answer in °C/minute to 3 significant figures. **(3)**

> Differentiate to find the rate of change.

....

....

(d) Explain why the temperature can never fall to $18°C$. **(1)**

....

....

2 A sample of radioactive material decays according to the formula $N = 60\,e^{-kt}$ where N is the number of grams of the material, t is the time, in years, and k is a positive constant.

(a) What was the initial mass of the sample? **(1)**

....

After 88 years, the sample has lost half its mass.

(b) Find the value of k to 3 significant figures. **(4)**

....

....

(c) How many grams of material are there after 120 years? **(2)**

....

(d) Find the rate of decay, in grams per year, after 50 years. Give your answer to 3 s.f. **(2)**

....

....

(e) Sketch a graph of N against t. **(2)**

Modelling with logs

1   The percentage of people visiting the theatre, P, has increased steadily since 1990.
It can be represented by the equation $P = at^n$, where t is the number of years after 1990 and
a and n are constants to be determined.

(a) Show that the graph of $\log_{10} P$ against $\log_{10} t$ will be a straight line of gradient n.   **(2)**

$\log_{10} P = \log_{10}(at^n) = \log_{10}a + \log_{10}t^n = \log_{10}a + \text{.....} \log_{10} \text{.....}$

(b) Write down, in terms of a, the intercept of this graph on the vertical axis.   **(1)**

Intercept = ...

(c) This sketch graph shows the relationship between t and P.
Use it to work out the equation for P in terms of t.   **(4)**

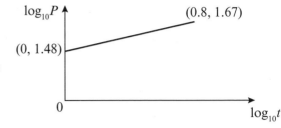

$n = \text{gradient} = \dfrac{1.67 - 1.48}{0.8} = \text{.......................}$

Intercept = $1.48 = \log_{10}a$, so $a = \text{.......................}$

So the equation is $P = \text{.......................}$

(d) Predict the percentage of people visiting the theatre in the year 2018, according to this model.   **(1)**

....

2   A 20-mile motorway extension is being planned, but there have been major delays in starting the construction.
The estimated cost, £y million, t years after the extension was first proposed can be modelled by an equation of the form $y = kb^t$, where k and b are constants to be determined.

(a) Show that the graph of $\log_{10}y$ against t will be a straight line of gradient $\log_{10}b$.   **(2)**

....

(b) Write down, in terms of k, the intercept of this graph on the vertical axis.   **(1)**

Intercept = ...

(c) This sketch graph shows the relationship between t and y.
Use it to work out the equation for y in terms of t.   **(4)**

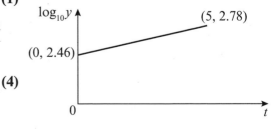

....

....

....

(d) Using this model, what was the estimated cost when the motorway extension was first proposed?   **(1)**

....

(e) What would be the delay in the project if the estimated cost rose to £650 million?
Give your answer to 1 decimal place.   **(2)**

....

You are the examiner!

> Checking through your work is a key skill for A Level Maths. Have a look at pages 54 and 55 of the *Revision Guide*, then practise with these questions. There are full worked solutions on page 201.

1   The line L has equation $2y = 5 - x$

Find the equation of the line perpendicular to L which passes through the point $(-1, 4)$

Give your answer in the form $ax + by + c = 0$ **(5)**

....

....

....

....

2   A curve has equation $y = 3x^2 - 2x + \dfrac{4}{x}$

Find the equation of the tangent to the curve at the point where $x = 2$

Give your answer in the form $y = mx + c$ **(6)**

....

....

....

....

....

3   Solve the simultaneous equations

$$2x - y = 9$$
$$x^2 - xy = 20 \qquad\qquad \textbf{(7)}$$

....

....

....

....

....

....

4   Solve, for $0 \leqslant x \leqslant 360°$, $\cos(x + 40°) = 0.85$

Give your answers to 1 decimal place.   **(5)**

....

....

....

....

....

You are the examiner!

Checking through your work is a key skill for A Level Maths. Have a look at pages 54 and 55 of the *Revision Guide*, then practise with these questions. There are full worked solutions on page 201.

5 (a) Find the exact solutions of the equation $2e^{3x} + 10e^x = 9e^{2x}$ **(5)**

....

....

....

....

....

(b) Solve $4^x e^{3x+2} = 5$

Give your answer in the form $\dfrac{\ln a + b}{\ln c + d}$ where a, b, c and d are integers.   **(5)**

....

....

....

....

....

6 The line with equation $y = 10 - 2x$ cuts the curve with equation $y = x^2 - 3x + 4$ at the points A and B, as shown in the diagram.

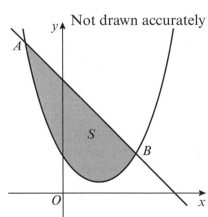

(a) Find the coordinates of A and B.   **(5)**

....

....

....

....

....

(b) The shaded area, S, is bounded by the line and the curve, as shown.
Find the exact area of S.   **(7)**

....

....

....

....

....

....

....

Proof by contradiction

Guided 1 Show that if $3n + 7$ is even, then n is odd. **(4)**

Assume that n is even, say $n = 2k$, then $3n + 7 = 3(\underline{\quad}) + 7 = \underline{\quad} + 7 = 6(\underline{\quad}) + 1$

But $6(\underline{\quad}) + 1 = 2(\underline{\quad}) + 1$ which is of the form $2m + 1$ and so is odd.

This contradicts the original assumption, so if $3n + 7$ is even then n must be odd.

Guided 2 Show that there are no positive integer solutions of the equation $x^2 - y^2 = 10$ **(5)**

Assume that x and y are different positive integers and $x^2 - y^2 = 10$ which means

$(x + y)(\underline{\quad}) = 10$

$(x + y)$ and $(\underline{\quad})$ must both be integers and since $(x + y)$ must be positive, the only

factors of 10 to consider are 1 and $\underline{\quad}$ or $\underline{\quad}$ and $\underline{\quad}$.

Suppose $x + y = \underline{\quad}$ and $x - y = 1$, solving simultaneously gives $x = \underline{\quad}$ and $y = \underline{\quad}$

Suppose $x + y = \underline{\quad}$ and $x - y = \underline{\quad}$, solving simultaneously gives $x = \underline{\quad}$ and $y = \underline{\quad}$

This contradicts the assumption that x and y are positive integers, so the original

assumption is incorrect.

So there are no positive integer solutions of the equation $x^2 - y^2 = 10$

3 Show that if m and n are two different positive real numbers, the arithmetic mean is always greater than the geometric mean. **(5)**

> The arithmetic mean is $\frac{m + n}{2}$, and the geometric mean is $\sqrt{mn}$.

> **Problem solving** Assume $\frac{m + n}{2} < \sqrt{mn}$ and square both sides, then rearrange and factorise.

....

....

....

....

....

....

....

4 Show that if θ is such that $0 \leqslant \theta < \frac{\pi}{2}$, then $\sin\theta + \cos\theta \geqslant 1$ **(5)**

> **Problem solving** Assume $\sin\theta + \cos\theta < 1$ and square both sides, then simplify.

....

....

....

....

....

Algebraic fractions

 1 Simplify fully $\dfrac{2x^2 + 7x - 30}{x^2 - 36}$ **(3)**

$$\frac{2x^2 + 7x - 30}{x^2 - 36} = \frac{(2x\ldots\ldots)(x\ldots\ldots)}{(x\ldots\ldots)(x\ldots\ldots)}$$

> Remember that $a^2 - b^2 = (a + b)(a - b)$.

$$= \frac{\ldots\ldots\ldots\ldots\ldots}{\ldots\ldots\ldots\ldots\ldots}$$

2 Simplify fully $\dfrac{6x^2 - 23x - 18}{2x^2 - 11x + 9}$ **(4)**

> Fully factorise the numerator and the denominator.

....

....

3 Simplify fully $\dfrac{2x^2 - 32}{5x^2 + 17x - 12}$ **(4)**

....

....

4 Express $\dfrac{3}{x(x - 1)} + \dfrac{2}{x}$ as a single fraction in its simplest form. **(2)**

> The LCM is $x(x - 1)$ because x is a factor of both denominators.

....

....

....

....

5 Express $\dfrac{3x^2 + 14x - 5}{x^2 - 25} - \dfrac{4x}{x(x - 5)}$ as a single fraction in its simplest form. **(5)**

> **Problem solving** Factorise fully, then look for a common denominator.

....

....

....

....

....

6 Express $\dfrac{2x - 3}{3x^2 - 7x - 6} + \dfrac{4}{3x + 2}$ as a single fraction in its simplest form. **(5)**

....

....

....

....

....

Partial fractions

Guided 1 Express in partial fractions $\dfrac{3x - 10}{(x - 2)(x - 4)}$ **(3)**

> You can use the cover-up rule when there are no repeated factors.

$\dfrac{3x - 10}{(x - 2)(x - 4)} = \dfrac{A}{x - 2} + \dfrac{B}{x - 4}$

Let $x = 2$ and work out $\dfrac{3x - 10}{x - 4}$:　　$A = \dfrac{3(2) - 10}{2 - 4} = \dfrac{-4}{-2} = 2$

Let $x = 4$ and work out $\dfrac{3x - 10}{x - 2}$:　　$B = \dfrac{3(............) - 10}{(............ - 2)} = \dfrac{............}{............} = ...$

So $\dfrac{3x - 10}{(x - 2)(x - 4)} \equiv \dfrac{2}{x - 2} + \dfrac{............}{x - 4}$

2 Express $\dfrac{10x - 1}{(2x + 1)(4x - 1)}$ in partial fractions. **(3)**

....

....

3 Express $\dfrac{6 - x}{x^3 - x^2 - 6x}$ in partial fractions. **(5)**

> First, fully factorise the denominator.

....

....

....

....

Guided 4 $\dfrac{x^2 - 13}{(x - 1)^2(x + 2)} = \dfrac{A}{x - 1} + \dfrac{B}{(x - 1)^2} + \dfrac{C}{x + 2}$

Find the values of the constants A, B and C. **(4)**

> **Problem solving** There is a repeated factor so you will need to substitute values of x and/or compare coefficients.

$x^2 - 13 = A(x - 1)(x + 2) + B(x + 2) + C(x - 1)^2$

When $x = -2$, $-9 = 9C$, so $\underline{C = -1}$

....

....

5 $\dfrac{x^3 - 3x^2 + 1}{x^2 - x - 2} = Ax + B + \dfrac{C}{x + 1} + \dfrac{D}{x - 2}$

Find the values of the constants A, B, C and D. **(5)**

> **Problem solving** It is easier to manage this if you write
> $x^3 - 3x^2 + 1 = (Ax + B)(x + 1)(x - 2) + C(x - 2) + D(x + 1)$

....

....

....

....

....

Algebraic division

Guided 1 Use long division to divide $2x^4 - 7x^3 - 10x^2 + 24x + 10$ by $x^2 - 3$ **(4)**

Remember to write $x^2 - 3$ as $x^2 + 0x - 3$.

$$x^2 + 0x - 3 \overline{\smash{\big)}\ 2x^4 - 7x^3 - 10x^2 + 24x + 10}$$

Quotient: $2x^2 \dotfill$

$$\underline{2x^4 + 0x^3 - 6x^2}$$

$$-7x^3 - 4x^2 + 24x + 10$$

$\dotfill$

Always line up the terms with the same power of x.

2 Given that

$$\frac{2x^4 - 5x^3 - x + 6}{x^2 - 2} \equiv ax^2 + bx + c + \frac{dx + e}{x^2 - 2}, \qquad x^2 \neq 2$$

find the values of the constants a, b, c, d and e. **(4)**

Problem solving Multiply through by $(x^2 - 2)$, expand brackets and collect like terms, then compare coefficients, starting with the highest power of x.

3 Given that

$$\frac{5x^4 - 2x^3 - 3x^2 - 8}{x^2 - x - 2} \equiv ax^2 + bx + c + \frac{dx + e}{x^2 - x - 2} \qquad x \neq -1, \ x \neq 2$$

find the values of the constants a, b, c, d and e. **(4)**

Domain and range

Guided   **1**   The functions f and g are defined by

$$f : x \mapsto x^2 - 2, \quad x \in \mathbb{R}, \ x^2 \neq 2 \qquad \text{and} \qquad g : x \mapsto 2 + \frac{3}{x}, \quad x \in \mathbb{R}, \ x \neq 0$$

(a) Show that the composite function gf is $\ gf : x \mapsto \dfrac{2x^2 - 1}{x^2 - 2}$ **(3)**

$$gf(x) = 2 + \frac{3}{x^2 - 2} = \frac{2(............) + 3}{x^2 - 2} = \frac{.............................}{.........................}$$

(b) Find $\ gf\left(\dfrac{1}{2}\right)$.   **(1)**

....

(c) Solve $\ gf(x) = 0$ **(2)**

....

2   The functions f and g are defined by

$$f : x \mapsto 1 - 5x, \quad x \in \mathbb{R} \qquad \text{and} \qquad g : x \mapsto \frac{2x}{x + 3}, \quad x \in \mathbb{R}, \ x \neq -3$$

(a) Show that the composite function gf is $\ gf : x \mapsto \dfrac{2 - 10x}{4 - 5x}$ **(2)**

....

....

(b) Find $\ gf(-4)$.   **(1)**

....

(c) Work out the composite function gg.   **(4)**

....

....

....

....

(d) Find $\ gg(-1)$.   **(1)**

....

(e) Solve the equation $\ gf(x) = f(x)$ **(4)**

....

....

....

....

Graphs and range

 1 The function f has domain $-5 < x < 6$.
Here is a sketch of the graph of $y = f(x)$.

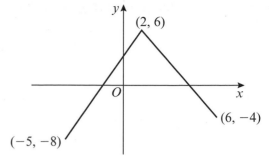

(a) Write down the range of f. **(1)**

Range of f is $-8 < f(x) < $ ....

(b) Find ff(6). **(2)**

ff(6) = f(−4) = ...

2 Find the range of the function defined by

> Use the gradient to work out f(−4).

(a) $f(x) = \dfrac{2x - 1}{x - 5}, \qquad 6 < x < 8$ **(2)**

....

....

(b) $g(x) = x^2 - 10x + 13, \qquad 0 < x < 11$ **(2)**

> Complete the square and draw a sketch graph of $y = g(x)$.

....

....

....

....

3 The function f is defined by

$$f : x \mapsto \frac{5x + 14}{x^2 + 4x - 12} - \frac{3}{x - 2}, \qquad x \in \mathbb{R}, \ -5 < x < 2$$

(a) Show that $f(x) = \dfrac{2}{x + 6}$ **(3)**

....

....

....

....

....

....

....

(b) Find the range of f. **(2)**

....

....

Inverse functions

Guided 1 The function f is defined by

$$f: x \mapsto \frac{2x}{3} - 4, \qquad x \in \mathbb{R}, \ -3 < x < 9$$

(a) Find $f^{-1}(x)$. **(2)**

$$y = \frac{2x}{3} - 4$$

$$3y = 2x - 12$$

$x = $ ....

so the inverse function f^{-1} is $x \mapsto$ ....

(b) Find the domain of f^{-1}. **(2)**

....

....

2 The function g is defined by

$$g: x \mapsto \frac{2x + 5}{x - 6}, \qquad x \in \mathbb{R}, \ x > 8$$

> Write the function in the form $y = \ldots$, then rearrange to make x the subject.

(a) Find $g^{-1}(x)$. **(3)**

....

....

....

....

(b) Find the domain of g^{-1}. **(2)**

> Consider the value of g when $x = 8$ and when $x \to \infty$.

....

....

3 The function h is defined by

$$h: x \mapsto \frac{x + 4}{3x + 1}, \qquad x \in \mathbb{R}, \ x > 0$$

(a) Find $h^{-1}(x)$. **(3)**

....

....

....

(b) Find the domain of h^{-1}. **(2)**

> Consider the value of h when $x = 0$ and when $x \to \infty$.

....

....

Inverse graphs

Guided **1** The diagram shows part of the curve with equation $y = f(x)$.
The curve intersects the coordinate axes at $(-2, 0)$ and $(0, 4)$.

On the same axes, sketch the curve with equation $y = f^{-1}(x)$.   **(2)**

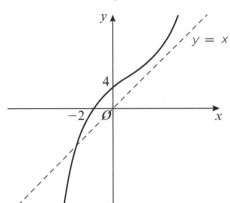

> Draw the line $y = x$, then reflect the graph of $y = f(x)$ in the line $y = x$ to find the graph of the inverse function.

> When reflecting points in the line $y = x$, the x- and y-coordinates swap over.

2 The function f has domain $-6 \leqslant x \leqslant 3$ and is linear from $(-6, -4)$ to $(0, -3)$ and from $(0, -3)$ to $(3, 5)$.
A sketch of the graph of $y = f(x)$ is shown.
On the same axes, sketch the graph of $y = f^{-1}(x)$.
Show the coordinates of the points corresponding to A and B.   **(3)**

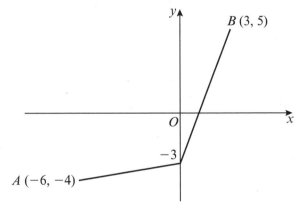

3 The diagrams show the graphs of four functions.
Which of these graphs have inverse functions?
For those that do not have inverse functions, explain why.   **(4)**

A 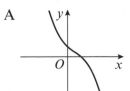   B 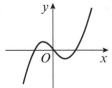   C 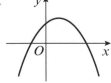   D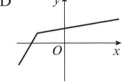

> The inverse of a function only exists if the function is a one-to-one function, which means that the function maps each point in the domain to a single point in the range.

....

....

Modulus

Guided 1　The diagram shows a sketch of the graph of $y = f(x)$.

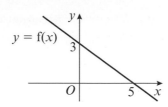

On separate diagrams, sketch the graphs of

(a) $y = |f(x)|$ **(3)**　　　　　　　　　　　　(b) $y = f(|x|)$ **(3)**

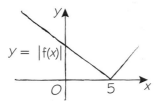

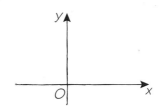

> For $y = |f(x)|$, any points on $f(x)$ below the x-axis are reflected in the x-axis. All the y-values must be positive.

> For $y = f(|x|)$, replace the graph for values of $x < 0$ with a reflection of the graph for values of $x > 0$.

Guided 2　For each of the following graphs of $y = f(x)$, sketch the graphs of

(i) $y = |f(x)|$　　　　　　　　　　　(ii) $y = f(|x|)$

Label any points of intersection with the axes or any turning points.

(a)

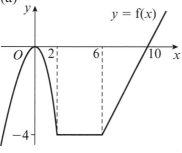

(i)

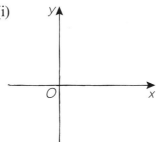

(ii)

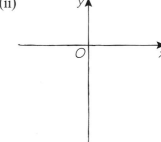

(2)

(b)

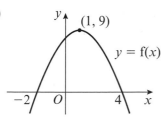

(2)

(c)

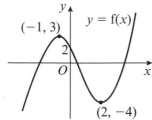

(2)

Modulus transformations

Guided

1 The diagram shows the graph of $y = f(x)$, which consists of two line segments meeting at $(-4, 2)$.

Sketch the graph of $y = 3|f(-x)|$ **(3)**

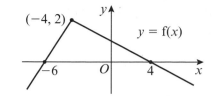

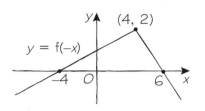

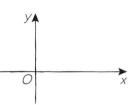

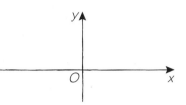

> You can do one step at a time; there are three steps which should be carried out in order.

2 The diagram shows the graph of $y = f(x)$.

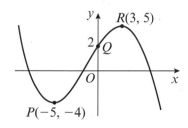

On separate diagrams, sketch the graphs of

(a) $y = f(-x) + 4$ **(3)**   (b) $y = |f(x + 3)|$ **(3)**

On each diagram, mark the positions of the points corresponding to P, Q and R.

> The order in which you do transformations is important.

Modulus equations

Guided

1 The function f is defined by

$$f : x \mapsto |7 - 2x|, \qquad x \in \mathbb{R}$$

(a) Sketch the graph with equation $y = f(x)$, showing the points where the graph crosses the axes. **(2)**

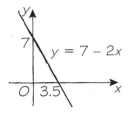 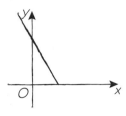

(b) Solve $f(x) = x + 3$ **(2)**

$7 - 2x = x + 3$ $\qquad\qquad$ $-(7 - 2x) = x + 3$

$x = \dots\dots\dots\dots$ $\qquad\qquad$ $x = \dots\dots\dots\dots$

> You need to solve two equations: a positive argument and a negative argument.

2 Solve $5 - |2x - 4| = 2 - \frac{1}{4}x$ **(5)**

....

....

....

....

3 The function f is defined by $f : x \mapsto |6 - 3x|, \; x \in \mathbb{R}$

(a) Sketch the graph of $y = f(x)$, showing the points where the graph crosses the axes. **(2)**

(b) Explain why $f(x) = -x$ has no solutions. **(1)**

....

(c) Solve $f(x) = x$ **(3)** > Use your graph to check that the solutions definitely exist.

....

....

....

Arithmetic sequences

Guided 1 The nth term of an arithmetic sequence is $(3n - 2)$.

(a) Write down the first three terms of this sequence. **(2)**

| To find the first three terms, substitute $n = 1$, 2 and 3 into the formula for the nth term. |

First term $n = 1$ $3 \times 1 - 2$ = ...

Second term $n = 2$ $3 \times$ .... = ...

Third term   .... = ...

(b) State the value of the common difference. **(1)**

| The common difference is the difference between any two consecutive terms in the sequence. |

....

Guided 2 The first term of an arithmetic sequence is 40 and the common difference is -2.5

(a) Find the value of the 20th term. **(2)**

| The general formula for the nth term of an arithmetic sequence is $a + (n - 1)d$. |

$a =$ .... $d =$ ....

20th term $= a + (20 - 1)d =$ .... $=$ ....

The rth term of the sequence is 0.

(b) Find the value of r. **(2)**

....

....

3 The first term of an arithmetic sequence is a and the common difference is d.
The 15th term of the sequence is 9 and the 20th term of the sequence is $16\frac{1}{2}$

(a) Use this information to write down two equations for a and d. **(2)**

....

....

(b) Find the values of a and d. **(2)**

....

....

....

4 An arithmetic sequence has first term $k^2 - 11k$ and common difference k, where $k > 0$
The sixth term of the sequence is 15.
Work out the value of k, giving your answer in the form $a + b\sqrt{6}$, where a and b are integers. **(5)**

....

....

....

....

....

Arithmetic series

> **Guided**　**1** Find the sum of the arithmetic sequence $-8, -5, -2, \ldots, 19$　　　　(3)

$a = $ ....　　$d = $ ....

$a + (n - 1)d = 19$

.... $= 19$

> To find the number of terms, n, solve $a + (n - 1)d = 19$, then use $S_n = \frac{1}{2}n[2a + (n - 1)d]$.

....

....

2 Find the sum of the odd numbers from 1 to 99 inclusive.

　　$1 + 3 + 5 + \ldots + 99$　　　　(3)

....

....

....

> **Guided**　**3** An arithmetic series has first term a and common difference d. The sum of the first 10 terms of the series is 150

> Use $S_n = \frac{1}{2}n[2a + (n - 1)d]$ and write in simplest form.

(a) Show that $2a + 9d = 30$　　　　(2)

$S_{10} = $ ....

....

Given also that the fifth term of the series is 14:

(b) write down a second equation in a and d　　　　(1)

....

(c) find the value of a and the value of d.　　　(4)　> Solve the two equations simultaneously.

....

....

4 An arithmetic series has first term 149 and common difference -2. The sum of the first n terms of the series is 5000

(a) Form an equation in n, and show that your equation may be written as

　　$n^2 - 150n + 5000 = 0$　　　　(3)

....

....

....

(b) Solve the equation in part (a).　　　　(3)

....

....

Geometric sequences

1 A geometric sequence has first term $a = 640$ and common ratio $r = \frac{5}{8}$
Find the 15th term of the sequence, giving your answer to 3 significant figures. **(2)**

....

....

> The nth term of a geometric
> sequence is $u_n = ar^{n-1}$.

> **Guided**

2 The fourth term of a geometric sequence is 72 and the seventh term of the sequence is 9

For this sequence, find:

(a) the common ratio **(2)**

> Divide ② by ① to eliminate a and find
> r. Note that, as the terms are getting
> smaller, r must be less than 1.

Fourth term: $ar^{\cdots} = 72$ ①

Seventh term: $ar^{\cdots} = 9$ ②

② ÷ ①: ....

....

(b) the first term. **(2)**

> Substitute your value of r into ①
> or ② to work out the value of a.

....

> **Guided**

3 The first three terms of a geometric sequence are
k, 15 and $k + 40$ respectively.
Find two possible values of k. **(5)**

> The common ratio is found by dividing any
> term of the sequence by the previous term.

> Rearrange to find a quadratic equation and
> solve by factorising.

$\dfrac{15}{k} = \dfrac{\cdots}{\cdots}$

....

....

....

4 The first three terms of a geometric sequence are $(k + 6)$, k and $(2k - 16)$ respectively, where k is a positive constant.

(a) Show that $k^2 - 4k - 96 = 0$ **(4)**

....

....

....

....

(b) Hence show that $k = 12$ **(2)**

....

....

(c) Find the common ratio of this sequence. **(2)**

....

....

Geometric series

Guided **1** A geometric series has first term 150 and common ratio $\frac{2}{3}$

Find the sum of the first 20 terms of the series, giving your answer to 1 decimal place. **(2)**

$$S_{20} = \frac{150(1 - (\ldots\ldots)^{\ldots\ldots})}{1 - (\ldots\ldots)} = \ldots\ldots\ldots\ldots\ldots$$

> The sum of the first n terms is $S_n = \dfrac{a(1 - r^n)}{1 - r}$

Guided **2** Find $\displaystyle\sum_{k=1}^{8} 10(3^k)$ **(3)**

> Write out some of the terms of the sequence to help you work out the values of a and r.

$$\sum_{k=1}^{8} 10(3^k) = 30 + \ldots\ldots\ldots + \ldots\ldots\ldots + \ldots\ldots\ldots + \ldots$$

$$a = \ldots\ldots\ldots \qquad r = \ldots\ldots\ldots$$

$$S_8 = \frac{\ldots\ldots\ldots(\ldots\ldots\ldots\ldots\ldots\ldots\ldots)}{\ldots\ldots\ldots\ldots\ldots\ldots\ldots} = \ldots\ldots\ldots\ldots\ldots = \ldots\ldots\ldots\ldots$$

3 A geometric series has first term 8 and common ratio -1.2

Find the sum of the first 50 terms of the series, giving your answer to 1 decimal place. **(2)**

....

....

....

4 In the geometric series $1 + 3 + 9 + 27 + \ldots$, each term is 3 times the previous term.

Find the sum of the first n terms of this series. **(4)**

....

....

....

5 Ms Burton will receive a salary of £38 000 in 2018. Each year she will receive an increase in salary of 3% so that her annual salaries form a geometric sequence. The first increase in salary is given in 2019.

(a) Find, to the nearest £100, Ms Burton's salary in the year 2021. **(2)**

....

....

(b) Find, to the nearest £1000, the total amount of salary she will receive from 2018 until 2030. **(4)**

....

....

....

Infinite series

Guided 1 Find the sum to infinity of the geometric series $\frac{2}{3} + \frac{1}{2} + \frac{3}{8} + \ldots$ **(3)**

$a = $ ....　　　$r = \dfrac{1}{2} \div \dfrac{\ldots}{\ldots} = $ ....

> Find r by working out $u_2 \div u_1$. You can check your answer by working out $u_3 \div u_2$.

$S_\infty = \dfrac{a}{1-r} = \dfrac{\ldots}{1 - \ldots} = $ ....

> $S_\infty = \dfrac{a}{1-r}$, provided $-1 < r < 1$.

Guided 2 The first term of a geometric series is 150 and the sum to infinity of the series is 375
Find the common ratio. **(3)**

$a = $ ....　　　$S_\infty = \dfrac{a}{1-r} = \dfrac{\ldots}{1 - \ldots} = 375$

> Rearrange the equation for S_∞ to find r.

....

3 The first three terms of a geometric series are 15, 13.5 and 12.15 respectively.

(a) Find the sum to infinity of the geometric series. **(3)**

....

....

(b) State the condition for an infinite geometric series with common ratio r to be convergent. **(1)**

....

(c) Find the difference between the sum to infinity of this series and the sum of the first 50 terms, giving your answer to 3 decimal places. **(3)**

....

....

....

4 A geometric series has first term a and common ratio r. The second term of the series is 12 and the sum to infinity of the series is 50

(a) Show that $25r^2 - 25r + 6 = 0$ **(4)**

....

....

....

....

....

(b) Find the two possible values of r and the corresponding values of a. **(4)**

....

....

....

Recurrence relations

Guided   **1**   A sequence $a_1, a_2, a_3, \ldots$ is defined by $a_1 = 2$

$$a_{n+1} = 2a_n - 3, \; n \geqslant 1$$

(a) Find the value of a_2 and the value of a_3.   **(2)**

$a_1 = 2$

$a_2 = 2a_1 - 3 = \; \ldots\ldots\ldots\ldots\ldots$

$a_3 = 2a_2 - 3 = \; \ldots\ldots\ldots\ldots\ldots$

> The recurrence relationship tells you how to find each term in the sequence from the previous term.

(b) Calculate the value of $\displaystyle\sum_{r=1}^{5} a_r$ **(3)**

> The Σ symbol means 'sum of'. You need to work out $a_1 + a_2 + a_3 + a_4 + a_5$.

$a_4 = \; \ldots\ldots\ldots\ldots\ldots$ $a_5 = \; \ldots\ldots\ldots\ldots\ldots$

$a_1 + a_2 + a_3 + a_4 + a_5 = \; \ldots\ldots\ldots\ldots\ldots\ldots\ldots\ldots\ldots\ldots\ldots\ldots \; = \; \ldots\ldots\ldots\ldots$

2   A sequence $a_1, a_2, a_3, \ldots$ is defined by $a_1 = k$

$$a_{n+1} = 3a_n - 2, \; n \geqslant 1$$

where k is a positive integer.

(a) Write down an expression for a_2 in terms of k.   **(1)**

$\ldots\ldots\ldots\ldots\ldots\ldots\ldots\ldots\ldots\ldots\ldots\ldots\ldots\ldots\ldots\ldots\ldots\ldots\ldots\ldots\ldots\ldots\ldots\ldots\ldots\ldots$

(b) Show that $a_3 = 9k - 8$ **(2)**

$\ldots\ldots\ldots\ldots\ldots\ldots\ldots\ldots\ldots\ldots\ldots\ldots\ldots\ldots\ldots\ldots\ldots\ldots\ldots\ldots\ldots\ldots\ldots\ldots\ldots\ldots$

(c) Given that $\displaystyle\sum_{r=1}^{4} a_r = 44$, find the value of k.   **(4)**

$\ldots\ldots\ldots\ldots\ldots\ldots\ldots\ldots\ldots\ldots\ldots\ldots\ldots\ldots\ldots\ldots\ldots\ldots\ldots\ldots\ldots\ldots\ldots\ldots\ldots\ldots$

$\ldots\ldots\ldots\ldots\ldots\ldots\ldots\ldots\ldots\ldots\ldots\ldots\ldots\ldots\ldots\ldots\ldots\ldots\ldots\ldots\ldots\ldots\ldots\ldots\ldots\ldots$

$\ldots\ldots\ldots\ldots\ldots\ldots\ldots\ldots\ldots\ldots\ldots\ldots\ldots\ldots\ldots\ldots\ldots\ldots\ldots\ldots\ldots\ldots\ldots\ldots\ldots\ldots$

$\ldots\ldots\ldots\ldots\ldots\ldots\ldots\ldots\ldots\ldots\ldots\ldots\ldots\ldots\ldots\ldots\ldots\ldots\ldots\ldots\ldots\ldots\ldots\ldots\ldots\ldots$

(d) State whether this sequence is increasing, decreasing or neither.   **(1)**

$\ldots\ldots\ldots\ldots\ldots\ldots\ldots\ldots\ldots\ldots\ldots\ldots\ldots\ldots\ldots\ldots\ldots\ldots\ldots\ldots\ldots\ldots\ldots\ldots\ldots\ldots$

3   A sequence $x_1, x_2, x_3, \ldots$ is defined by $x_1 = 1$

$$x_{n+1} = px_n + 3, \; n \geqslant 1$$

where p is a constant.

(a) Write down an expression for x_2 in terms of p.   **(1)**

$\ldots\ldots\ldots\ldots\ldots\ldots\ldots\ldots\ldots\ldots\ldots\ldots\ldots\ldots\ldots\ldots\ldots\ldots\ldots\ldots\ldots\ldots\ldots\ldots\ldots\ldots$

(b) Show that $x_3 = p^2 + 3p + 3$ **(2)**

$\ldots\ldots\ldots\ldots\ldots\ldots\ldots\ldots\ldots\ldots\ldots\ldots\ldots\ldots\ldots\ldots\ldots\ldots\ldots\ldots\ldots\ldots\ldots\ldots\ldots\ldots$

(c) Given that $x_3 = 31$, find the possible values of p.   **(3)**

$\ldots\ldots\ldots\ldots\ldots\ldots\ldots\ldots\ldots\ldots\ldots\ldots\ldots\ldots\ldots\ldots\ldots\ldots\ldots\ldots\ldots\ldots\ldots\ldots\ldots\ldots$

$\ldots\ldots\ldots\ldots\ldots\ldots\ldots\ldots\ldots\ldots\ldots\ldots\ldots\ldots\ldots\ldots\ldots\ldots\ldots\ldots\ldots\ldots\ldots\ldots\ldots\ldots$

$\ldots\ldots\ldots\ldots\ldots\ldots\ldots\ldots\ldots\ldots\ldots\ldots\ldots\ldots\ldots\ldots\ldots\ldots\ldots\ldots\ldots\ldots\ldots\ldots\ldots\ldots$

Modelling with series

Guided   1   Kelly pays into a savings scheme. In the first year she pays £600. Her payments then increase by £100 each year so she pays £700 in the second year, £800 in the third year and so on.

(a) Find the amount that Kelly will pay in the 25th year. **(2)**

$a =$ .... $d =$ ....

> This is an arithmetic sequence. Use the formula for the nth term, $u_n = a + (n-1)d$.

25th year: $u_n =$ ....

(b) Find the total amount that Kelly will pay in over the 25 years. **(2)**

$S_{25} =$ ....

> Find the sum of the first 25 terms. Use $S_n = \frac{1}{2}n[2a + (n-1)d]$.

....

....

Guided   2   Micah saves some money each week over a period of w weeks. He saves 50p in week 1, 60p in week 2, 70p in week 3 and so on, so that his weekly savings form an arithmetic sequence. Micah saves a total of £121.50 over the period of w weeks.

> Use $S_n = \frac{1}{2}n[2a + (n-1)d]$. Remember to work with consistent units.

Show that $w(w + 9) = 45 \times 54$ and hence write down the value of w. **(5)**

$a =$ .... $d =$ ....

$S_w = \frac{1}{2}w($ ....$) =$ ....

....

....

....

3   A company, which makes racing bikes, plans to increase its production.

The number of racing bikes produced is to be increased by 10 each week from 150 in week 1 to 160 in week 2, to 170 in week 3 and so on, until it is producing 500 in week N.

(a) Find the value of N. **(2)**

....

....

The company plans to continue to produce 500 racing bikes each week.

(b) Find the total number of racing bikes that will be made in the first 52 weeks, starting from and including week 1. **(5)**

....

....

....

....

Series and logs

Guided **1** A geometric series has first term 12 and common ratio 2.5
Find the smallest value of n for which the sum of the
first n terms exceeds 20 000. **(4)**

> Remember that in an inequality, if you multiply or divide by a **negative** number, the **direction** of the inequality changes.

$a = $ .... $r = $ .... $S_n = \dfrac{a(1 - r^n)}{1 - r}$

$\dfrac{12(1 - \text{............})}{1 - \text{............}} > 20\,000$

> Remember to round n up to the nearest whole number.

....

....

Guided **2** A motorcycle was purchased for £25 000 on 1 January.
On 1 January each following year, the value of the motorcycle
is 85% of its value on 1 January in the previous year. The value
of the motorcycle falls below £1500 for the first time m years
after it was purchased. Find the value of m. **(4)**

> You need to identify the first **term** in the series that is less than £1500.

$a = $ .... $r = $ ....   nth term $= ar^{n-1}$

.... < 1500

> Remember that if $0 < a < 1$, then $\log a$ is negative.

....

....

....

....

3 A geometric series has first term 12 and common ratio 0.8
Find the smallest value of n for which the sum of the first n terms exceeds 40. **(4)**

....

....

....

....

....

4 The adult population of a town is 250 000 at the end of Year 1. A model predicts that the adult
population of the town will increase by 4% each year, forming a geometric sequence.
The model predicts that Year N will be the first year in which the adult population of the town
exceeds 500 000.

(a) Show that $(N - 1) \log 1.04 > \log 2$ **(3)**

....

....

....

(b) Find the value of N. **(2)**

....

....

Binomial expansion 2

> **Guided** 1 $f(x) = (1 + 4x)^{\frac{3}{2}}, \qquad |x| < \frac{1}{4}$

Find the binomial expansion of f(x),
in ascending powers of x, up to and
including the term in x^3. Give each coefficient in its simplest form.   **(5)**

> Take great care working out the coefficients.
> For x^2: $\dfrac{\left(\frac{3}{2}\right)\left(\frac{1}{2}\right)(4^2)}{1 \times 2} = \dfrac{\frac{3}{2} \times \frac{1}{2} \times 16}{1 \times 2} = \dfrac{3 \times 4}{1 \times 2} = 6$

$$(1 + 4x)^{\frac{3}{2}} = 1 + \left(\tfrac{3}{2}\right)(4x) + \frac{\left(\frac{3}{2}\right)\left(\frac{1}{2}\right)(4x)^2}{1 \times 2} + \frac{\dots\dots\dots\dots\dots(4x)^3}{1 \times 2 \times 3} + \dots\dots\dots$$

$$= 1 + 6x + 6x^2 \dots\dots\dots\dots\dots\dots$$

> **Guided** 2   Find the series expansion of $\sqrt{4 - x}$, $|x| < 4$, up to and
including the term in x^3, simplifying each term.   **(7)**

> Don't forget to multiply all the terms by 2.

$$\sqrt{4 - x} = (4 - x)^{\frac{1}{2}} = \left[4\left(1 - \tfrac{x}{4}\right)\right]^{\frac{1}{2}} = 4^{\frac{1}{2}}\left(1 - \tfrac{x}{4}\right)^{\frac{1}{2}} = 2\left(1 - \tfrac{x}{4}\right)^{\frac{1}{2}}$$

$$2\left(1 - \tfrac{x}{4}\right)^{\frac{1}{2}} = 2\left[1 + \left(\tfrac{1}{2}\right)\left(\tfrac{-x}{4}\right) + \frac{(\dots\dots)(\dots\dots)\left(\frac{-x}{4}\right)^2}{1 \times 2} + \frac{\dots\dots\dots\dots\dots\dots}{\dots\dots\dots\dots\dots\dots} + \dots\dots\dots\right]$$

....

....

3   (a)   Expand $\dfrac{1}{\sqrt{4 + 5x}}$ in ascending powers of x up to and including the term in x^3, simplifying
each term, and state the range of values of x for which the expansion is valid.   **(6)**

....

....

....

....

....

....

   (b)   Use your expansion, with a suitable value of x, to work out an approximate value

of $\dfrac{1}{\sqrt{3.9}}$, giving your answer to 5 decimal places. State the value of x which you
use in your expansion, and show all your working.   **(3)**

....

....

   (c)   Find the first three terms in the series expansion of $\dfrac{x + 4}{\sqrt{4 + 5x}}$, simplifying each term.   **(3)**

....

....

....

....

Radians, arcs and sectors

Guided 1 In the diagram, OAB is a sector of a circle, radius 6 cm.
The arc AB is 9 cm long.
Find:

(a) the size of $\angle AOB$ in radians **(2)**

> Use arc length $= r\theta$ to work out the size of $\angle AOB$.

$9 = \text{..........}\ \theta \qquad \theta = \text{.....................}$

(b) the area of the sector AOB. **(2)**

Area $= \frac{1}{2}r^2\theta = \frac{1}{2} \times \text{..........}^2 \times \text{..........} = \text{..........}\ cm^2$

> Use area $= \frac{1}{2}r^2\theta$ to work out the area of the sector.

Guided 2 In the diagram, ABC is a sector of a circle, radius 10 cm.
Given that the size of $\angle BAC$ is 0.65 radians, find:

(a) the perimeter of the sector ABC **(3)**

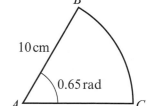

> Perimeter = arc length + 2 × radius

Arc length $= r\theta = \text{..............} = \text{..........}\ cm$

Perimeter $= \text{..........} + \text{..........} + \text{..........} = \text{..........}\ cm$

(b) the area of the sector. **(2)**

Area $= \frac{1}{2}r^2\theta = \frac{1}{2} \times \text{..............} = \text{..........}\ cm^2$

3 In the diagram, PQR is a sector of a circle, radius 7 cm
and angle $PQR = \frac{2\pi}{3}$
Find:

(a) the exact length of arc PR **(2)**

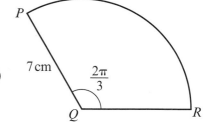

> Watch for questions which ask for **exact** answers. This usually means giving your answer in terms of π or in surd form.

....

(b) the exact value of the area of the sector. **(2)**

....

4 In the diagram, AOB is a sector of a circle radius 8 cm.
The area of the sector is 45 cm².
Find:

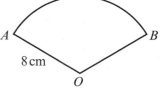

(a) the size of $\angle AOB$ in radians to 3 significant figures **(3)**

....

....

(b) the perimeter of sector AOB. **(3)**

....

....

Areas of triangles

> **Guided**

1 In the diagram, $PQRS$ is a sector of a circle with centre Q and radius $5\sqrt{2}$ cm.
Given that the length of the straight line PR is 10 cm:

(a) find the exact size of angle PQR in radians **(3)**

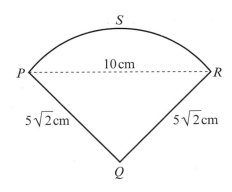

$$\cos Q = \frac{PQ^2 + QR^2 - PR^2}{2 \times PQ \times QR}$$

$$= \frac{(\ldots\ldots)^2 + (\ldots\ldots)^2 - (\ldots\ldots)^2}{2 \times \ldots\ldots \times \ldots\ldots}$$

$$= \frac{\ldots\ldots\ldots - \ldots\ldots\ldots}{\ldots\ldots\ldots} = \ldots\ldots\ldots$$

$Q = \ldots\ldots\ldots$

(b) show that the area of $PQRS$ is $\frac{25}{2}\pi$ cm^2. **(2)**

Area of sector $= \frac{1}{2}r^2\theta = \frac{1}{2} \times \ldots\ldots\ldots\ldots\ldots\ldots = \ldots\ldots\ldots$

Area $= \ldots\ldots\ldots$ cm^2

(c) Find the exact area of the triangle PQR. **(2)**

> When you know two sides and the included angle of a triangle you can use area $= \frac{1}{2} ab \sin\theta$

Area of triangle $= \frac{1}{2} ab\sin\theta$

$$= \frac{1}{2} \times \ldots\ldots\ldots\ldots\ldots\ldots = \ldots\ldots\ldots$$

Area $= \ldots\ldots\ldots$ cm^2

> **Guided**

2 In the diagram, ABC is a triangle and ABD is a sector of a circle with centre A. Find the shaded area, R, giving your answer to 3 significant figures. **(5)**

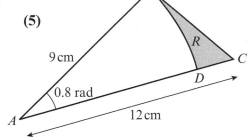

> Area of R = area of triangle ABC – area of sector ABD

Area of $ABC = \ldots\ldots\ldots\ldots\ldots\ldots\ldots\ldots$

Area of $ABD = \ldots\ldots\ldots\ldots\ldots\ldots\ldots\ldots$

Area of $R = \ldots\ldots\ldots\ldots\ldots\ldots\ldots\ldots$

3 The diagram shows ABC, a sector of a circle with centre A and radius 7 cm. The size of $\angle BAC$ is 0.8 radians and D is the midpoint of AC. Find the area of R, giving your answer to 3 significant figures. **(6)**

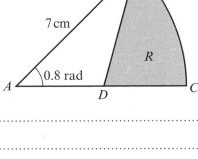

$\ldots\ldots\ldots\ldots\ldots\ldots\ldots\ldots\ldots\ldots\ldots\ldots\ldots\ldots\ldots\ldots\ldots\ldots\ldots\ldots\ldots\ldots\ldots$

$\ldots\ldots\ldots\ldots\ldots\ldots\ldots\ldots\ldots\ldots\ldots\ldots\ldots\ldots\ldots\ldots\ldots\ldots\ldots\ldots\ldots\ldots\ldots$

$\ldots\ldots\ldots\ldots\ldots\ldots\ldots\ldots\ldots\ldots\ldots\ldots\ldots\ldots\ldots\ldots\ldots\ldots\ldots\ldots\ldots\ldots\ldots$

$\ldots\ldots\ldots\ldots\ldots\ldots\ldots\ldots\ldots\ldots\ldots\ldots\ldots\ldots\ldots\ldots\ldots\ldots\ldots\ldots\ldots\ldots\ldots$

$\ldots\ldots\ldots\ldots\ldots\ldots\ldots\ldots\ldots\ldots\ldots\ldots\ldots\ldots\ldots\ldots\ldots\ldots\ldots\ldots\ldots\ldots\ldots$

Sec, cosec and cot

> **Guided** **1** Sketch the graph of $y = 2 \operatorname{cosec} \left(\frac{1}{2}\theta\right)$

for $-360° < \theta < 360°$ **(2)**

Start with the graph of $y = \operatorname{cosec} \theta$

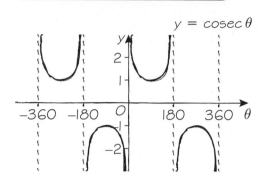

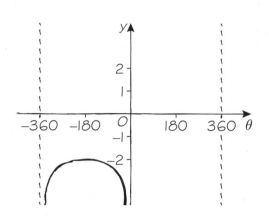

You need to apply two transformations: horizontal stretch scale factor 2, and vertical stretch scale factor 2.

2 Sketch the graph of $y = 2 \sec\left(x - \frac{\pi}{2}\right)$ for $0 < x < 2\pi$ **(2)**

You need to be able to work with radians.

Start with $y = \sec x$

3 Sketch the graph of $y = \cot\left(\theta + \frac{\pi}{2}\right) - 1$ for $-\pi < \theta < \pi$ **(2)**

Trigonometric equations 3

Guided 1 Solve, for $-180° \leqslant x \leqslant 180°$

$\sqrt{3} \operatorname{cosec} 2x = 2$

Give your answers in degrees. **(5)**

$\operatorname{cosec} 2x = \dfrac{2}{\sqrt{3}}, \qquad \dfrac{1}{\sin 2x} = \dfrac{2}{\sqrt{3}}, \qquad \sin 2x = \dfrac{\sqrt{3}}{2}$

$-180° \leqslant x \leqslant 180° \quad so \quad -360° \leqslant 2x \leqslant 360°$

> Remember to double the range for $2x$.

$2x = -300°, \ldots\ldots\ldots, \ldots\ldots\ldots, \ldots\ldots\ldots$

$x = \ldots\ldots\ldots, \ldots\ldots\ldots, \ldots\ldots\ldots, \ldots\ldots\ldots$

2 Solve $\cot 2\theta = \sqrt{3}$ for $0 \leqslant \theta \leqslant \pi$
Give your answers in terms of π. **(5)**

....

....

....

....

3 Solve $2 \sec^2 x = 9 \sec x + 5$ for $0° \leqslant x \leqslant 360°$
Give your answer in degrees to 1 decimal place. **(6)**

> Substitute A for $\sec x$ to give an equation you can more easily rearrange as a quadratic and factorise.

....

....

....

....

....

....

4 Solve $2 \operatorname{cosec} \theta - 3 = 5 \sin \theta$ for $0° \leqslant \theta \leqslant 360°$
Give your answers in degrees to 1 decimal place. **(6)**

....

....

....

....

....

....

Trigonometric identities 2

Guided **1** Prove that $\operatorname{cosec}\theta - \sin\theta \equiv \cot\theta\cos\theta$ **(3)**

$$\operatorname{cosec}\theta - \sin\theta \equiv \frac{1}{\sin\theta} - \sin\theta \equiv \frac{1 - \sin^2\theta}{\sin\theta} \equiv \text{..................} \equiv \text{..}$$

> Use $1 - \sin^2\theta = \cos^2\theta$, then rewrite $\cos^2\theta$ as $\cos\theta\cos\theta$ to obtain the result.

> Always start with one side of the identity and use trig manipulation to achieve the expression on the other side.

2 Solve $\sec^2\theta + \tan\theta = 1$ for $0 \le \theta \le 2\pi$
Give your answers in terms of π. **(5)**

> Use $\sec^2\theta \equiv 1 + \tan^2\theta$

....

....

....

....

3 Prove that $\sec^2\theta + \operatorname{cosec}^2\theta \equiv \sec^2\theta\operatorname{cosec}^2\theta$ **(4)**

....

....

....

....

4 Solve $4\sec^2 2\theta = 5\tan 2\theta + 3\tan^2 2\theta$
for $0° \le \theta \le 180°$
Give your answers in degrees to 1 decimal place. **(7)**

> **Problem solving** Use $\sec^2 2\theta \equiv 1 + \tan^2 2\theta$ and form a quadratic in $\tan 2\theta$. Remember to double the range.

....

....

....

....

....

5 Solve $4\cot^2\theta - 3\operatorname{cosec}^2\theta = 2\cot\theta$ for $0° \le \theta \le 360°$
Give your answers in degrees to 1 decimal place. **(7)**

....

....

....

....

....

Arcsin, arccos and arctan

1   Write down the value of each of the following in radians.

    (a) $\arcsin\left(\dfrac{1}{2}\right)$ **(1)**   (b) $\arccos\left(\dfrac{-\sqrt{3}}{2}\right)$ **(1)**   (c) $\arctan(-1)$ **(1)**

....

Guided

2   The function f is defined by

$$f : x \mapsto \arccos x + \frac{\pi}{4}, \qquad x \in \mathbb{R},\ -1 \leqslant x \leqslant 1$$

    (a)   Find $f\left(\dfrac{\sqrt{3}}{2}\right)$, giving your answer in terms of π.   **(2)**

$$f\left(\frac{\sqrt{3}}{2}\right) = \arccos\left(\frac{\sqrt{3}}{2}\right) + \frac{\pi}{4} = \frac{\pi}{6} + \frac{\pi}{4} = \frac{\text{............}}{\text{............}}$$

    (b)   Solve the equation $f(x) = \dfrac{7\pi}{12}$, giving your answer as an exact value.   **(3)**

....

....

    (c)   Find $f^{-1}(x)$ and state its domain, and sketch the graph of $y = f^{-1}(x)$, showing the coordinates of the point where the graph crosses the x-axis.   **(6)**

Let $y = \arccos x + \dfrac{\pi}{4}$, so $y - \dfrac{\pi}{4} = \arccos x$

$\cos(............) = x$

So $f^{-1}(x) = ...$

Domain of f^{-1} = range of f,

so ....

3   The function g is defined by

$$g : x \mapsto 2 \arcsin x + \frac{\pi}{2}, \qquad x \in \mathbb{R},\ -1 \leqslant x \leqslant 1$$

Problem solving   The domain of g^{-1} is the range of g.

Find $g^{-1}(x)$ and state its domain, and sketch the graph of $y = g^{-1}(x)$, showing the coordinates of the point where the graph crosses the x-axis.   **(5)**

....

....

....

....

Addition formulae

Guided 1 Find, without using a calculator, an expression in surd form for tan 105°.   **(4)**

$$\tan 105° = \tan(60° + 45°) = \frac{\tan 60° + \tan 45°}{1 - \tan 60° \tan 45°} = \frac{\sqrt{3} + 1}{1 - (\sqrt{3})(1)} = \frac{(\sqrt{3} + 1)(1 + \sqrt{3})}{(1 - \sqrt{3})(1 + \sqrt{3})}$$

$$= \frac{\ldots\ldots\ldots\ldots}{\ldots\ldots\ldots} = \ldots\ldots\ldots\ldots$$

2 Solve, for $0° \leqslant \theta \leqslant 360°$

(a) $\cos(\theta - 30°) = 2\sin\theta$ **(4)**

....

....

....

....

(b) $2\tan\theta = 3\tan(45° - \theta)$
Give your answers in degrees to 1 decimal place.   **(5)**

> Use the addition formula for tan to write this as a quadratic in $\tan\theta$.

....

....

....

....

3 Angle A is acute and angle B is obtuse.

$$\cos A = \frac{5}{7}, \qquad \sin B = \frac{1}{5}$$

(a) Work out the value of $\sin(A - B)$.   **(4)**

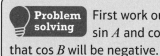

> **Problem solving** First work out the values of $\sin A$ and $\cos B$. Remember that $\cos B$ will be negative.

....

....

....

....

....

(b) Work out the value of $\cos(A - B)$.   **(4)**

....

....

....

....

Double angle formulae

Guided   **1**   Solve, for $-180° \leqslant \theta \leqslant 180°$, $1 = 2\sin\theta + 4\cos 2\theta$ **(6)**
Give your answers correct to 1 decimal place.

$$1 = 2\sin\theta + 4(1 - 2\sin^2\theta)$$

$$8\sin^2\theta - 2\sin\theta - 3 = 0$$

$(\text{.........................})\,(\text{.........................}) = 0$

$\sin\theta = \text{............}$ or $\sin\theta = \text{............}$

$\theta = \text{............}, \text{............}$ $\theta = \text{............}, \text{............}$

> The single term in the equation is $\sin\theta$, so choose the appropriate version of the $\cos 2\theta$ formula to produce a quadratic in $\sin\theta$. Factorise and solve.

2 θ is an obtuse angle and $\sin\theta = \frac{2}{3}$

     Use the double angle formulae to work out the values of

     (a) $\sin 2\theta$ **(2)**   (b) $\cos 2\theta$ **(2)**   (c) $\tan 2\theta$ **(2)**

> $\cos\theta$ and $\tan\theta$ will be negative.

3   Prove that $\dfrac{\sin 3A}{\sin A} + \dfrac{\cos 3A}{\cos A} = 4\cos 2A$ **(5)**

> **Problem solving**   Start with the LHS and write it as a fraction with common denominator $\sin A \cos A$. Use the addition formulae and double angle formulae. Remember that $\sin 2\theta = 2\sin\theta\cos\theta$ also implies that $\sin 4\theta = 2\sin 2\theta \cos 2\theta$.

4   Solve, for $0° \leqslant x \leqslant 360°$

     $\cos 2x - 3 = 5\cos x$

     Give your answers correct to 1 decimal place.   **(6)**

> **Problem solving**   First use a double angle formula for $\cos 2x$, then solve a quadratic in $\cos x$. You will need to use the quadratic formula.

$a\cos\theta \pm b\sin\theta$

> **Guided**

1 (a) Express $4\cos\theta + 2\sin\theta$ in the form $R\cos(\theta - \alpha)$ where $R > 0$ and $0° < \alpha < 90°$ **(4)**

$$4\cos\theta + 2\sin\theta \equiv R(\cos\theta\cos\alpha + \sin\theta\sin\alpha)$$

$$R\cos\alpha = 4, \qquad R\sin\alpha = 2, \qquad \tan\alpha = \tfrac{1}{2}, \qquad \alpha = \ldots\ldots\ldots$$

$$R = \sqrt{4^2 + \ldots\ldots} = \sqrt{\ldots\ldots}$$

So $4\cos\theta + 2\sin\theta \equiv \sqrt{\ldots\ldots}\ \cos(\theta - \ldots\ldots\ldots)$

(b) Hence, or otherwise, solve
$$4\cos\theta + 2\sin\theta = 1$$
for $0° \leqslant \theta \leqslant 360°$
Give your answers correct to 1 decimal place.   **(5)**

> Use the result from part (a). Look at the range of values of θ and check that you have found all the solutions in the range.

(c) State the maximum and minimum values of $4\cos\theta + 2\sin\theta$ **(2)**

2 (a) Express $5\sin x - 8\cos x$ in the form
$$R\sin(x - \alpha)$$
where $R > 0$ and $0 < \alpha < \dfrac{\pi}{2}$ **(4)**

(b) Hence, or otherwise, solve
$$5\sin x - 8\cos x = 6, \qquad 0 \leqslant x \leqslant 2\pi$$
giving your answers to 2 decimal places.   **(5)**

> Remember to put your calculator into radians mode. Don't round prematurely, and check that you have found all the solutions in the specified range.

Trig modelling

Guided 1 (a) Express $6\cos\theta + 8\sin\theta$ in the form $R\cos(\theta - \alpha)$ where $R > 0$ and $0 < \alpha < \dfrac{\pi}{2}$ **(4)**

$6\cos\theta + 8\sin\theta \equiv R(\cos\theta\cos\alpha + \sin\theta\sin\alpha)$

$R\cos\alpha = 6, \quad R\sin\alpha = 8, \quad \tan\alpha = \dfrac{8}{6}, \quad \alpha = \text{..................}$

$R = \sqrt{\text{...........} + \text{...........}} = \sqrt{\text{...........}} = \text{...........}$

So $6\cos\theta + 8\sin\theta \equiv \text{...........} \cos(\theta - \text{...................})$

> Don't round any values until the end of the calculation. Work in radians and show at least 4 decimal places in your answers.

(b) (i) Find the maximum value of $6\cos\theta + 8\sin\theta$

....

(ii) Find the smallest value of θ for which this maximum occurs. **(2)**

....

The temperature, in °C, of a storage depot, is modelled by the function

$\qquad f(t) = 14 + 6\cos(0.25t) + 8\sin(0.25t)$

where t is the time in hours after midday, $0 \leqslant t \leqslant 24$.

(c) Calculate the maximum and minimum temperatures predicted by this model and find the values of t for which the maximum and minimum temperatures occur. **(4)**

....

....

....

....

(d) Find the times, to the nearest minute, when the temperature of the depot is 12 °C. **(6)**

> t is the time in hours. Remember to convert to hours and minutes, then round to the nearest minute.

....

....

....

....

....

....

(e) Sketch a graph of $f(t) = 14 + 6\cos(0.25t) + 8\sin(0.25t)$, showing clearly the coordinates of the maximum and minimum points. **(3)**

Parametric equations 1

Guided 1 The curve C has parametric equations

$$x = 1 - t, \qquad y = t^2 - 4$$

Find a cartesian equation of the curve. **(3)**

$t = 1 - x$, so $t^2 = (1 - x)^2 = $ ....

$y = t^2 - 4 = $ .... $- 4$ so $y = $ ....

2 Work out cartesian equations for these curves.

(a) $x = e^{2t}, \qquad y = 3e^{-t}$ **(3)**

....

....

....

(b) $x = t^2 - 1, \qquad y = t^4 + 1$ **(3)**

....

....

....

(c) $x = \sec\theta, \qquad y = 5\tan\theta$ **(3)**

....

....

....

(d) $x = 1 + \cos\theta, \qquad y = 1 - 2\sin\theta$ **(3)**

....

....

....

3 A curve C has parametric equations

$$x = t - 1, \qquad y = \frac{1}{t}$$

A line L has equation $3x - 2y = 2$

Find the points of intersection of C and L. **(6)**

 Problem solving Substitute the expressions for x and y in terms of t into the equation of the line, then solve the resulting quadratic in t. Don't forget to state the (x, y) solutions.

....

....

....

....

....

....

4 The curve C has parametric equations

$$x = 2\cos\theta + \sin\theta, \qquad y = \cos\theta - \sin\theta$$

Find a cartesian equation of the curve. **(3)**

 Problem solving Solve simultaneous equations for $\sin\theta$ and $\cos\theta$, then use $\sin^2\theta + \cos^2\theta = 1$.

....

....

....

....

Differentiating sin x and cos x

> **Guided**

1 Prove, from first principles, that the derivative of $\sin 2x$ is $2\cos 2x$.
You may assume that as $h \to 0$,

$$\frac{\sin h}{h} \to 1 \quad \text{and} \quad \frac{\cos h - 1}{h} \to 0 \tag{5}$$

Let $f(x) = \sin 2x$

$$f'(x) = \lim_{h\to 0} \frac{f(x+h) - f(x)}{h} = \lim_{h\to 0} \frac{\sin 2(x+h) - \sin 2x}{h} = \lim_{h\to 0} \frac{\sin(2x + 2h) - \sin 2x}{h}$$

$$= \lim_{h\to 0} \frac{\sin 2x \cos 2h + \text{.................} - \sin 2x}{h}$$

$$= \lim_{h\to 0} \left[2\sin 2x \frac{(\cos 2h - 1)}{2h} + \text{.................} \frac{\text{.................}}{2h} \right]$$

$$= \lim_{h\to 0} 2\sin 2x \frac{(\cos 2h - 1)}{2h} + \lim_{h\to 0} \text{.................} \frac{\text{.................}}{2h}$$

> Introduce a factor of 2 in the numerator and the denominator.

Since $\lim_{h\to 0} \dfrac{\cos 2h - 1}{2h} = 0$ and $= \lim_{h\to 0} \dfrac{\text{.................}}{\text{.................}} = 1$

$f'(x) = \text{.................}$

2 Given that x is small and measured in radians, find approximate values for each of the following.

> Assume $2x$, $3x$ and $4x$ are sufficiently small.

(a) $\dfrac{\tan 3x}{2x}$ **(2)**

....

....

(b) $\dfrac{x \sin x}{1 - \cos x}$ **(3)**

....

....

(c) $\dfrac{1 - \cos 2x}{x^2}$ **(3)**

....

....

(d) $\dfrac{\sin 2x \tan x}{1 - \cos 3x}$ **(3)**

....

....

(e) $\dfrac{\cos 3x - \cos x}{\cos 4x - \cos 2x}$ **(4)**

....

....

....

(f) $\dfrac{(\cos 2x - 1)(\cos x - 1)}{x^3 \sin 3x}$ **(4)**

....

....

....

The chain rule

Guided   **1**   Find $\dfrac{dy}{dx}$ for each of the following:

(a) $y = (5 - 3x)^7$ **(2)**

$u = 5 - 3x$ $y = u^7$

$\dfrac{du}{dx} = -3$ $\dfrac{dy}{du} = 7u^6$

$\dfrac{dy}{dx} = \dfrac{dy}{du} \times \dfrac{du}{dx} = \ldots\ldots\ldots \times \ldots\ldots\ldots = \ldots\ldots\ldots\ldots\ldots\ldots$

> Remember to write your final answer in terms of x, not u.

(b) $y = (4 - x^2)^{-4}$ **(2)**

$\dfrac{dy}{dx} = -4 \times (4 - x^2)^{-5} \times (\ldots\ldots\ldots) = \ldots\ldots\ldots\ldots\ldots\ldots\ldots\ldots$

> The missing term is the derivative of $(4 - x^2)$. Always simplify your answer.

(c) $y = (1 + 6x)^{\frac{3}{2}}$ **(3)**   (d) $y = (4x + 5)^{\frac{1}{2}}$ **(3)**

....

....

(e) $y = \dfrac{1}{\sqrt{3 - 2x^2}}$ **(4)**   (f) $y = \dfrac{2}{\sqrt[3]{3x^2 + 4}}$ **(4)**

> $y = 2(3x^2 + 4)^{-\frac{1}{3}}$

....

....

....

2   A curve has equation $y^3 + 3y^2 - 4y - 5 = x$

(a) Find $\dfrac{dy}{dx}$ in terms of y.   **(3)**

> Use $\dfrac{dy}{dx} = \dfrac{1}{\frac{dx}{dy}}$

....

....

(b) Find the gradient of the curve at the point $(7, -2)$.   **(2)**

....

> $\dfrac{dy}{dx}$ is given in terms of y so substitute the y-coordinate to find the gradient.

3 $f(x) = (4\sqrt{x} + 3)^3$

Find $f'(x)$.   **(2)**   > Simplify your answer as much as possible.

....

....

Differentiating standard functions

Guided   **1**   Differentiate with respect to x

(a) $y = \sin^3 x$ **(2)**   (b) $y = \cos(5 - 4x)$ **(2)**

$u = \sin x$ $y = u^3$ ....

$\dfrac{du}{dx} = \cos x$ $\dfrac{dy}{du} = 3u^2$ ....

$\dfrac{dy}{dx} = \dfrac{dy}{du} \times \dfrac{du}{dx} = \text{...........} \times \text{...........} = \text{.....................................}$

(c) $y = e^{x^2+1}$ **(2)**   (d) $y = \ln(x^3 + 2)$ **(2)**

> When using the chain rule, don't forget to differentiate the expression inside the brackets.

....

....

2   Work out $\dfrac{dy}{dx}$ for each of the following.

(a) $y = \cos^4 x$ **(2)**   (b) $y = \sin 2x + \cos 3x$ **(2)**

....

....

(c) $y = 2x^3 - e^{5-3x}$ **(3)**   (d) $y = \ln(\cos 2x)$ **(2)**   > Simplify your answer.

....

....

3   (a) Given that $y = \operatorname{cosec} x$, show that $\dfrac{dy}{dx} = -\operatorname{cosec} x \times \cot x$ **(3)**

....

....

....

(b) Hence, or otherwise, differentiate $\ln(\operatorname{cosec} x)$ with respect to x.   **(2)**

....

....

....

....

....

The product rule

Guided **1** Differentiate with respect to x

(a) $y = (x^2 + 3)(2x^3 - 1)$ **(3)**

$u = x^2 + 3$ $\qquad$ $v = 2x^3 - 1$

$\dfrac{du}{dx} = 2x$ $\qquad$ $\dfrac{dv}{dx} = 6x^2$

> Expand the brackets and simplify.

$\dfrac{dy}{dx} = u\dfrac{dv}{dx} + v\dfrac{du}{dx} = (x^2 + 3)(6x^2) + (2x^3 - 1)(2x) =$ ....

....

(b) $y = x^4 \sin x$ **(3)**

$u = x^4$ $\qquad$ $v = \sin x$

$\dfrac{du}{dx} = 4x^3$ $\qquad$ $\dfrac{dv}{dx} =$ ....

$\dfrac{dy}{dx} = x^4$ .... $+ \sin x(4x^3)$

(c) $y = 2x^2 e^{2x}$ **(3)** $\qquad$ (d) $y = (x^3 - 4x)\ln 2x$ **(3)**

.... $\qquad$ ....

.... $\qquad$ ....

2 (a) Given that $h(x) = e^{4x} \sec x$, find $h'(x)$. **(4)**

....

....

(b) Solve, for $-\dfrac{\pi}{2} < x < \dfrac{\pi}{2}$, the equation $h'(x) = 0$.
Give your answer correct to 3 s.f. **(4)**

> Make sure your calculator is in radians mode.

....

....

3 If $y = x^2\sqrt{1 + x^2}$, show that $\dfrac{dy}{dx} = \dfrac{3x^3 + 2x}{\sqrt{1 + x^2}}$ **(5)**

> Use the product rule, then use $\sqrt{1 + x^2}$ as a common denominator.

....

....

....

4 A curve has equation $y = (x^2 - 2x - 1)e^{2x}$
Find the coordinates of the turning points on the curve. **(6)**

....

....

....

The quotient rule

1 Differentiate with respect to x, simplifying your answers.

(a) $y = \dfrac{x^2}{2x + 1}$ **(4)**

$u = x^2$ $\qquad\qquad$ $v = 2x + 1$

$\dfrac{du}{dx} = 2x$ $\qquad\qquad$ $\dfrac{dv}{dx} = 2$

$\dfrac{dy}{dx} = \dfrac{v\dfrac{du}{dx} - u\dfrac{dv}{dx}}{v^2} = \dfrac{(2x + 1)(2x) - (x^2)(2)}{(2x + 1)^2} = \dfrac{\cdots\cdots\cdots\cdots}{(2x + 1)^2}$

(b) $y = \dfrac{x^3}{\sqrt{1 - 2x^2}}, \qquad x^2 \neq \frac{1}{2}$ **(5)**

$u = x^3$ $\qquad\qquad$ $v = (1 - 2x^2)^{\frac{1}{2}}$

$\dfrac{du}{dx} = 3x^2$ $\qquad\qquad$ $\dfrac{dv}{dx} = \frac{1}{2}(1 - 2x^2)^{\frac{-1}{2}}(-4x) = (-2x)(1 - 2x^2)^{\frac{-1}{2}}$

....

....

2 Differentiate with respect to x, simplifying your answers.

(a) $f(x) = \dfrac{x^2 + x - 1}{1 - x^2}, \qquad x \neq \pm 1$ **(4)** $\qquad$ (b) $f(x) = \dfrac{4x}{\sqrt{3x^2 + 1}}$ **(5)**

3 Differentiate with respect to x, simplifying your answers.

(a) $\dfrac{\ln 2x}{3x}$ **(4)** $\qquad$ (b) $\dfrac{\cos 3x}{1 + \sin 3x}$ **(5)** $\qquad$ (c) $\dfrac{2 \sin x - 3 \cos x}{e^{2x}}$ **(5)**

Differentiation and graphs

Guided 1 A curve C has equation $y = 3x^2 \ln x$

   (a) Find $\dfrac{dy}{dx}$ $\dfrac{dy}{dx} = (3x^2)\left(\dfrac{1}{x}\right) + (\ln x)(6x) = 3x + 6x\ln x$ **(3)**

   (b) Find an equation of the tangent to C at the point where $x = e$ **(3)**

When $x = e$, $y = 3e^2 \ln e = $ ....

When $x = e$, $\dfrac{dy}{dx} = 3e + 6e\ln e = $ .... $= $ ....

Equation of tangent is .... $\boxed{\text{Use } y - y_1 = m(x - x_1)}$

   (c) The tangent to C when $x = e$ intersects the x-axis at point A.
       Find the exact values of the coordinates of A.   **(2)**

....

....

2 A curve C has equation $y = e^{2x}\cos 3x$, $-\dfrac{\pi}{2} < x < \dfrac{\pi}{2}$ $\boxed{\begin{array}{l}\text{A curve has a turning} \\ \text{point when } \dfrac{dy}{dx} = 0.\end{array}}$

   (a) Show that turning points on C occur when $\tan 3x = \dfrac{2}{3}$ **(4)**

....

....

....

   (b) Find an equation of the normal to C at the point where $x = 0$.
       Give your answer in the form $ax + by = c$, where a, b and c are integers.   **(4)**

....

....

....

3 A curve C has equation $y = \dfrac{4x}{x^2 + 4}$

   (a) Find the maximum and minimum points on the curve.   **(7)**

....

....

....

....

   (b) Find an equation of the tangent to C at the point where $x = 1$.
       Give your answer in the form $ax + by + c = 0$, where a, b and c are integers.   **(3)**

....

....

....

Parametric differentiation

1 A curve C has parametric equations

$$x = 4\cos t, \qquad y = 3\sin t, \qquad 0 < t < \frac{\pi}{2}$$

(a) Find $\dfrac{dy}{dx}$ in terms of t. **(4)**

$$\frac{dx}{dt} = -4\sin t, \qquad \frac{dy}{dt} = \text{.................}$$

$$\frac{dy}{dx} = \frac{dy}{dt} \div \frac{dx}{dt} = \frac{\text{.................}}{\text{.................}} = \text{.........................}$$

(b) Find an equation of the tangent to C when $t = \dfrac{\pi}{3}$. **(5)**

....

....

....

....

2 A curve C has parametric equations

$$x = 4e^{-2t} - 3, \qquad y = 2e^{2t} - 5$$

(a) Find $\dfrac{dy}{dx}$ in terms of t. **(3)**

....

....

The point P, where $t = \ln 2$, lies on curve C.

(b) Find the gradient of the tangent at P. **(1)**

....

(c) Find the coordinates of P. **(2)**

....

....

The normal at P crosses the x-axis at Q.

(d) Find the coordinates of Q. **(4)**

....

....

(e) Find a cartesian equation of C in the form $xy + ay + bx = k$ where a, b and k are integers. **(5)**

....

....

....

....

Implicit differentiation

> **Guided**

1 A curve C has equation $x^2 + 4y - y^2 = 7$

Find an equation of the normal to C at the point $(-2, 3)$.

Give your answers in the form $ax + by + c = 0$, where a, b and c are integers. **(7)**

Differentiating implicitly, $2x + 4\dfrac{dy}{dx} - 2y\dfrac{dy}{dx} = 0$

$$2x = (2y - 4)\dfrac{dy}{dx}$$

$$\dfrac{dy}{dx} = \dfrac{\text{.................}}{\text{.................}} = \dfrac{\text{...........}}{\text{...........}}$$

When $x = -2$ and $y = 3$, $\dfrac{dy}{dx} = $ .... So gradient of normal = ...

Equation of normal is $y - 3 = $ .... $(x - -2)$

> Remember to write your final equation in the correct form.

....

2 A curve C has equation

$$3x^2 - y^2 + 3xy + 28 = 0$$

Find the coordinates of the points on C where $\dfrac{dy}{dx} = 0$

> Differentiate implicitly and equate to zero. This will give a connection between x and y. Use this to substitute into the equation for C and solve an equation in one variable.

(7)

....

....

....

....

....

3 A curve C has equation $\cos 2y + y\,e^{2x} = \pi$

The point $P(\ln 2, \dfrac{\pi}{4})$ lies on C.

(a) Find an expression for $\dfrac{dy}{dx}$ in terms of x and y. **(5)**

....

....

....

....

(b) Find the exact value of the gradient of the tangent at P. **(2)**

....

....

(c) The tangent at P crosses the x-axis at Q. Find the exact value of the x-coordinate of Q. **(2)**

....

....

Differentiating a^x

Guided 1   Given that $y = 4^{2x}$, find $\dfrac{dy}{dx}$ (2)

> You can use the chain rule, and the rule $\dfrac{d}{dx}(a^x) = a^x \ln x$.

Let $u = 2x$ $y = 4^u$

$\dfrac{du}{dx} = 2$ $\dfrac{dy}{du} = 4^u \ln 4$

$\dfrac{dy}{dx} = \dfrac{dy}{du} \times \dfrac{du}{dx} = \text{................} = \text{................} = \text{................}$

2   Differentiate with respect to x

    (a) $y = 3^{\tan x}$ (2)   (b) $y = x^3\, 6^{2x}$ (3)   (c) $y = 5^{x^2} \ln 2x$ (3)

    ....

    ....

    ....

    ....

3   A curve has equation $2xy + 3^y = 9$
    Find an equation of the normal to
    the curve at the point $(0, 2)$.   (6)

> The gradient of the normal is $\dfrac{-1}{\frac{dy}{dx}}$

    ....

    ....

    ....

    ....

4   A curve C has equation $4^x - 3y^2 = 4xy$

    (a) Find the coordinates of the two points on C where $x = 2$.   (3)

    ....

    ....

    ....

    ....

    (b) Find the exact value of $\dfrac{dy}{dx}$ at each of the points where $x = 2$.   (7)

    ....

    ....

    ....

    ....

    ....

    ....

Points of inflexion

> **Guided** 1 A curve has equation $y = x^3 - 6x^2 + 9x - 1$

(a) Find $\dfrac{dy}{dx}$ and $\dfrac{d^2y}{dx^2}$ **(4)**

$y = x^3 - 6x^2 + 9x - 1$, $\dfrac{dy}{dx} = 3x^2$ ...., $\dfrac{d^2y}{dx^2} = 6x$ ....

(b) Find the coordinates of the stationary points and determine their nature. **(5)**

Stationary points occur when $\dfrac{dy}{dx} = 0$, $3x^2$ .... $= 0$, x^2 .... $= 0$

$(x\text{.........})(x\text{.........}) = 0$, $x = $ .... and $x = $ ....

When $x = $ ...., $y = $ .... $= $ ....

When $x = $ ...., $y = $ .... $= $ ....

When $x = $ ...., $\dfrac{d^2y}{dx^2} = $ .... $= $ ...., so there is a .... point at (.........., ...)

When $x = $ ...., $\dfrac{d^2y}{dx^2} = $ .... $= $ ...., so there is a .... point at (.........., ...)

(c) Find the coordinates of the point of inflexion. **(3)**

A point of inflexion occurs when $\dfrac{d^2y}{dx^2} = 0$ and $\dfrac{d^2y}{dx^2}$ changes sign either side of this point.

$\dfrac{d^2y}{dx^2} = 0$, $6x$ .... $= 0$, $x = $ .... and $y = $ .... $= $ ....

When $x < $ ...., $\dfrac{d^2y}{dx^2} < 0$; when $x > $ ...., $\dfrac{d^2y}{dx^2} > 0$, so point of inflexion at (.........., ...)

2 A curve, C, has equation $y = (4 - 3x)e^x$

(a) Find the stationary point on C and determine its nature. **(6)**

....

....

....

....

....

....

(b) Show that C has one point of inflexion and find its coordinates. **(4)**

....

....

....

(c) State, with reasons, whether C is concave or convex in the interval $[1, 2]$. **(2)**

....

....

Rates of change

Guided

1 Water is poured into a conical vessel at a rate of $8\,\text{cm}^3\,\text{s}^{-1}$.

After t seconds, the volume $V\,\text{cm}^3$ of water is given by $V = \frac{2}{9}\pi x^3$, where x is the depth of the water.

Find, in terms of π, the rate at which the water is rising when $x = 6$. **(5)**

$$\frac{dV}{dt} = 8, \qquad V = \frac{2}{9}\pi x^3, \qquad so\ \frac{dV}{dx} = \dots\dots\dots$$

$$\text{Rate required} = \frac{dx}{dt} = \frac{dx}{dV} \times \frac{dV}{dt} = \frac{dV}{dt} \div \frac{dV}{dx} = 8 \div \dots\dots\dots = \dots\dots\dots$$

When $x = 6$, $\frac{dx}{dt} = \dots\dots\dots \text{cm}\,\text{s}^{-1}$

> Use the chain rule.

2 The volume of a spherical bubble is increasing at the rate of $5\,\text{cm}^3\,\text{s}^{-1}$.
Find the rate at which the radius is increasing when the radius is $4\,\text{cm}$.
Give your answer correct to 3 significant figures. **(4)**

> Volume of sphere $= \frac{4}{3}\pi r^3$

....

....

....

....

3 A horizontal trough is $4\,\text{m}$ long and $1\,\text{m}$ deep.
Its cross-section is an isosceles triangle of
width $1.5\,\text{m}$. When the depth of the water is $h\,\text{m}$,
the volume is $V\,\text{m}^3$ and the width of the
cross-section of the water is $x\,\text{m}$.

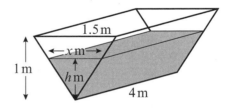

(a) Show that $V = 3h^2$ **(3)**

....

....

....

....

(b) Water runs into the trough at the rate of $0.03\,\text{m}^3\,\text{s}^{-1}$.
Find the rate at which the water level is rising at the instant when the water has
been running for 25 seconds. **(8)**

....

....

....

....

....

....

....

Iteration

Guided   **1** $f(x) = e^{-x} - 3 + 2\sqrt{x}$

(a) Show that the equation $f(x) = 0$ has a root, α, between 2 and 3.   **(2)**

> You need to show that f(2) is negative and f(3) is positive, and write a conclusion.

$f(2) = e^{-2} - 3 + 2\sqrt{2} = \ldots\ldots\ldots$

$f(3) = e^{-3} - 3 + 2\sqrt{3} = \ldots\ldots\ldots$

Hence there is a root between 2 and 3 because there is a change of sign.

(b) Show that the equation $f(x) = 0$ can be written as $x = \frac{1}{4}(3 - e^{-x})^2$ **(3)**

$e^{-x} - 3 + 2\sqrt{x} = 0, \qquad 2\sqrt{x} = 3 - e^{-x}, \qquad \sqrt{x} = \ldots\ldots\ldots\ldots, \qquad x = \ldots\ldots\ldots$

(c) Starting with $x_0 = 2.1$, use the iterative formula $x_{n+1} = \frac{1}{4}(3 - e^{-x_n})^2$ to calculate x_1, x_2 and x_3, giving your answers correct to 4 decimal places.   **(3)**

$x_1 = \frac{1}{4}(3 - e^{-2.1})^2 = \ldots\ldots\ldots\ldots\ldots\ldots\ldots\ldots\ldots\ldots\ldots\ldots\ldots\ldots\ldots$

> Take great care using your calculator and show at least 6 d.p. before you round to 4 d.p.

$x_2 = \ldots\ldots\ldots\ldots\ldots\ldots\ldots\ldots\ldots\ldots\ldots\ldots\ldots\ldots\ldots\ldots\ldots\ldots\ldots\ldots$

$x_3 = \ldots\ldots\ldots\ldots\ldots\ldots\ldots\ldots\ldots\ldots\ldots\ldots\ldots\ldots\ldots\ldots\ldots\ldots\ldots\ldots$

(d) By choosing a suitable interval, show that $\alpha = 2.064$, correct to 3 decimal places.   **(3)**

> Substitute 2.0635 and 2.0645 into the expression for f(x) and look for a change of sign. Write 'change of sign' and write down the interval that contains the root.

....

....

....

....

....

....

2 $f(x) = x^3 + 3x^2 - 4x - 2$

(a) Show that the equation $f(x) = 0$ has a root, α, between 1 and 2.   **(2)**

....

(b) Show that the equation $f(x) = 0$ can be written as $x = \sqrt{\dfrac{4x + 2}{x + 3}}$, $x \neq -3$ **(2)**

....

(c) Starting with $x_0 = 1.5$, use the iterative formula $x_{n+1} = \sqrt{\dfrac{4x_n + 2}{x_n + 3}}$ to calculate x_1, x_2 and x_3, giving your answers correct to 4 decimal places.   **(3)**

....

(d) By choosing a suitable interval, show that $\alpha = 1.2924$, to 4 decimal places.   **(3)**

....

....

The Newton–Raphson method

 Guided 1 $f(x) = x^3 - 3x^2 + 1$

(a) Show that $f(x) = 0$ has a root, α, in the interval $[2, 3]$. **(2)**

$f(2) = 8$ .... = ..., $f(3) = 27$ .... = ...

so the graph crosses the x-axis between $x = 2$ and $x = 3$

(b) Find $f'(x)$. **(2)**

$f'(x) = $ .... $x^2 - $ ....

(c) Explain why $x_0 = 2$ would not be a suitable first approximation when applying the Newton–Raphson method to find α. **(2)**

$f'(x) = $ .... $x^2 - $ .... $= $ .... $x(x$ ....$)$ so there are stationary points at

$x = $ .... and $x = $ .... and the tangent at $x = $ .... would be ....

and .... intersect the x-axis.

(d) Taking $x_0 = 3$ as a first approximation, apply the Newton–Raphson procedure twice to obtain an approximate value of α. Give your answer to 3 decimal places. **(5)**

$x_{n+1} = x_n - \dfrac{f(x_n)}{f'(x_n)} = x_n - \dfrac{x_n^3 - 3x_n^2 + 1}{\text{......................}}$ $x_1 = 3 - \dfrac{27\text{..........}}{\text{................}} = $ ....

$x_2 = $ .... $- \dfrac{\text{..}}{\text{..}} = $ .... $= $ .... (3 d.p.)

(e) By considering the change of sign in $f(x)$ over an appropriate interval, show that your answer to part (d) is accurate to 3 decimal places. **(2)**

> Use values ±0.0005 either side of your answer to (d) and look for a change of sign.

$f($................$) = $ .... , $f($................$) = $ ....

so the change of sign means that .... is correct to 3 d.p.

2 $f(x) = \ln x - 3\cos x$

(a) Show that $f(x) = 0$ has a root, α, in the interval $[1, 2]$. **(2)**

....

(b) Find $f'(x)$. **(2)**

....

(c) Taking $x_0 = 1.5$ as a first approximation, apply the Newton–Raphson procedure twice to obtain an approximate value of α. Give your answer to 3 decimal places. **(5)**

....

....

(d) By considering the change of sign in $f(x)$ over an appropriate interval, show that your answer to (c) is accurate to 3 decimal places. **(2)**

....

....

Integrating standard functions

> **Guided** 1   Find:

> Check your answer by differentiating to ensure you have the correct coefficient.

(a) $\int 6\cos 2x\,dx$ **(2)**   (b) $\int \sec^2 \frac{x}{2}\,dx$ **(2)**

= .... $\sin 2x + c$ = ...

(c) $\int \frac{1}{2}\sin 3x\,dx$ **(2)**   (d) $\int \operatorname{cosec} 2\theta \cot 2\theta\,d\theta$ **(2)**

= .... $\cos 3x + c$ = ...

2   Find:

(a) $\int -12\sin 4x\,dx$ **(2)**   (b) $\int 4\cos \frac{\theta}{2}\,d\theta$ **(2)**

....

(c) $\int 5\sin 10x\,dx$ **(2)**   (d) $\int \frac{1}{2}\cos(3x+5)\,dx$ **(2)**

....

3   Find:

(a) $\int 2e^{3x}\,dx$ **(2)**   (b) $\int \frac{3}{5}e^{\frac{\theta}{4}}\,d\theta$ **(2)**

....

(c) $\int \frac{5}{2x-1}\,dx$ **(2)**   (d) $\int \frac{2}{1+8x}\,dx$ **(2)**

....

4   Find:

(a) $\int \sqrt{x+6}\,dx$ **(2)**   (b) $\int \frac{1}{2}\sqrt{2x-3}\,dx$ **(2)**

....

(c) $\int (4-3x)^{\frac{3}{2}}\,dx$ **(2)**   (d) $\int \sqrt[3]{1+4x}\,dx$ **(2)**

....

5   Show that $\displaystyle\int_{2}^{6} \frac{1}{\sqrt{5x+2}}\,dx = \frac{4}{5}(2\sqrt{2}-\sqrt{3})$ **(4)**

....

6   Find the value of $\displaystyle\int_{-1}^{0} \frac{1}{\sqrt[3]{1-7x}}\,dx$ **(4)**

....

Reverse chain rule

Guided

1 Find:

(a) $\int \dfrac{3x-4}{3x^2-8x}\,dx$ (3)

$= \ldots\ldots\ldots \ln(3x^2-8x)+c$

(b) $\int 6x^2(7-4x^3)^6\,dx$ (3)

$= \ldots\ldots\ldots (7-4x^3)^7+c$

2 Find:

(a) $\int x(6x^2-2)^5\,dx$ (3)

(b) $\int \dfrac{3\sin 2\theta}{\cos 2\theta}\,d\theta$ (3)

3 Find:

(a) $\int 3\cos^3 x \sin x\,dx$ (3)

(b) $\int \frac{1}{3}x\cos(x^2)\,dx$ (3)

4 Find:

(a) $\int 2\sec^2\theta \tan^3\theta\,d\theta$ (3)

(b) $\int 3\operatorname{cosec}^5 x \cot x\,dx$ (3)

5 Find:

(a) $\int 4x\sqrt{3x^2-2}\,dx$ (3)

(b) $\int \dfrac{2x^2-4x}{\sqrt{2x^3-6x^2+5}}\,dx$ (3)

6 Find the exact value of $\displaystyle\int_0^4 \dfrac{x}{x^2+2}\,dx$ (5) | Simplify your answer fully.

7 Find the exact value of $\displaystyle\int_0^{\ln 3} \dfrac{e^{-x}}{1+e^{-x}}\,dx$ (5) | Try $\ln|1+e^{-x}|$, and take care with the signs.

8 The function $f(x)$ is defined by $f(x)=\dfrac{2x^2-1}{4x^3-6x+5},\ x\geqslant 1$

Find the area enclosed by $y=f(x)$, the lines $x=1$, $x=3$ and the x-axis.
Give your answer correct to 3 decimal places. (5)

Identities in integration

> **Guided**

1 Find the exact value of $\int_{\frac{\pi}{6}}^{\frac{\pi}{2}} \cos^2\left(\frac{x}{2}\right) dx$ **(5)**

$\cos 2A = 2\cos^2 A - 1$

When $A = \dfrac{x}{2}$, $\cos x = 2\cos^2\left(\dfrac{x}{2}\right) - 1$

So $\cos^2\left(\dfrac{x}{2}\right) = \dfrac{1}{2}(\cos x + 1)$

$\int_{\frac{\pi}{6}}^{\frac{\pi}{2}} \cos^2\left(\dfrac{x}{2}\right) dx = \int_{\frac{\pi}{6}}^{\frac{\pi}{2}} \dfrac{1}{2}(\cos x + 1) dx = \dfrac{1}{2}\Big[\text{...........} + x\Big]_{\frac{\pi}{6}}^{\frac{\pi}{2}}$

$= \dfrac{1}{2}\Big[\Big(\text{...........} + \dfrac{\pi}{2}\Big) - \Big(\text{...........} + \dfrac{\pi}{6}\Big)\Big] = \text{...........}$

> Leave your answer as an expression involving π.

2 Find the value of $\int_{0}^{\frac{\pi}{8}} \sin 2\theta \cos 2\theta \, d\theta$ **(5)**

> Use $\sin 2A = 2\sin A \cos A$ with $A = 2\theta$.

....

....

....

3 (a) By writing $\cos 5x$ as $\cos(3x + 2x)$ and $\cos x$ as $\cos(3x - 2x)$, show that $\cos 5x + \cos x = 2\cos 3x \cos 2x$ **(4)**

> Use the addition formulae.

....

....

(b) Hence find the value of $\int_{0}^{\frac{\pi}{6}} (\cos 3x \cos 2x) \, dx$ **(2)**

....

....

4 Find the exact value of $\int_{-\frac{\pi}{8}}^{\frac{\pi}{8}} \sin^2(2x) \, dx$ **(5)**

....

....

....

....

....

5 Find the exact value of $\int_{\frac{\pi}{6}}^{\frac{\pi}{3}} \cot^2(2x) \, dx$ **(5)**

....

....

....

....

....

....

Integration by substitution

Guided

1 Use the substitution $u = \sin 2x$ to find the exact value of $\int_{\frac{\pi}{12}}^{\frac{\pi}{4}} \sin^3 2x \cos 2x \, dx$ **(5)**

$u = \sin 2x$

$\dfrac{du}{dx} = 2\cos 2x$ so $\dfrac{du}{2} = \cos 2x \, dx$

When $x = \dfrac{\pi}{12}$, $u = \sin\dfrac{\pi}{6} = \ldots\ldots\ldots$ When $x = \dfrac{\pi}{4}$, $u = \sin\dfrac{\pi}{2} = \ldots\ldots\ldots$

$\int_{\frac{\pi}{12}}^{\frac{\pi}{4}} \sin^3 2x \cos 2x \, dx = \int_{....}^{....} \ldots\ldots\ldots\ldots\ldots\ldots\ldots\ldots\ldots$

$\qquad\qquad\qquad = \Big[\ldots\ldots\ldots\ldots\ldots\ldots\Big]_{....}^{....}$

$\qquad\qquad\qquad = \ldots\ldots\ldots = \ldots\ldots\ldots$

> Remember to transform the limits when using integration by substitution.

2 Use the substitution $x = 3\sin\theta$ to find the exact value of $\int_{\frac{3}{2}}^{\frac{3\sqrt{3}}{2}} \dfrac{1}{x^2\sqrt{9 - x^2}} \, dx$ **(5)**

....

....

....

....

....

....

3 Use the substitution $t = e^x$ to find the exact value of $\int_0^1 \dfrac{e^x}{(1 + e^x)^2} \, dx$ **(5)**

....

....

....

....

....

4 Use the substitution $x = 2\sin\theta$ to find the exact value of $\int_0^2 \sqrt{4 - x^2} \, dx$

> You will also need to use $\cos 2A = 2\cos^2 A - 1$.

(7)

....

....

....

....

....

....

Integration by parts

Guided   **1**   Use integration by parts to find $\int x\,e^{-x}\,dx$ **(4)** $\boxed{\int u\dfrac{dv}{dx}\,dx = uv - \int v\dfrac{du}{dx}\,dx}$

$$u = x \qquad\qquad \frac{dv}{dx} = e^{-x}$$

$$\frac{du}{dx} = 1 \qquad\qquad v = -e^{-x}$$

$$\int x\,e^{-x}\,dx = x(-e^{-x}) - \int(-e^{-x})(1)\,dx$$

$$= -xe^{-x}\ldots\ldots\ldots\ldots\ldots\ldots = \ldots\ldots\ldots\ldots\ldots\ldots = \ldots\ldots\ldots\ldots\ldots$$

2   Use integration by parts to show that

$$\int x^3 \ln x\,dx = \frac{x^4}{16}(4\ln x - 1) + c \qquad\qquad \textbf{(4)} \qquad \boxed{\text{Always set } \ln x \text{ as } u.}$$

....

....

....

....

....

....

3   (a) Use integration by parts to find $\int 2x\sin x\,dx$ **(3)**

....

....

....

     (b) Use integration by parts and your answer to part (a) to find $\int x^2\cos x\,dx$ **(4)**

....

....

....

....

4   Use integration by parts to find the exact value of $\int_1^2 x^2 e^{2x}\,dx$ **(8)** $\boxed{\begin{array}{l}\text{You will need to use}\\ \text{integration by parts twice.}\end{array}}$

....

....

....

....

....

....

....

Integrating partial fractions

 1 (a) Express $\dfrac{5 - 8x}{(2 + x)(1 - 3x)}$ in partial fractions. **(3)**

$\dfrac{5 - 8x}{(2 + x)(1 - 3x)} = \dfrac{A}{2 + x} + \dfrac{B}{1 - 3x}$ so $5 - 8x = A(1 - 3x) + B(2 + x)$

When $x = -2$, $21 = 7A$, so $A = 3$

When $x = $ ....

> You can use the cover-up rule to find A and B.

So $\dfrac{5 - 8x}{(2 + x)(1 - 3x)} \equiv \dfrac{3}{2 + x} + \dfrac{\text{..........}}{1 - 3x}$

(b) Hence find the exact value of $\displaystyle\int_{-1}^{0} \dfrac{5 - 8x}{(2 + x)(1 - 3x)}\, dx$,

giving your answer in the form $p \ln q$, where p and q are constants to be found. **(4)**

> Both of these are logarithm integrals. Use the rules of logarithms to simplify your answer.

$\displaystyle\int_{-1}^{0} \dfrac{5 - 8x}{(2 + x)(1 - 3x)}\, dx = \int_{-1}^{0}\left(\dfrac{3}{2 + x} + \dfrac{\text{..........}}{1 - 3x}\right) dx$

....

....

....

2 (a) Express $\dfrac{2x + 9}{4x^2 - 9}$ in the form $\dfrac{A}{2x + 3} + \dfrac{B}{2x - 3}$ where A and B are integers. **(3)**

....

....

....

(b) Show that $\dfrac{12x^3 - 31x - 18}{4x^2 - 9}$ can be written as $3x - \dfrac{2(2x + 9)}{4x^2 - 9}$ **(3)**

....

....

(c) Hence find $\displaystyle\int_{0}^{1} \dfrac{12x^3 - 31x - 18}{4x^2 - 9}\, dx$, giving your answer in the form $p + \ln q$,

where p and q are constants to be found. **(5)**

....

....

....

....

....

....

....

Area between two curves

Guided **1** The diagram shows two quadratic curves with
equations $y = 4 + 2x - x^2$ and $y = x^2 + 2x - 4$

Find the total area of the region bounded by
the two curves.   **(6)**

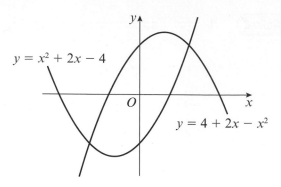

For x values of points of intersection, solve

$4 + 2x - x^2 = x^2$ ....

$0 = 2x^2$ .... $= 2(..........) = 2(..........)(..........)$

so $x = ...$ and $x = ...$

Area $= \int_{....}^{....} \big((4 + 2x - x^2) - (............................)\big)dx = \int_{....}^{....} (8 - ....)\,dx = \big[8x..........\big]_{....}^{....}$

$= (.......... - ....) - (.......... - ....) = ...$

2 The diagram shows the curves with equations
$y = x^3 - x^2 - 2x + 2$ and $y = x^2 + 3x - 4$

The curves intersect at the points P, Q and R.

(a) Find the coordinates of the points P, Q and R.   **(5)**

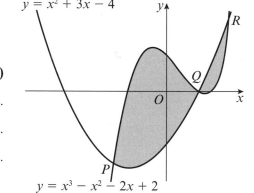

....

....

....

(b) Find the total area of the two shaded regions
bounded by the two curves.   **(8)**

....

....

....

....

....

3 The diagram shows the curves with equations
$y = 3 \sin x$ and $y = \sqrt{3} \cos x$ in the range 0 to 2π.

The curves intersect at the points P and Q.

(a) Find the coordinates of the points P and Q.   **(3)**

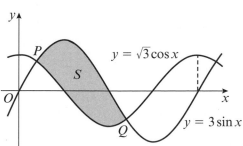

....

(b) Find the area of the finite region S bounded by the curves.   **(7)**

....

....

....

....

Areas and parametric curves

 Guided

1 The diagram shows the curve with parametric equations

$$x = 2t - \sin t, \qquad y = 1 - \cos t, \qquad 0 \leqslant t \leqslant 2\pi$$

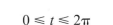

Find the area bounded by the curve and the x-axis.   **(5)**

$$x = 2t - 2\sin t, \qquad \frac{dx}{dt} = 2 - \cos t, \qquad y = 1 - \cos t$$

When $y = 0$, $\cos t = 1$, so $t = 0$ or 2π

> Use $\cos 2A = 2\cos^2 A - 1$ to express $\cos^2 t$ in terms of $\cos 2t$. Tidy up, then integrate.

$$\text{Area} = \int_{x=0}^{x=4\pi} y\, dx = \int_{t=0}^{t=2\pi} y \frac{dx}{dt}\, dt = \int_{0}^{2\pi} (1 - \cos t)(2 - \cos t)\, dt$$

$$= \int_{0}^{2\pi} (2 - 3\cos t + \cos^2 t)\, dt = \int_{0}^{2\pi} \left(2 - 3\cos t + \tfrac{1}{2} + \tfrac{1}{2}\cos 2t\right) dt$$

= .... = ... = ... = ...

2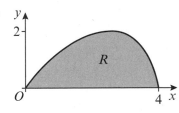

The diagram shows a curve with parametric equations

$$x = 4\cos t, \qquad y = 2\sin 2t, \qquad 0 \leqslant t \leqslant \frac{\pi}{2}$$

Find the area of the region marked R.   **(8)**

> 💡 **Problem solving** Write the integral in the form $k\int \cos t(\sin t)^2\, dt$, then use the substitution $u = \sin t$.

....

....

....

....

....

....

3 The diagram shows a curve with parametric equations

$$x = t^3, \qquad y = e^t, \qquad 0 \leqslant t \leqslant 1$$

Find the area of the region marked R.   **(8)**

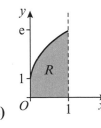

> You will need to use integration by parts twice.

....

....

....

....

....

....

The trapezium rule

> **Guided**

1. (a) Given that $y = \dfrac{x}{x^2 + 2}$, complete the table.

x	0	0.8	1.6	2.4	3.2	4
y	0	0.30303	0.35088			0.22222

(2)

   (b) Use the trapezium rule with all the values of y in the completed table to obtain an estimate for $\displaystyle\int_0^4 \dfrac{x}{x^2 + 2}\,dx$

   Show all the steps of your working and give your answer to 4 decimal places. **(3)**

$$\int_0^4 \frac{x}{x^2 + 2}\,dx \approx \frac{0.8}{2}[0 + 0.22222 + 2(0.30303 + \ldots\ldots\ldots + \ldots\ldots\ldots + \ldots\ldots\ldots)]$$

$$= \ldots\ldots\ldots\ldots\ldots \text{ (4 d.p.)}$$

   (c) Integrate $\displaystyle\int_0^4 \dfrac{x}{x^2 + 2}\,dx$, giving your answer in the form $\ln k$ where k is an integer. **(5)**

   ....

   ....

   (d) Calculate the percentage error in the estimate you obtained in part (b). **(2)**

   ....

   ....

2. The diagram shows a sketch of the curve
   $y = (2x - 1)\ln x, \qquad x > 0$

   (a) Complete this table of values.

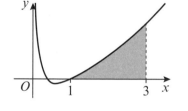

x	1	1.5	2	2.5	3
y	0	0.81093			

(2)

   (b) Use the trapezium rule with all the values of y in the completed table to obtain an estimate of the area under the curve between $x = 1$ and $x = 3$.
   Show your working and give your answer to 4 decimal places. **(3)**

   ....

   ....

   (c) Show that the exact value of $\displaystyle\int_1^3 (2x - 1)\ln x\,dx$ is $p\ln q + r$ where p, q and r are integers to be determined. **(7)**

   ....

   ....

   ....

   ....

   ....

   ....

   ....

Solving differential equations

> **Guided**

1 (a) Show that $\dfrac{10}{(x-3)(3x+1)}$ can be written as $\dfrac{1}{x-3} - \dfrac{3}{3x+1}$ **(2)**

....

....

(b) Hence find $\displaystyle\int \dfrac{10}{(x-3)(3x+1)}\,\mathrm{d}x$ where $x>3$ **(3)**

> These are log integrals. You need not simplify your answer at this stage.

$$\int \dfrac{10}{(x-3)(3x+1)}\,dx = \int\left(\dfrac{1}{x-3} - \dfrac{3}{3x+1}\right)dx$$

$$= \;...$$

(c) Find the particular solution of the differential equation

> Separate the variables and integrate.

$$(x-3)(3x+1)\dfrac{\mathrm{d}y}{\mathrm{d}x} = 10y, \qquad x>3$$

for which $y=4$ at $x=5$. Give your answer in the form $y=\mathrm{f}(x)$. **(6)**

....

....

....

....

....

....

2 The platform of a fairground ride oscillates vertically for the first 60 seconds of the ride.
The height, h metres, and the time, t seconds, are connected by the differential equation

> You will need to use integration by parts.

$$\dfrac{\mathrm{d}h}{\mathrm{d}t} = \dfrac{t\cos\left(\frac{\pi}{8}t\right)}{40h}$$

At $t=0$, the height of the platform is 3.5 metres.

Find the height of the platform after 36 seconds, giving your answer to the nearest centimetre. **(9)**

....

....

....

....

....

....

....

You are the examiner!

Checking through your work is a key skill for A Level Maths. Have a look at pages 110 and 111 of the *Revision Guide*, then practise with these questions. There are full worked solutions on page 210.

1 $f(x) = \dfrac{x^2 + 2}{2x^2 - x - 1}$

Show that $f(x)$ can be written in the form $A + \dfrac{B}{x - 1} + \dfrac{C}{2x + 1}$ where A, B and C are constants to be found.   **(5)**

....

....

....

2   A right circular cone has a height of 4 cm. The radius of the base of the cone is increasing at a rate of 0.5 cm s^{-1}. Find the rate of increase of the volume of the cone when the radius is 3 cm.   **(5)**

....

....

3   (a) $y = \cos^3 x \sin 3x$ Find $\dfrac{dy}{dx}$ in its simplest form.   **(3)**

....

....

....

     (b)   By writing $\tan 2x = \dfrac{\sin 2x}{\cos 2x}$, show clearly that $\dfrac{d}{dx}(\tan 2x) = 2\sec^2 2x$ **(3)**

....

....

....

4   (a)   Given that θ is small, use the small angle approximation for $\cos \theta$ to show that:

$$6\cos^2 \theta - \cos \theta - 2 \approx 3 - \frac{11}{2}\theta^2$$

  (3)

....

....

Liz uses $\theta = 4°$ to test the approximation in part (a). Here is her working:

> Calculator: $6\cos^2 4° - \cos 4° - 2 \approx 2.973$ (3 d.p.)
>
> Approximation: $3 - \dfrac{11}{2}\theta^2 = 3 - \dfrac{11}{2}(4)^2 = -85$
>
> So the approximation is not true for $\theta = 4°$.

     (b)   Identify Liz's mistake and show that the approximation is correct to 3 decimal places when $\theta = 4°$.   **(2)**

....

....

You are the examiner!

Checking through your work is a key skill for A Level Maths. Have a look at pages 110 and 111 of the *Revision Guide*, then practise with these questions. There are full worked solutions on page 210.

5 (a) Use integration by parts to find $\int x \cos x \, dx$ **(2)**

....

(b) Using your answer to part (a), find $\int_0^{\frac{\pi}{2}} x^2 \sin x \, dx$ **(4)**

....

....

....

....

6 A football travels through the air along a path modelled by the function

$$h(t) = 48 \sin \frac{t}{5} - 12 \cos \frac{t}{5} + 12 - t^2$$

(a) Show that the football has zero height again after T seconds, where $7 \leqslant T \leqslant 8$ **(2)**

....

....

(b) Find $h'(t)$. **(2)**

....

(c) Taking $t_0 = 8$ as a first approximation, apply the Newton–Raphson method once to find a second approximation for the time when the ball next has zero height.
Give your answer to 3 decimal places. **(3)**

....

....

7 A curve, C, has equation $y = 4x^3 - 3x^2 - 18x + 10$

(a) Find $\dfrac{dy}{dx}$ and $\dfrac{d^2y}{dx^2}$ **(3)**

....

(b) Find the coordinates of the stationary points on C and determine their nature. **(5)**

....

....

....

....

(c) Show that C has one point of inflexion and find its coordinates. **(3)**

....

....

....

Sampling

1   Beth is investigating how often students visit the local leisure centre. She wants a sample of 30 students from her year group of 245 students. She selects the first person from an alphabetical list by choosing a random number from 1 to 6, then selects every 8th person after that.

   (a) What sampling technique is Beth using?   **(1)**

   ....

   (b) State two advantages this system of sampling has over a simple random sample.   **(2)**

   ....

   ....

> **Guided**

2   A youth club has 450 members. Each member can play one of football, tennis, rugby and squash. The table shows the number of members who play each of these sports.

Sport	Football	Tennis	Rugby	Squash
Number of members	97	68	151	134

Bill takes a sample of 65 members, stratified by the sport they play.

Find the number of members in the sample for each of these sports.   **(3)**

Sampling fraction = $\dfrac{..........}{450}$

| You might need to round to the nearest integer. |

Number in sample playing football = $\dfrac{..........}{450} \times 97 = ...$

Number in sample playing:

Tennis = ...   Rugby = ...   Squash = ...

| Make sure the numbers of members in the sample add up to 65. |

3   A golf club has 582 members. A stratified sample is taken, by age.
The table shows the age grouping of the members and some information about the sample.

Age (years)	16–24	25–44	45–64	65+
Number of members	96			110
Number in sample	16		34	

Complete the table.   **(5)**

   ....

   ....

   ....

   ....

   ....

Mean

1   Over a period of weeks, 36 blackbirds were caught in a nature reserve.

They were weighed and then released.

Their masses, x grams, were such that $\sum x = 3362$

(a) Find the mean of these data.   **(1)**

....

....

The next five blackbirds caught weighed

       101.6 g, 104 g, 89.5 g, 94.1 g and 112.8 g.

(b) Find the mean mass of all the birds caught so far.   **(2)**

> There are now 41 blackbirds. Calculate the new total mass.

....

....

....

Guided   **2**   These are the times taken, to the nearest minute, by a class of 32 students to travel to school on a particular day.

Time, t (minutes)	1–5	6–12	13–20	21–30
Frequency	6	11	7	8
Midpoint, x	3			25.5

(a) Find the midpoints of the 6–12 minutes and the 13–20 minutes groups.   **(2)**

....

....

(b) Estimate the mean of the journey times for the whole class.   **(2)**

$$\bar{x} = \frac{\sum fx}{\sum f} = \frac{6 \times 3 + \text{................} + \text{................} + 8 \times 25.5}{32}$$

$= $ ....

....

3   The table shows the distances some people travelled to work each day.

Estimate the mean distance travelled.   **(4)**

Distance, d (km)	Frequency
$0 < d \leqslant 4$	9
$4 < d \leqslant 10$	17
$10 < d \leqslant 15$	33
$15 < d \leqslant 25$	24
$25 < d \leqslant 30$	11

....

....

....

....

....

Median and quartiles

> **Guided**

1 The numbers of driving lessons taken by 23 people before they passed their test are given below.

8   17   20   32   13   23   11   33   19   33   28   35
20   28   14   27   9   28   35   26   11   34   18

(a) Write down the modal number of lessons. **(1)**

....

(b) Find the values of the lower quartile, the median and the upper quartile. **(3)**

....

....

$n = 23$, $\frac{n}{2} = 11.5 \Rightarrow$ 12th value, so median, $Q_2 = 23$

$\frac{n}{4} = 5.75 \Rightarrow$ 6th value, so $Q_1 = $ ....

$\frac{3n}{4} = $ .... $\Rightarrow$ ....th value, so $Q_3 = $ ....

2 Here are the ages of some people queuing for tickets at the theatre.

32   25   29   46   18   52   55   25   34   28   54   46   50
48   61   68   38   29   20   48   25   32   36   60   54   44

For these people, find the modal age, the median age and the interquartile range. **(4)**

....

....

....

....

....

....

3 The daily mean air pressure (kPa) at Leeming for the first 26 days in August 2017 was measured and recorded in the large data set. The data are given below:

1011   1010   998   1007   1014   1019   1014   1013   1019
1025   1015   1013   1021   1015   1012   1016   1007   1005
1010   1021   1022   1019   1015   1014   1016   1016

For this period, find:

(a) the median air pressure **(1)**

....

....

....

(b) the interquartile range. **(2)**

....

....

Linear interpolation

> **Guided**

1 The table gives the weights, w (kg), of 270 items of baggage checked in on a flight at Gatwick airport.

Use interpolation to estimate the median, Q_2, of these weights. Give your answer correct to 1 decimal place. **(2)**

Weight, w (kg)	Number of items
$0 < w < 10$	29
$10 \leqslant w < 15$	121
$15 \leqslant w < 22$	73
$22 \leqslant w < 30$	47

$\frac{n}{2} = 135$, so the median is

$(135 - 29) = 106$ values into the $10 \leqslant w < 15$ group.

This group is 5 kg wide so each member is worth $\frac{5}{121}$ kg.

$Q_2 = 10 + 106 \times \frac{5}{121}$ kg

     = ... = ... kg (1 d.p.)

2 The table shows the speeds, v (mph), of 90 vehicles travelling along a country road.

(a) Use interpolation to estimate the median, Q_2, the lower quartile, Q_1, and the upper quartile, Q_3, of these items.
Give your answers correct to 1 decimal place. **(4)**

Speed, v (mph)	Number of vehicles
$10 \leqslant v < 20$	12
$20 \leqslant v < 30$	16
$30 \leqslant v < 45$	36
$45 \leqslant v < 60$	18
$60 \leqslant v < 70$	8

....

....

....

....

....

> Start by working out $\frac{n}{4}$, $\frac{n}{2}$ and $\frac{3n}{4}$ to locate the positions of Q_1, Q_2 and Q_3, then follow the same procedure as in Question 1.

(b) Local residents claim that at least 20% of vehicles are breaking the 50 mph speed limit.

Investigate their claim. **(3)**

> Work out the 80th percentile.

....

....

3 The table shows the lengths of caterpillars, measured to the nearest millimetre.

Use interpolation to estimate the median, Q_2, the lower quartile, Q_1, and the upper quartile, Q_3, of these items. Give your answers correct to 1 decimal place. **(4)**

Length (mm)	Frequency
1–10	16
11–25	33
26–45	38
46–65	27
66–75	10

....

....

> **Problem solving**   Be aware of the upper and lower class boundaries, e.g. 11–25 really means lengths from 10.5 to 25.5 mm.

....

....

....

Standard deviation 1

> **Guided**

1 The table shows the marks obtained (out of 80) by students in a maths exam.

Given that $\sum x^2 = 195\,600$, calculate estimates for the mean and the standard deviation for the data. **(6)**

Mark	Frequency (f)	Midpoint (x)	$f \times x$
$0 < x \leq 10$	16	5	80
$10 < x \leq 30$	32	20	
$30 < x \leq 50$	38		
$50 < x \leq 60$	24		
$60 < x \leq 80$	10		

....

....

....

2 The ages, x years, of 34 people in a restaurant can be summarised as follows:

$$\sum x = 1262 \text{ and } \sum x^2 = 54\,431$$

Calculate the mean and the standard deviation of these ages. **(3)**

....

....

3 Here is a record of the numbers of letters received, in a week, by households in a street.

     13   20   31   15   18   29   20   31   18

     26   21   32   26   19   24   34   15   24

Calculate the mean and the standard deviation of the data. **(3)**

....

....

....

4 The monthly hours of sunshine, n hours, in Hurn was recorded in the large data set. The data can be summarised as follows:

$$\sum n = 1763.7 \qquad \sum n^2 = 319\,235.65$$

(a) Calculate the mean and standard deviation, giving both answers correct to 1 decimal place. **(2)**

....

....

The mean and standard deviation for the monthly hours of sunshine in 2005 for Leuchars were 129.5 hours and 58.7 hours respectively.

(b) State, with a reason, whether these results support the conclusion that southern locations have more hours of sunshine than northern locations. **(2)**

....

....

Standard deviation 2

> **Guided**

1 The table shows the times taken by 160 people to travel to work one morning.

Estimate the standard deviation of the data. **(5)**

Time, t (minutes)	Number of people	Midpoint
$0 \leqslant t < 10$	12	5
$10 \leqslant t < 15$	27	12.5
$15 \leqslant t < 30$	85	22.5
$30 \leqslant t < 50$	36	40

$$\sum f = 160$$

$$\sum fx = 12 \times 5 + 27 \times 12.5 + 85 \times 22.5 + 36 \times 40$$

$$= 3750$$

$$\sum fx^2 = 12 \times 5^2 + 27 \times 12.5^2 + \text{..................} + \text{..................}$$

$$= \text{.....................}$$

$$\text{Variance} = \frac{\text{.....................}}{160} - \left(\frac{3750}{160}\right)^2 = \text{.....................}$$

> Start by finding the midpoint of each group – these will be the x values. Work out $\sum fx$ and $\sum fx^2$, then use the formula for the variance. Don't forget to square root to find the standard deviation.

....

....

2 The profits of 92 businesses are given in the table.

Estimate the standard deviation of the data. **(5)**

Profit, p (£ million)	Number of businesses
$1.0 \leqslant p < 2.0$	19
$2.0 \leqslant p < 2.8$	34
$2.8 \leqslant p < 3.6$	26
$3.6 \leqslant p < 5.0$	13

....

....

....

....

....

....

....

3 The table shows the lengths of some earthworms, measured to the nearest millimetre.

(a) Find the midpoints of the 30–46 and 66–75 groups. **(2)**

....

....

(b) Estimate the standard deviation of the lengths of these earthworms. **(3)**

Length (mm)	Frequency	Midpoint
11–29	16	20
30–46	36	
47–65	40	56
66–75	24	
76–100	10	88
101–120	14	110.5

[You may use $\sum fx^2 = 551\,493.5$]

....

....

....

....

....

Coding

Guided **1** The table shows the yields of potatoes, w kg, from some allotments.

Yield, w (kg)	Frequency, f	Midpoint, w	$u = w - 80$	$f \times u$	u^2	$f \times u^2$
$65 \leqslant w < 75$	21	70	-10	-210	100	2100
$75 \leqslant w < 85$	18	80	0			
$85 \leqslant w < 105$	11					
$105 \leqslant w < 125$	7					

Use the coding $u = w - 80$ to work out estimates of the mean and the standard deviation of the data. Give your answers to 3 significant figures. **(6)**

> Coding simplifies the calculations in the table significantly.

Mean for $u = \dfrac{\sum fu}{n} = \dfrac{\ldots\ldots}{57} = \ldots\ldots$, so mean for $w = \ldots\ldots + 80 = \ldots\ldots$ kg (3 s.f.)

Variance for $u = \dfrac{\sum fu^2}{n} - \left[\dfrac{\sum fu}{n}\right]^2 = \dfrac{\ldots\ldots}{57} - (\ldots\ldots)^2 = \ldots\ldots$

Standard deviation for $u = \ = \sqrt{\ldots\ldots} = \ldots\ldots$, so standard

> The mean for w needs adjusting but the SD does not.

deviation for $w = \ldots\ldots$ kg (3 s.f.)

2 The time taken, t minutes, for a task is coded using $y = \dfrac{t - 12.5}{8}$

The mean of the coded data is $\bar{y} = 1.6$
The standard deviation of the coded data is $\sigma_y = 1.12$
Find the mean and the standard deviation of the original data. **(2)**

....

....

3 The scores, x, in a test for 50 people are shown in the table.

Score, x	Frequency
$100 < x \leqslant 106$	6
$106 < x \leqslant 114$	12
$114 < x \leqslant 126$	23
$126 < x \leqslant 140$	9

(a) Find estimates of the mean and the standard deviation of the scores.
You may use the fact that $\sum x^2 = 699\,255$ **(4)**

....

....

(b) It was discovered that there had been an error in the marking, and all the scores were adjusted by subtracting 3 marks and then increasing them by 5%.
Find estimates of the mean and the standard deviation of the adjusted marks. **(2)**

....

....

Box plots and outliers

> **Guided**

1 Carla recorded the ages of some people at a concert.

This table summarises her data.

For this data, an outlier is defined as a value that is greater than Q_3 plus 1.25 times the interquartile range or less than Q_1 minus 1.25 times the interquartile range.

Draw a box plot to represent the data, indicating clearly any outliers.

(5)

Two lowest values	11, 14
Lower quartile	28
Median	37
Upper quartile	40
Two highest values	43, 61

IQR = 40 − 28 = 12

1.25 × IQR = 1.25 × 12 = ...

Q_3 + ... = ...

....

....

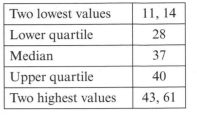

10 15 20 25 30 35 40 45 50 55 60 65

2 The box plot shows a summary of the marks gained by students in a test.

(a) (i) Write down the mark that 75% of the students scored more than.

     (ii) State the name given to this mark. **(2)**

....

....

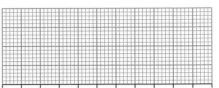

5 10 15 20 25 30 35 40 45 50 55
Mark

An outlier is defined as a value greater than Q_3 plus 1.5 times the interquartile range or less than Q_1 minus 1.5 times the interquartile range.

(b) Show working to explain why 10 is an outlier. **(2)**

....

....

3 A town centre car park was monitored every half hour, over an 11-hour period, to record how many cars were parked.

These are the results:

     26   18   27   36   27   43   9   30   48   36   29

     15   28   7   26   19   53   26   31   37   28   31

An outlier is defined as a value that is greater than Q_3 plus 1.5 times the interquartile range or less than Q_1 minus 1.5 times the interquartile range.

Draw a box plot to represent the data, indicating clearly any outliers. **(7)**

....

....

....

....

....

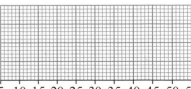

5   10 15 20 25 30 35 40 45 50 55

....

....

Cumulative frequency diagrams

Guided 1 The table shows the lengths of some insects in a zoo, measured to the nearest millimetre.

Length, l (mm)	Number of insects	Cumulative frequency
$0 < l \leqslant 5$	65	65
$5 < l \leqslant 10$	50	115
$10 < l \leqslant 20$	60	
$20 < l \leqslant 30$	25	
$30 < l \leqslant 40$	15	
$40 < l \leqslant 50$	10	

(a) Draw a cumulative frequency diagram to represent the data. **(3)**

(b) Use your cumulative frequency diagram to estimate the 20th to 80th interpercentile range. **(3)**

For the 20th percentile, read across from $\frac{20n}{100}$ on the vertical axis then down to the horizontal axis.

20th percentile $= \dfrac{20}{100} \times 225 = \ldots\ldots$ th value

80th percentile $= \dfrac{80}{100} \times 225 = \ldots\ldots$ th value

Interpercentile range $= \ldots\ldots - \ldots\ldots = \ldots\ldots$ mm

2 Katie did a survey of the amounts of money spent by customers in a supermarket one morning. The table shows her results.

Amount spent, x (£)	$0 < x \leqslant 10$	$10 < x \leqslant 20$	$20 < x \leqslant 40$	$40 < x \leqslant 60$	$60 < x \leqslant 80$	$80 < x \leqslant 100$
Number of customers	12	42	70	28	20	8

(a) Draw a cumulative frequency diagram to represent the data. **(3)**

(b) Use your cumulative frequency diagram to find the median and the interquartile range of the amounts spent. **(3)**

....

....

....

....

(c) Estimate how many people spent more than £75. **(2)**

....

(d) Estimate the 10th to 90th interpercentile range. **(2)**

....

Histograms

Guided **1** The histogram shows information about how much time cars spent in a car park.

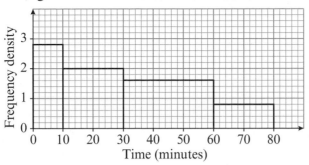

Complete the table. **(2)**

Frequency for $0 < t \leqslant 10$ class = 2.8 × 10 = 28

Frequency for $10 < t \leqslant 30$ class = 2 × .... = ...

....

....

Time, t (minutes)	Number of cars
$0 < t \leqslant 10$	28
$10 < t \leqslant 30$	
$30 < t \leqslant 60$	
$60 < t \leqslant 80$	16

Frequency $\times$ class width = frequency (density)

2 The speeds of cars along a stretch of road were recorded.

The histogram and the frequency table show the same information.

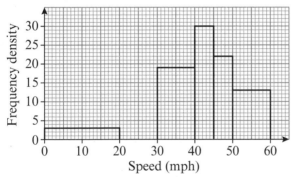

Speed, v (mph)	Number of cars
$0 < v \leqslant 20$	60
$20 < v \leqslant 30$	110
$30 < v \leqslant 40$	190
$40 < v \leqslant 45$	150
$45 < v \leqslant 50$	
$50 < v \leqslant 60$	130

(a) Complete the histogram and fill in the missing number in the frequency table. **(2)**

....

(b) Estimate how many cars were travelling at between 25 mph and 43 mph. **(3)**

....

....

....

3 Poppy recorded the heights of 80 plant seedlings, to the nearest mm. This table shows her results.

Height (mm)	6–7	8–9	10–13	14–19
Frequency	8	32	24	18

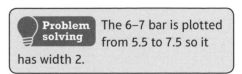

Problem solving The 6–7 bar is plotted from 5.5 to 7.5 so it has width 2.

A histogram was drawn and the bar representing the 8–9 class was 1 cm wide and 4 cm high. Find the width and the height of the bar representing the 10–13 class. **(3)**

....

....

....

Comparing distributions

Guided **1** The box plots show the marks scored in an exam by the boys and the girls in a class.

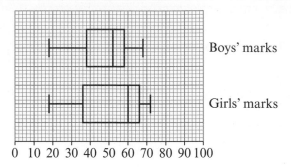

Boys' marks

Girls' marks

0 10 20 30 40 50 60 70 80 90 100

Compare and contrast the two sets of results. **(4)**

The median for the boys' marks (52) is less than the median for the girls' marks (60),

so the boys did less well overall.

The IQR for the boys was .... compared with .... for the girls.

....

....

> **Problem solving** You need to compare data sets using a measure of location and a measure of spread.

2 The daily mean air temperature, in °C, is measured in Beijing in September 1997 and September 2015.

The results are recorded in the large data set and are summarised as shown in the table.

	Min	Q_1	Q_2	Q_3	Max	$\sum x$	$\sum x^2$
1997	13.3	16.6	17.7	21.1	25.5	556.1	10 577.11
2015	15.5	18.8	20.8	21.6	25.5	614.8	12 766.42

(a) Calculate the mean and standard deviation of the data for each of the two years. **(4)**

....

....

....

....

....

(b) Compare the distributions for the two years. How far do the data support the conclusion that average air temperatures in Beijing have increased between 1997 and 2015? **(4)**

....

....

....

ρ

....

....

Correlation and cleaning data

Guided   **1**   A scientist is testing a model which proposes that an increase in weight is accompanied by an increase in height in teenage boys. This table shows the weights and the heights of 12 teenage boys.

	A	B	C	D	E	F	G	H	I	J	K	L
Weight, w (kg)	72	80	58	71	68	72	67	55	72	73	77	70
Height, h (cm)	175	182	166	173	172	180	169	173	176	182	178	174

The following statistics were calculated for the data on weight:

$$Q_1 = 67.5 \quad Q_2 = 71.5 \quad Q_3 = 72.5$$

An outlier is defined as a value that is less than $Q_1 - 1.5 \times IQR$, or greater than $Q_3 + 1.5 \times IQR$.

(a) Show that $x = 55$ is an outlier. **(1)**

IQR = 72.5 − 67.5 = 5, 1.5 × IQR = 7.5, Q_1 − 7.5 ....; since 55 < ...., 55 is an outlier.

(b) It was decided to remove boy H from the data. Comment on the validity of this decision. **(2)**

....

....

(c) Draw a scatter diagram for the remaining 11 results. **(3)**

(d) Describe the correlation shown on your scatter diagram and interpret this in the context of the model. **(2)**

....

....

....

2   Simon is conducting an experiment on memory.
He randomly selects ten people and gives them 20 minutes to try to remember 30 words.
Then, after a gap of 10 minutes, he asks them to recall as many words as possible.
The table shows the age of each person, x years, and the number of words remembered, y.

	A	B	C	D	E	F	G	H	I	J
Age, x (years)	19	32	16	70	48	34	30	39	29	36
Number of words, y	15	15	19	20	17	18	12	13	23	14

(a) Find Q_1, Q_2 and Q_3 for the ages of the people. **(3)**

....

An outlier is defined as a value that is less than $Q_1 - 1.5 \times IQR$, or greater than $Q_3 + 1.5 \times IQR$

(b) Show that $x = 70$ is an outlier. **(1)**

....

(c) Simon decides to retain person D in his results. Comment on his decision. **(2)**

....

....

Regression

> **Guided**

1 Measurements of annual average CO_2 levels have been recorded at Mauna Loa in Hawaii.

The scatter diagram shows the CO_2 level, y, in parts per million and the number of years, x, since 1991.

The equation of the regression line of y on x for the data is

$$y = 351.64 + 2.11x$$

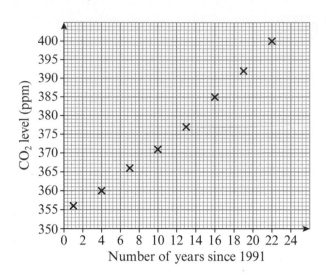

(a) Give an interpretation of the gradient of the regression line.   **(1)**

The gradient is 2.11, so every year the

average CO_2 level ....

....

(b) Comment on the validity of a linear regression model for the data.   **(2)**

There is .... correlation so a linear model ....

2 The scatter diagram shows the average daily temperature, $x°C$, and a household's daily energy consumption, y kWh, on 8 winter days.

The equation of the regression line of y on x for the data is

$$y = 25.7 - 2.25x$$

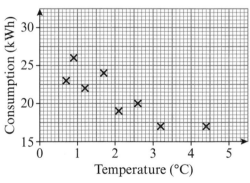

(a) Give an interpretation of the gradient of the regression line.   **(1)**

....

....

....

(b) Give an interpretation of the y-intercept of the regression line.   **(1)**

....

....

(c) Comment on the validity of a linear regression model for the data.   **(2)**

....

....

....

Using regression lines

1 Explain what is meant by

(a) interpolation **(1)**

....

(b) extrapolation. **(2)**

....

2 Look at the information and scatter diagram from Question 1 on page 124.

The equation of the regression line of y on x is $y = 351.64 + 2.11x$, where x is the number of years since 1991 and y is the average level of CO_2 in parts per million.

(a) Comment on the reliability of using this regression equation to estimate the average level of CO_2 in

(i) 2005

(ii) 2016. **(2)**

....

....

....

(b) Laura uses the above regression model to predict the year in which CO_2 levels reached 375 parts per million. Give a reason why this regression model would not be suitable for this prediction. **(1)**

....

3 Look at the information and scatter diagram from Question 2 on page 124.

The equation of the regression line of y on x is $y = 25.7 - 2.25x$, where x is the temperature in °C and y is the daily energy consumption in kWh.

(a) Comment on the reliability of using this regression equation to estimate

(i) the daily energy consumption when the average temperature is 4 °C

(ii) the average temperature on a day when the household used 20 kWh of energy. **(2)**

....

....

....

(b) Tom states that the regression model predicts that each additional °C of temperature reduces energy usage by 2.25 kWh. He predicts that if the weather is warmer than 12 °C, the household will use no energy.

Give two reasons why Tom's prediction is unlikely to be accurate. **(2)**

....

....

Drawing Venn diagrams

Guided 1 80 children were asked whether they had a cat, a dog or a rabbit as a pet.

31 of them had a cat
35 of them had a dog
18 of them had a rabbit
11 of them had a cat and a dog
7 of them had a cat and a rabbit
5 of them had a dog and a rabbit
2 of them had all three pets

(a) Draw a Venn diagram to represent this information.   (5)

The 11 children who had a cat and a dog include the 2 children who had all three pets.

So 11 − 2 = 9 children had a cat and a dog but
not a rabbit. This is $C \cap D \cap R'$.

....

....

....

....

....

....

(b) How many of the 80 children did not have a cat or a dog?   (1)

....

2 160 people were asked which of the countries France, Italy and Germany they had visited.

78 of them had been to France
43 of them had been to Italy
69 of them had been to Germany
21 of them had been to France and Italy
31 of them had been to France and Germany
20 of them had been to Italy and Germany
14 of them had been to all three countries

> Draw a rectangle to denote
> the whole sample space
> and draw three closed,
> intersecting circles for the
> three events, labelled *F*, *I*
> and *G*, inside the rectangle.

(a) Draw a Venn diagram to represent this information.   (5)

....

....

....

....

....

....

....

(b) How many of the 160 people had been to exactly two of the three countries?   (1)

....

Using Venn diagrams

Guided   **1**   The Venn diagram shows the numbers of students who take maths, English and history.

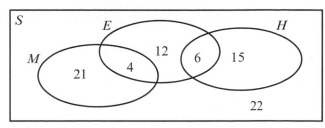

One of these students is selected at random.

(a) Show that the probability that the student takes only one of the subjects is $\frac{3}{5}$ **(2)**

The total number of students = 21 + 4 + 12 + 6 + 15 + 22 = 80

The number taking only one subject = 21 + 12 + ... = ...

So the probability is ....

(b) Find the probability that the student takes maths or English, or both.   **(2)**

....

2   For the events A and B, $P(A \cap B) = 0.23$, $P(A \cup B)' = 0.17$ and $P(B) = 0.54$

(a) Draw a Venn diagram to illustrate the complete sample space for events A and B.   **(4)**

> Instead of totals you write probabilities in the appropriate places on the Venn diagram. Remember that the total in the whole sample space must be 1.

(b) Write down the value of $P(A)$ and the value of $P(A' \cap B)$.   **(2)**

....

3   A survey showed that 68% of the people in a town shopped at Warners supermarket and 46% shopped at Johnsons supermarket. 17% of the people in the town did not shop at either of these supermarkets.

(a) Draw a Venn diagram to represent this information.   **(4)**

A person from the town is chosen at random.

(b) Write down the probability that this person shops at either Warners or Johnsons, but not both.   **(2)**

....

Independent events

1 Given that $P(Q) = q$ and $P(R) = r$, express $P(Q \cup R)$ in terms of q and r when

(a) Q and R are mutually exclusive **(1)**

....

(b) Q and R are independent. **(1)**

....

> **Guided**

2 The Venn diagram shows the numbers of people who chose a chocolate biscuit (C), a wafer biscuit (W) or a ginger biscuit (G) from a box of biscuits.

Determine whether choosing a chocolate biscuit and choosing a ginger biscuit are statistically independent. **(3)**

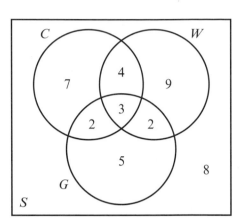

Total number of people

$$= 7 + 4 + 9 + 2 + 3 + 2 + 5 + 8 = \text{...........}$$

$$P(C) = \frac{7 + 4 + 2 + 3}{\text{.........}} = \frac{16}{\text{.........}}$$

$$P(G) = \frac{5 + 2 + \text{.........} + \text{.........}}{\text{.........}} = \text{.................}$$

Next, work out $P(C \cap G)$ and compare it to $P(C) \times P(G)$.

....

....

3 Two events A and B are independent.

$$P(B \cap A') = \frac{3}{25} \qquad P(A' \cap B') = \frac{1}{5}$$

Draw a Venn diagram and mark on it the probabilities that are given.

(a) Find $P(A)$ **(3)**

....

....

....

(b) Find $P(A \cap B)$ **(4)**

Problem solving Let $P(A \cap B) = x$
Use the fact that A and B are independent and set up an equation to find x.

....

....

....

....

....

Tree diagrams

Guided 1 Marcus either gets up immediately when his alarm goes off or sleeps for a little while longer. The probability that he gets up immediately is 0.3

If he gets up immediately, the probability that he eats breakfast is 0.85 but if he sleeps for a little while longer, the probability that he eats breakfast is 0.45

(a) Draw a tree diagram to represent this information. **(2)**

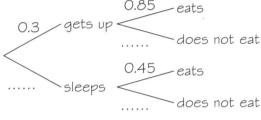

(b) Find the probability that Marcus does not eat breakfast. **(3)**

> Remember to include both cases, P(gets up and does not eat) + P(sleeps and does not eat).

....

(c) Given that he does not eat breakfast, find the probability that he got up immediately when his alarm went off. **(3)**

....

....

(d) Find the probability that Marcus does not eat breakfast on two days out of three. **(3)**

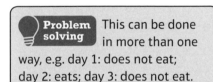

> **Problem solving** This can be done in more than one way, e.g. day 1: does not eat; day 2: eats; day 3: does not eat.

....

....

2 When Keisha goes to a restaurant she always eats pizza or risotto for her main course and always eats apple pie or lemon tart for dessert.

The probability that she eats pizza is $\frac{3}{8}$

If she eats pizza, the probability that she eats apple pie is $\frac{4}{5}$

If she eats risotto, the probability that she eats lemon tart is $\frac{2}{3}$

(a) Draw a tree diagram to represent this information. **(2)**

(b) Find the probability that Keisha eats either risotto or lemon tart, but not both. **(3)**

....

....

(c) Given that Keisha eats apple pie, find the probability that she ate pizza for her main course. **(4)**

....

....

....

Random variables

Guided 1 The discrete random variable X can only take the values 1, 2, 3 and 4

   X has probability function

$$P(X = x) = \begin{cases} kx^2, & x = 1, 2, 3 \\ 3kx, & x = 4 \end{cases}$$

   where k is a constant.

   (a) Find the value of k and construct a table giving the probability distribution of X. **(3)**

   $P(X = 1) = k \times 1^2 = k$, $P(X = 2) = k \times 2^2 = 4k$, $P(X = 3) = $ ...., $P(X = 4) = $ ....

   $k + 4k + $ .... $ + $ .... $ = 1$, giving $k = $ ....

x	1	2	3	4
$P(X = x)$				

   (b) Find $P(X < 3)$. **(2)**

   ....

2 The discrete random variable Y can only take the values 1, 2, 3, 4 and 5

   Y has probability function $P(Y = y) = k(6y - y^2)$ for $y = 1, 2, 3, 4, 5$, where k is a constant.

   (a) Construct a table giving the probability distribution of Y. **(3)**

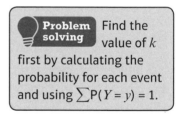

Problem solving Find the value of k first by calculating the probability for each event and using $\sum P(Y = y) = 1$.

   (b) Find $P(Y \geqslant 3)$. **(2)**

   ....

3 The discrete random variable W has the probability distribution given by

w	-4	-1	0	1	3	6
$P(W = w)$	0.15	$2a$	a	0.05	0.1	$0.5a$

   where a is a constant.

   (a) Find the value of a. **(2)**

   ....

   ....

   ....

   (b) Find $P(2W + 5 \geqslant 4)$. **(2)**

   ....

   ....

   ....

   ....

The binomial distribution

Guided 1 Research shows that 5% of people are allergic to a particular brand of hand cream.
A group of 40 people, randomly chosen, agree to test the product.

(a) Justify the use of the binomial distribution to model the number of people in the group who are allergic. **(2)**

....

(b) Find the probability that exactly two of the people are allergic to the hand cream. **(2)**

$P(X = 2) = \dbinom{40}{2} \times (0.05)^2 \times (\text{.............})^{38} = \text{.............}$

(c) Find the probability that no more than two of the people are allergic to the hand cream. **(2)**

This is P(0) + P(1) + P(2), or $P(X \leq 2)$, using the binomial cumulative distribution.

....

....

2 In one category of a quiz there are eight questions.
For each question there is a choice of three possible answers, only one of which is correct.
Jack has no knowledge of this topic so decides to guess every answer.

(a) Find the probability that he gets exactly five questions correct. **(2)**

....

(b) Find the probability that he gets at least two correct answers. **(2)**

....

....

3 Ellie has a bag containing 20 liquorice sweets and 20 toffees. She eats 10 sweets at random, and records the number of toffees, T, that she eats. Ellie decided to model T as B(10, 0.5). Explain why this model is not suitable. **(1)**

....

....

4 The probability that a plant produces pink flowers is 0.35
A garden centre sells these plants in trays of 12 plants of mixed colours.
A tray is selected at random.
Find the probability that, in this tray, the number of plants that will produce pink flowers is

(a) exactly 4 **(2)**

....

(b) more than 5 **(2)**

....

(c) between 3 and 6 (inclusive). **(3)**

....

....

Hypothesis testing

Guided   **1**   When playing a game involving dice, Elaine noticed that a score of 1 seemed to occur more than might be expected.

She tested her theory that the dice was biased towards the number 1 by throwing it 30 times and recording the scores. Her results are shows in the table.

Score	1	2	3	4	5	6
Frequency	8	4	5	3	6	4

Test, at the 10% significance level, whether there is sufficient evidence that the dice is biased towards the number 1.   **(6)**

H_0: $P(1) = \frac{1}{6}$ (unbiased) H_1: $P(1) > \frac{1}{6}$ (biased)

Assume H_0, so that $X \sim B(30, \frac{1}{6})$ where X is the number of 1s

$P(X \leqslant 7) = $ .... $P(X \geqslant 8) = 1 - $ .... $ = $ ....

Since .... 0.10 , there is .... evidence to reject H_0

So the conclusion is that ....

2   In a local football team, the striker who takes the penalties thinks he has a fairly unimpressive 55% chance of scoring from a penalty.
His coach thinks he is underestimating his chances.
The striker takes 18 penalties and scores 14 times.
Test, at the 5% significance level, whether he has underestimated his chances of scoring.
State your hypotheses clearly.   **(6)**

....

....

....

....

....

3   In the 2016 UK referendum, 51.9% of those voting voted for the UK to leave the EU.
In a sample of 50 Scottish voters, 19 said they voted to leave.
Test, at the 5% significance level, whether this result is different from the UK average.
State your hypotheses clearly.   **(6)**

 Problem solving   Work out the mean (np) and compare it with your value of x, then decide whether to calculate $P(X \leqslant x)$ or $P(X \geqslant x)$.

....

....

....

....

....

....

....

Finding critical regions

Guided **1** Peppered moths can be light or dark. In a village, 20% of the moths are dark.
Atmospheric pollution can be identified by an increase in the proportion of dark moths.
A scientist wants to investigate whether pollution levels are changing so she catches a sample
of 30 moths and counts how many of them are dark.
Find the critical values, at the 10% significance level, which would indicate that pollution levels
are changing. **(3)**

Model this by $X \sim B(30, 0.2)$ $H_0: \rho = 0.2$ $H_1: \rho$ .... (two-tailed test)

$P(X \leqslant 2) =$ .... 0.05 $P(X \leqslant$ ......$) =$ 0.05

$P(X \geqslant$ ......$) =$ .... 0.05 $P(X \geqslant$ ......$) =$ 0.05

> You are finding probabilities as close as possible to 0.05 but < 0.05.

The critical region is .... and ....

So catching fewer than .... or more than .... dark moths would indicate that

pollution levels are changing.

2 In the UK, 22% of the people have brown eyes.
It is suspected that in the South-West of England, this figure is higher.
To test this theory, a sample of 40 people living in the South-West were randomly selected.

(a) Using a 5% significance level, find the critical region for this test, stating your hypotheses
clearly. **(3)**

....

....

....

(b) State the actual significance level of this test. **(1)**

....

(c) The number of people found to have brown eyes in the sample was 12.
Comment on this observation in the light of your critical region. **(2)**

....

....

3 A random variable, X, is modelled as $X \sim B(36, p)$
A single observation of X is taken and used to test $H_0: \rho = 0.73$ against $H_1: \rho \neq 0.73$

(a) Using a 5% significance level, find the critical region for this test. **(2)**

....

....

(b) State the actual significance level. **(1)**

....

(c) The observed value of X is 19.
Comment on this observation in the light of your critical region. **(2)**

....

....

You are the examiner!

Checking through your work is a key skill for A Level Maths. Have a look at pages 134 and 135 of the *Revision Guide*, then practise with these questions. There are full worked solutions on page 214.

1   An inspector is checking a company's vehicles.

There are 3 large-load vehicles, 135 light vans and 24 company cars.

The inspector decides to sample 15% of the vehicles. Each type of vehicle should be included in the sample.

(a) What is this sampling procedure called? **(1)**

....

(b) How many of each type of vehicle should be inspected? **(3)**

....

....

2   The numbers of goals scored, x, and points gained, y, by 10 netball teams are shown in the table.

Team	A	B	C	D	E	F	G	H	I	J
Goals, x	37	51	51	46	48	30	56	60	45	50
Points, y	15	21	14	18	17	10	19	14	11	16

(a) Find the values of the median and the interquartile range for the goals scored. **(3)**

....

....

An outlier is defined as a value that is less than $Q_1 - 1.5 \times IQR$, or greater than $Q_3 + 1.5 \times IQR$.

(b) Show that $x = 30$ is an outlier. **(1)**

....

(c) Explain why the data for team F should be retained. **(2)**

....

....

(d) Draw a scatter diagram for all 10 data items.   **(3)**

(e) Describe and interpret the correlation shown
on your scatter diagram.   **(2)**

....

....

....

....

....

You are the examiner!

Checking through your work is a key skill for A Level Maths. Have a look at pages 134 and 135 of the *Revision Guide*, then practise with these questions. There are full worked solutions on page 214.

3   Electric cable is sold on reels which are supposed to hold 100 m of cable.

For quality control purposes the length is checked by measuring randomly chosen reels.

The lengths are recorded as differences, in centimetres, from 100 m, so, for example, a sample of 99.87 m is recorded as −13

For a sample of $n = 20$ reels, the data are summarised as follows:

$$\sum x = -88 \text{ and } \sum x^2 = 4292$$

(a) Calculate the mean and the standard deviation of the values of x. **(3)**

....

....

(b) Hence find the mean and the standard deviation, in metres, of the lengths of cable on the 20 reels. **(2)**

....

....

Someone notices that one of the x values is −38, and thinks it might be an error, so it is discarded.

(c) Find the new mean and the standard deviation, in metres, of the lengths of cable on the other 19 reels. **(3)**

....

....

....

....

4   In a tea shop, 65% of the customers take tea with milk, 15% take tea with lemon and the rest take tea with neither milk nor lemon.

Of those taking tea with milk, $\frac{2}{5}$ take sugar.

Of those taking tea with lemon, $\frac{1}{4}$ take sugar.

Of those taking tea with neither milk nor lemon, $\frac{3}{8}$ take sugar.

(a) Represent this information on a fully labelled tree diagram. **(3)**

(b) Find the probability that a customer does not take sugar. **(4)**

....

....

Measuring correlation

Guided 1 The heights, in centimetres, and weights, in kilograms, of 8 people are shown in the table.

Height, h (cm)	170	168	179	175	171	172	180	178
Weight, w (kg)	73	72	82	78	77	70	75	74

(a) Calculate the product moment correlation coefficient between h and w. **(1)**

$r =$ .... (3 d.p.)

(b) Use your answer to part (a) to describe the correlation between height and weight, based on this sample. **(2)**

$r =$ .... indicates a .... correlation between height and weight.

A linear model .... be the best; a different model might be a .... fit.

2 This table records the numbers of hours of sunshine and the numbers of centimetres of rainfall over a six-month period.

Month	January	February	March	April	May	June
Sunshine, x (hours)	85	105	115	91	124	130
Rainfall, y (cm)	4.8	4.2	3.1	4.6	2.7	3.2

(a) Calculate the product moment correlation coefficient for these data. **(1)**

....

(b) Describe the nature of the linear relationship of these data, if any, based on this sample. **(2)**

....

....

3 Data are recorded for two variables x and y.

x	2	6	7	9	12	14	15	16
y	1.5	2	2.5	3	4	4.5	6.5	8

Calculate the product moment correlation coefficient for the given data, using each of these relationships to find which relationship most closely models the data

(i) a relationship of the form $y = mx + c$, where m and c are constants

(ii) a relationship of the form $y = ax^n$, where a and n are constants

(iii) a relationship of the form $y = kb^x$, where k and b are constants. **(9)**

....

....

....

....

....

....

....

....

....

Hypothesis testing for 0 correlation

Guided   **1**   An athletics coach thinks there is a positive correlation between performances on the high jump and the long jump. Data was collected for nine athletes.

Athlete	A	B	C	D	E	F	G	H	I
High jump, x (m)	2.0	2.1	1.6	1.8	1.9	1.6	2.1	1.8	1.7
Long jump, y (m)	8.1	7.5	7.1	6.6	8.0	7.0	7.3	6.9	6.7

(a) Calculate the product moment correlation coefficient for these data.   **(1)**

$r = $ ....

(b) Test the coach's claim at the 5% significance level, stating your hypotheses clearly.   **(3)**

$H_0: \rho = 0$ $H_1: \rho$ ....   sample size, $n = $ ....   significance level $= 0.05$

From the critical values table, the critical value of r is ...., so the critical region is

$r >$ .... 0. .... 0. .... The observed value of r ....

in the critical region, so .... at the 5% level to .... H_0.

The data .... the coach's claim.

> Remember to state your conclusions in the context of the question.

2   Ten students took two aptitude tests. The table shows their scores in each test.

Student	1	2	3	4	5	6	7	8	9	10
Verbal test (x)	67	81	56	51	86	65	48	74	67	69
Spatial test (y)	48	65	49	52	81	69	46	62	55	77

(a) Calculate the product moment correlation coefficient for these data.   **(1)**

....

(b) Test, at the 1% level of significance, whether there is evidence of a positive correlation between the verbal score and the spatial score. State your hypotheses clearly.   **(3)**

....

....

....

3   The table shows the weights of 7 lorries and their average fuel consumption in miles per gallon.

Weight, x (tonnes)	3.5	4	6	7.5	10	11	14
Fuel consumption, y (mpg)	17	12.5	10	9.5	8.5	8.5	8

The product moment correlation coefficient for these data is $r = -0.8174$.
Jack thinks there is a negative correlation between the weight and the fuel consumption.
He use the hypothesis:

$H_0: \rho = 0$, $H_1: \rho < 0$ to test his theory.

Given that these data provided him with sufficient evidence to reject his null hypothesis, suggest the least possible significance level for the test.   **(2)**

....

....

Conditional probability

Guided 1   The Venn diagram shows the ice-cream flavours chosen
by a group of 48 children at a party.

The choices are vanilla (V), choc-chip (C) and toffee (T).

A child is selected at random.

(a) Given that the child chooses choc-chip, find the
probability that they also choose toffee.   **(2)**

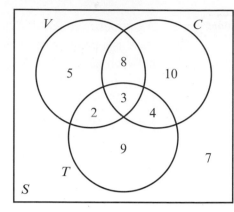

The number choosing choc-chip = 10 + 8 + 4 + 3 = 25

Of these 25, ... choose toffee, so the probability = $\frac{\text{............}}{25}$

(b) Given that the child chooses vanilla or toffee,
find the probability that they choose choc-chip.   **(2)**

....

> The denominator of the probability
> fraction will be the total choosing
> vanilla or toffee or both of these.

....

....

2   The Venn diagram shows the sports played by a group
of 80 students.

The three most popular sports were tennis (T), golf (G)
and basketball (B).

A student is selected at random.

(a) Given that the student plays tennis, find the
probability that they play all three sports.   **(2)**

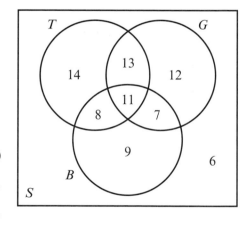

....

....

....

(b) Given that the student plays at least two of the three sports, find the probability that
they play golf and basketball.   **(2)**

....

....

....

(c) Given that the student does not play tennis, find the probability that they only play
basketball.   **(2)**

....

....

....

Probability formulae

Guided 1 Two events A and B are such that $P(A \cup B) = 0.85$, $P(A) = 0.7$ and $P(B) = 0.45$

Find the value of:

(a) $P(A' \cap B')$ **(1)**

$P(A' \cap B') = 1 - P(A \cup B) = $ ....

(b) $P(A \cap B)$ **(2)**

$P(A \cap B) = P(A) + P(B) - P(A \cup B)$

$= 0.7 + 0.45 - 0.85$

$= $ ....

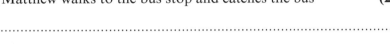

Write in the probabilities as you work them out.

(c) $P(A \cap B')$ **(1)**

....

(d) $P(A' \cup B)$ **(1)**

....

2 Matthew either walks or runs to the bus stop on his way to school.

The probability that he walks is 0.6

The probability that he catches the bus is 0.49

If he walks to the bus stop, the probability that he catches the bus is 0.35

Find the probability that:

(a) Matthew walks to the bus stop and catches the bus **(2)**

....

....

....

....

....

....

....

Problem solving Draw a Venn diagram representing the events W (for walking to the bus stop) and C (for catching the bus). Use the formula $P(C \mid W) = \dfrac{P(C \cap W)}{P(W)}$ to find $P(C \cap W)$.

(b) Matthew runs to the bus stop but does not catch the bus **(3)**

....

....

(c) Matthew catches the bus, given that he runs to the bus stop. **(2)**

....

....

Problem solving On your Venn diagram, fill in the probabilities for $P(W \cap C')$, $P(C \cap W')$ and $P(W' \cap C')$. Remember that $P(\text{runs to the bus stop}) = P(W') = 1 - P(W)$.

....

....

The normal distribution 1

1   The random variable $X \sim N(15, 4^2)$.

    (a) Find $P(X < 9)$ **(1)**

....

    (b) Find $P(12 < X < 17)$ **(1)**

....

    (c) Find $P(X > 20)$ **(1)**

....

> Make sure you know how to use your calculator to find these values.

> Draw a sketch of the distribution so you can see the probability required.
>
>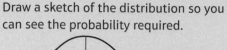
>
>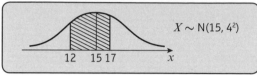
>
>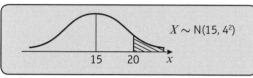

2   The random variable $X \sim N(48, 25)$

    (a) Find $P(X > 45)$ **(1)**

....

    (b) Find $P(X < 56)$ **(1)**

....

    (c) Find $P(X < 40$ or $X > 58)$ **(1)**

....

> 25 is the variance. Take the square root to find the standard deviation.

> Work out each probability separately then add the answers. Or you could use $P(40 < X < 58)$ and subtract from 1.

3   The random variable $Y \sim N(18, 12)$.

    (a) Find $P(Y < 23)$ **(1)**

....

> 12 is the variance. Take the square root to find the standard deviation.

    (b) Find $P(10 < Y < 15)$ **(1)**

....

    (c) Find $P(10 < Y < 15$ or $Y > 23)$ **(1)**

....

4   The heights of 13–year–old boys, H, are normally distributed, $H \sim N(162, 9.5^2)$

    (a) Find $P(155 < H < 170)$ **(1)**

....

    (b) Find $P(H > 175)$ **(1)**

....

    (c) Three 13–year–old boys are selected at random.
       What is the probability that all of them are taller than 175 cm?   **(2)**

....

The normal distribution 2

> **Guided**   **1**   Test scores are modelled as being normally distributed with a mean of 80 and a standard deviation of 12. Students who score more than 100 are awarded a distinction. A class of 30 students take the test.

    (a) Find the probability of any student scoring more than 100.   **(1)**

> Use the Normal CD function on your calculator.

$X \sim N(80, 12^2)$ $P(X > 100) =$ ....

    (b) Find the probability that more than three students are awarded a distinction.   **(3)**

> Use the Binomial CD function with $n = 30$ and $p =$ the probability found in part (a). There are two options – they will either be awarded a distinction or they will not – and each student's chance of success is independent from every other student.

Let S be the number of students who are awarded a

distinction.

$S \sim B(30, \text{...........})$ $P(S > 3) = 1 - P(S \leqslant 3)$

$$= 1 - \text{...........} = \text{...........}$$

2   The weights of oranges are normally distributed with a mean of 135 g and a standard deviation of 40 g. Class 1 oranges weigh more than 174 g. Class 3 oranges weigh less than 92 g. Class 2 oranges are oranges in between these weights.

    (a) Find the percentage of oranges in each class.   **(3)**

....

....

....

    (b) In a sample of 20 oranges, find the probability that at least five of them are Class 1.   **(3)**

....

....

....

3   A type of light bulb lasts H hours, where H is normally distributed with a standard deviation of 55 hours.

    (a) Given that 2.5% of the light bulbs last longer than 1957.8 hours, find the mean of the distribution.   **(3)**

> Use the standard normal distribution, $Z \sim N(0, 1^2)$, with the appropriate value of z from the percentage points table.

....

....

....

    (b) Elaine buys a pack of 10 of these light bulbs.
        Find the probability that at least eight of them will last more than 1770 hours.   **(4)**

....

....

....

The inverse normal function

> **Guided**

1 The random variable X is normally distributed with mean 80 and standard deviation 10.

(a) Find a such that $P(X < a) = 0.305$ **(2)**

$P(X < a) = 0.305$ so $a =$ .... (2 d.p.)

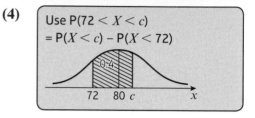

Use the inverse normal function on your calculator with area = 0.305, $\sigma = 10$ and $\mu = 80$

(b) Find b such that $P(X > b) = 0.102$ **(2)**

$P(X > b) = 0.102$ so $P(X < b) =$ ....

so $b =$ ....

The inverse normal function represents the area to the **left** of the value you key in, so use area = ..., $\sigma = 10$ and $\mu = 80$

(c) Find c such that $P(72 < X < c) = 0.4$ **(4)**

$P(X < c) = P(72 < X < c) + P(X < 72)$

$= 0.4 +$ .... $=$ .... so $c =$ ....

Use $P(72 < X < c)$
$= P(X < c) - P(X < 72)$

72 80 c x

2 The length of the life of a car tyre, L, is normally distributed with mean 18 000 miles and standard deviation 1600 miles.

(a) Find the upper quartile, Q_3, of this distribution. **(2)**

....

(b) Find the lower quartile, Q_1, of this distribution. **(1)**

....

3 The weights, W kg, of female jaguars can be modelled by a normal distribution with mean 68 kg and standard deviation 8.5 kg.

(a) Find w such that $P(65 < W < w) = 0.35$ **(4)**

....

....

Conservationists in Costa Rica monitor the jaguars there. Records are kept of the weight and general health of the jaguars.

(b) Find the probability that two female jaguars, captured and weighed, both weigh more than w kg. **(3)**

....

....

4 A batch of cylindrical pipes have internal diameters, d mm, modelled by $D \sim N(105, 6)$.

(a) Find d such that $P(D > d) = 0.15$ **(2)**

....

(b) Find the 10% to 80% interpercentile range of diameters. **(3)**

....

....

....

Finding μ and σ

1   Tins of soup are filled automatically by a machine. The tins are meant to contain 440 ml of soup. The amounts of soup in a tin are normally distributed with mean 452 ml.

The law states that 99% of the tins of soup the company makes must contain at least 440 ml, as advertised.

Find the standard deviation of the amount of soup in a tin if the company obeys the law.   **(5)**

$$P(X > 440) = P\left(Z > \frac{440 - 452}{\sigma}\right) = 0.99$$

$P(Z > \text{...................}) = 0.99$ (using the percentage points table)

since $P(Z > 2.3263) = 0.01$

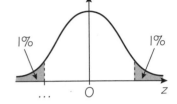

$$\frac{440 - 452}{\sigma} = - \text{......................}$$

....

....

2 X is a normally distributed random variable with mean μ and standard deviation σ.

$P(X > 20.6) = 0.4$

(a) Show that $\mu = 20.6 - 0.2533\sigma$ **(3)** | Use the percentage points table: $P(Z > 0.2533) = 0.4$

....

....

....

....

....

You are also given that $P(X < 13.2) = 0.15$

(b) Form a second equation in μ and σ and hence find the values of the mean and the standard deviation of X.   **(5)**

.... | The percentage points table tells you that $P(Z > 1.0364) = 0.15$. Be careful because the z-value needs to be negative.

....

....

....

....

....

....

....

....

Normal approximations

> **Guided**

1 An apple crop can be damaged by a fungal disease. It is claimed that 45% of the crop can be damaged. A random sample of 150 apples are selected.

(a) Write down a binomial model for X, the number of damaged apples. **(1)**

$X \sim B(\ldots\ldots, \ldots\ldots)$

(b) Use a normal approximation to estimate the probability that fewer than 55 apples are damaged. **(3)**

> **Problem solving** First find μ and σ then apply the continuity correction. Fewer than 55 means 55 is **not** included.

$\mu = np = \ldots\ldots \times \ldots\ldots = \ldots\ldots,$

$\sigma = \sqrt{np(1-p)}$

$= \sqrt{\ldots\ldots \times \ldots\ldots \times \ldots\ldots} = \ldots\ldots$

$Y \sim N(\ldots\ldots, \ldots\ldots^2)$

$P(X < 55) \approx P(Y < \ldots\ldots) = \ldots\ldots$

(c) Estimate the probability that between 60 and 75, inclusive, of the apples are damaged. **(2)**

> **Problem solving** 60 and 75 are both included. Make sure the continuity correction takes this into account.

$P(60 \leqslant X \leqslant 75) \approx P(\ldots\ldots < Y < \ldots\ldots) = \ldots\ldots$

2 Flowers sown from seed have a 60% chance of germinating. Monty sows 120 seeds.

(a) Write down a binomial model for X, the number of seeds that germinate. **(1)**

....

(b) Explain why X can be approximated by a normal distribution and state its mean and standard deviation. **(3)**

....

....

(c) Use a normal approximation to estimate the probability that at least 80 seeds germinate. **(2)**

....

....

3 Voting patterns from previous general elections show that party A in a particular constituency usually gets 54% of the vote. An opinion poll is conducted of 800 people who are eligible to vote.

(a) Write down a binomial model for X, the number of people who are likely to vote for the candidate from party A. **(1)**

....

(b) Write down two conditions under which the normal distribution may be used as an approximation to the binomial distribution. **(1)**

....

(c) By using a normal approximation, find the probability that between 420 and 450, inclusive, of these people say they will vote for the candidate from party A. **(4)**

....

....

Normal hypothesis testing

> **Guided**

1. Resistors are produced in a factory such that the resistance is normally distributed with a mean of 100 ohms and standard deviation 9 ohms. A technician thinks that the mean resistance is less than 100 ohms and takes a random sample of 15 resistors, which are found to have a mean resistance of 96.3 ohms.

   Test the technician's theory at the 5% level of significance, stating your hypotheses clearly. **(4)**

   $H_0: \mu = 100$ $H_1:$ ....

   Let X represent the resistance and assume H_0 to be true, so that $X \sim N(100, 9^2)$

   So for the sample mean, $\overline{X} \sim N(100, $ ....$)$ or $\overline{X} \sim N(100, $ ....$^2)$

   $P(\overline{X} < 96.3) = $ ....

   .... 0.05, so there is .... to reject H_0

   So the mean resistance ....

2. The heights of male students at a particular college were measured in 2010, and it was found that they were normally distributed with a mean height of 177 cm and a standard deviation of 7.5 cm. In 2017 it was thought that the mean male student height had increased, so a random sample of 30 students was selected and the mean height was found to be 179.8 cm.

   Test, at the 2.5% level of significance, whether this is evidence of an increase in the mean height, stating your hypotheses clearly. **(4)**

   ....

   ....

   ....

   ....

   ....

3. Wheels are manufactured to be normally distributed with a mean diameter of 42 cm and a standard deviation of 1.5 cm. To test whether this is true, a random sample of 22 wheels is taken.

   > **Problem solving** We are testing whether this is true. The diameter might be more or less than 42 cm, so use a two-tailed test and halve the probability in each tail.

   (a) Find the critical region for this test, at the 5% level, stating your hypotheses clearly. **(3)**

   ....

   ....

   ....

   ....

   (b) The observed mean diameter from the sample of 22 wheels is 41.6 cm.
   Comment on this in the light of the critical region. **(2)**

   ....

   ....

You are the examiner!

Checking through your work is a key skill for A Level Maths. Have a look at pages 146 and 147 of the *Revision Guide*, then practise with these questions. There are full worked solutions on page 216.

1   An auto parts retailer claims that 28% of the tail light bulbs sent to them by their supplier are faulty.

(a) Explain why a binomial distribution would be a suitable model to use to determine the number of faulty bulbs in a sample. **(2)**

....

....

The suppliers of the tail light bulbs make a slight change to their manufacturing process and claim that there will now be fewer faulty bulbs. A random sample of 40 bulbs was selected to test this claim, and seven of them were found to be faulty.

(b) Test, at the 5% significance level, whether there is evidence to support the claim that there will now be fewer faulty tail light bulbs State your hypotheses clearly. **(6)**

....

....

....

....

....

....

2   A supermarket chain sells coffee in packets containing 250 g of coffee granules. The packets are filled by machines dispensing 250 g. The fills are normally distributed with a mean of 250 g and a variance of 42 g.

Find the probability that packets contain

(a) more than 265 g   **(1)**   (b) less than 240 g   **(1)**   (c) between 245 g and 260 g. **(1)**

....

....

(d) If six out of 400 packets are rejected, what is the weight of coffee below which the packets are rejected? Give your answer to the nearest gram. **(2)**

....

....

....

....

You are the examiner!

> Checking through your work is a key skill for A Level Maths. Have a look at pages 146 and 147 of the *Revision Guide*, then practise with these questions. There are full worked solutions on page 217.

3   A machine producing metal bolts cuts them to a length X cm, where X is normally distributed with a mean of 9.4 cm.

   (a) Given that 5% of the bolts exceed 9.65 cm, show that the standard deviation of the distribution is 0.152 cm (3 s.f.)   **(3)**

....

....

   (b) If all bolts in the range 9.1 cm to 9.6 cm can be used, find the probability that a randomly selected bolt can be used.   **(2)**

....

   (c) If two bolts are selected at random for a particular job, what is the probability that neither of them can be used?   **(2)**

....

4   Given that $P(A' \cap B) = 0.28$ and $P(A' \cap B') = 0.38$

   (a) find $P(A)$ **(1)**   (b) find $P(A \cup B)$ **(1)**

   Given that $P(A \mid B) = \frac{1}{3}$

   (c) find $P(A \cap B)$ **(3)**   (d) write down $P(B)$ **(1)**

....

....

   (e) determine whether the events A and B are independent.   **(2)**

....

   Event C has $P(C) = 0.32$ and the events A and C are mutually exclusive.

   Given that $P(B \cup C) = 0.64$:

   (f) find $P(B \cap C)$ **(2)**

....

   (g) draw a Venn diagram to illustrate the events A, B and C, giving the probabilities for each region.   **(3)**

Modelling in mechanics

1   A block of wood *A* rests on a smooth table and is attached to one end of a light inextensible string. The string passes over a smooth pulley *P* fixed at the edge of the table. The other end of the string is attached to a ball *B* which hangs freely below the pulley.

The system is released from rest with the string taut. In the resulting motion *A* and *B* are modelled as particles. State how you can use in your calculations the assumptions that

(a) the plane is smooth   **(1)**

Think about the friction.

....

(b) the string is light   **(1)**

Think about the weight.

....

(c) the string is inextensible   **(1)**

Think about the acceleration.

....

(d) the pulley is smooth   **(1)**

....

(e) *A* and *B* are modelled as particles.   **(1)**

....

2   A mass of 1 kg is attached to a fixed point by a string.
It hangs vertically, in equilibrium.
The mass is pulled to one side and released.

Consider the string, the mass and the motion of the mass.

Make a list of the assumptions you might make to create a simple model for this situation.   **(3)**

....

....

....

3   A football is kicked and its path can be modelled by the equation $h = 0.8x - 0.009x^2$ where *h* m is the height of the ball above the ground and *x* m is the horizontal distance travelled.

(a) Find the height of the ball when it has travelled 20 m horizontally.   **(2)**

....

....

(b) How far will the ball travel before it hits the ground? Give your answer to 3 s.f.   **(2)**

....

....

(c) What is the greatest height reached by the ball? Give your answer to 3 s.f.   **(2)**

....

....

(d) What assumptions have been made in calculations using this model for the path of the football?   **(2)**

....

Motion graphs

> **Guided**   1   A car is moving along a straight horizontal road. The speed of the car as it passes the point A is $30\,\text{m s}^{-1}$, and the car maintains this speed for $40\,\text{s}$. The car then decelerates uniformly to a speed of $20\,\text{m s}^{-1}$. The speed of $20\,\text{m s}^{-1}$ is then maintained until the car passes the point B. The time taken to travel from A to B is $100\,\text{s}$, and $AB = 2500\,\text{m}$.

(a) Sketch a velocity–time graph to show the motion of the car from A to B.   **(2)**

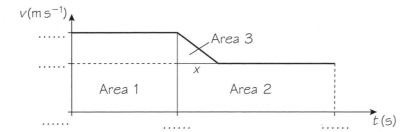

> Divide the area under the graph into separate sections to calculate the total area.

(b) Calculate the deceleration of the car as it decelerates from $30\,\text{m s}^{-1}$ to $20\,\text{m s}^{-1}$.   **(7)**

Area = Area 1 + Area 2 + Area 3

$\quad$ = $(30 \times 40) + (20 \times \,\text{.........}\,) + (\frac{1}{2} \times \,\text{.........}\, \times x) = 2500$

.... $x =$ ....

$x = \dfrac{\text{.........}}{\text{.........}} =$ ....   Deceleration $= \dfrac{\text{.........}}{\text{.........}} =$ ....$\,\text{m s}^{-2}$

> Distance travelled = area under graph

> Find the gradient of the graph to work out the deceleration.

2   A train is travelling at $12\,\text{m s}^{-1}$ on a straight horizontal track. The driver sees a red signal $150\,\text{m}$ ahead and immediately applies the brakes. The train immediately decelerates with constant deceleration for $10\,\text{s}$, reducing its speed to $4\,\text{m s}^{-1}$. The driver then releases the brakes and allows the train to travel at a constant speed of $4\,\text{m s}^{-1}$ for a further $10\,\text{s}$. He then applies the brakes again and the train slows down with constant deceleration, coming to rest as it reaches the signal.

(a) Sketch a velocity–time graph to show the motion of the train.   **(3)**

(b) Find the distance travelled by the train from the moment when the brakes are first applied to the moment when its speed first reaches $4\,\text{m s}^{-1}$.   **(2)**

....

....

....

(c) Find the total time from the moment when the brakes are first applied to the moment when the train comes to rest.   **(5)**

....

....

....

....

Constant acceleration 1

Guided 1   A car moves with constant acceleration along a straight horizontal road. The car passes the point A with speed $5\,\text{m s}^{-1}$, and 4 s later it passes the point B with a speed of $20\,\text{m s}^{-1}$.

(a) Find the acceleration of the car. (2)

$s = ?$ $u = 5$ $v = 20$ $a = ?$ $t = 4$

$v = u + at$

.... = ... + $a \times 4$

....

....

> Constant acceleration means using the *suvat* formulae. Write down the five letters and all the values you know.

> Use $v = u + at$ and solve to find a.

(b) Find the distance AB. (2)

$s = ?$ $u = 5$ $v = 20$ $a =$ .... $t = 4$

$s = \dfrac{1}{2}($.........................$)$......... = ... m

> Use $s = \frac{1}{2}(u + v)t$.

2   A particle P is moving with constant acceleration along a straight horizontal line ABC where $AC = 25\,\text{m}$. Initially P is at A and is moving with speed $6\,\text{m s}^{-1}$ in the direction AB. After 2.5 s, P is at B with speed $10.5\,\text{m s}^{-1}$.

> When the question involves **three points**, draw a sketch to help you.

(a) Find the acceleration of the particle. (2)

....

....

....

....

(b) Find the distance BC. (3)

....

....

....

3   The driver of a train begins the approach to a station by applying the brakes when the speed is $40\,\text{m s}^{-1}$. The train takes 30 s to come to rest at the station.

> When the train comes to rest, $v = 0$.

(a) Find the deceleration of the train. (2)

....

....

....

(b) Find the distance between the train and the station when the driver applied the brakes. (2)

....

....

....

Constant acceleration 2

Guided 1 Three posts P, Q and R are fixed in that order at the side of a straight horizontal road. The distance from P to Q is 45 m and the distance from Q to R is 120 m. A car is moving along the road with constant acceleration a m s^{-2}. The speed of the car, as it passes P, is u m s^{-1}. The car passes Q 2 seconds after passing P, and the car passes R 4 seconds after passing Q.

Find the value of u and the value of a. **(7)**

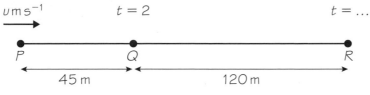

u m s^{-1}	$t = 2$		$t = \ldots$	

P Q R

45 m   120 m

> When the question involves **three points**, draw a sketch to help you.

PQ: $s = 45$ $u = u$ $\cancel{v = ?}$ $a = a$ $t = 2$

$45 = u \times \ldots\ldots + \dfrac{1}{2}a \times \ldots\ldots^2$ ①

> Use $s = ut + \frac{1}{2}at^2$ for PQ and PR and solve simultaneously.

PR: $s = \ldots\ldots$ $u = u$ $\cancel{v = ?}$ $a = a$ $t = \ldots\ldots$

$\ldots\ldots = u \times \ldots\ldots + \dfrac{1}{2}a \times \ldots\ldots^2$ ②

....

....

....

....

2 Two cars A and B are moving in the same direction along a straight horizontal road. At time $t = 0$, they are side by side, passing a point O on the road. Car A travels at a constant speed of 40 m s^{-1}. Car B passes O with a speed of 25 m s^{-1}, and has constant acceleration of 5 m s^{-2}. Find:

(a) the speed of B when it has travelled 80 m from O **(2)**

> Use $v^2 = u^2 + 2as$ for B.

....

....

....

(b) the distance from O of A when B is 80 m from O **(4)**

> Find the time taken for B to travel 80 m from O.

....

....

> For constant speed, $a = 0$ so you can use $s = vt$.

....

(c) the time when B overtakes A. **(5)**

> **Problem solving** Find the time when the cars are the same distance from O.

....

....

....

....

Motion under gravity

Guided **1** A ball is projected vertically upwards with speed 21 m s^{-1} from a point A, which is 1.5 m above the ground. After projection, the ball moves freely under gravity until it reaches the ground. Modelling the ball as a particle, find:

(a) the greatest height above A reached by the ball **(3)**

$s = ?$ $u = \text{.........}$ $v = 0$ $a = -9.8$ $\cancel{t = ?}$

$v^2 = u^2 + 2as$ so $0^2 = \text{.........}^2 - 2 \times 9.8 \times h$

$h = \text{..}$

> Remember that at the greatest height, $v = 0$. When travelling upwards, acceleration is negative and due to gravity, so use $a = -9.8 \text{ m s}^{-2}$.

(b) the speed of the ball as it reaches the ground **(3)**

$s = -1.5$ $u = 21$ $v = ?$ $a = -9.8$ $\cancel{t = ?}$

$v^2 = u^2 + 2as$ so $v^2 = 21^2 + \text{.........} = \text{.........}$

so $v = \text{.........} \text{ m s}^{-1}$

> Remember that the ball starts 1.5 m above the ground.

> Upwards is positive so s and a will both be negative.

(c) the time between the instant when the ball is projected from A and the instant when the ball reaches the ground. **(4)**

$\cancel{s = ?}$ $u = 21$ $v = \text{.............}$ $a = -9.8$ $t = ?$

$v = u + at$

> Upwards is positive so v will be negative.

....

....

Guided **2** A firework rocket starts from rest at ground level and moves vertically. In the first 4 s of its motion, the rocket rises 50 m. The rocket is modelled as a particle moving with constant acceleration $a \text{ m s}^{-2}$. Find:

(a) the value of a **(2)**

> Use $s = ut + \frac{1}{2}at^2$.

$s = \text{.........}$ $u = 0$ $\cancel{v = ?}$ $a = ?$ $t = \text{.........}$

....

....

(b) the speed of the rocket 4 s after it has left the ground. **(2)**

> Use $v = u + at$.

....

....

After 4 s, the rocket burns out. The motion of the rocket is now modelled as that of a particle moving freely under gravity.

(c) Find the height of the rocket above the ground 7 s after it has left the ground. **(4)**

> Consider motion from $t = 4$ to $t = 7$; use $s = ut + \frac{1}{2}at^2$.

....

....

....

....

Forces

> **Guided**

1 A breakdown van of mass 2500 kg is towing a car of mass 1500 kg along a straight horizontal road. The two vehicles are joined by a tow-bar which remains parallel to the road. The van and the car experience constant resistances to motion of magnitudes 900 N and 250 N respectively. There is a constant driving force acting on the van of 2750 N. Find:

> Draw a clear diagram to help you see what is going on. Consider the **resultant** force in the direction of motion.

(a) the magnitude of the acceleration of the van and the car   **(3)**

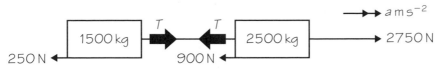

Van and car: $2750 - \ldots\ldots - \ldots\ldots = (2500 + 1500)a$

....

....

> Consider the breakdown van and car as a single system and apply $F = ma$. The two tensions in the tow-bar cancel out because they are equal and opposite.

(b) the tension in the tow-bar.   **(4)**

Car: $T - \ldots\ldots = 1500a$

> Consider the forces acting on the car and apply $F = ma$.

....

....

....

2 A man of mass 85 kg travels in a lift of mass 900 kg to the top of a tall building. The lift starts from rest on the ground floor and moves vertically upwards with an acceleration of $3\,\mathrm{m\,s^{-2}}$. It then moves with constant speed and finally decelerates with a constant deceleration of $2\,\mathrm{m\,s^{-2}}$ before coming to rest at the top floor. The lift is pulled up by means of a vertical cable attached to the top of the lift. By modelling the cable as a light inextensible string, find:

> The force due to gravity on a mass m kg is mg N. Take $g = 9.8\,\mathrm{m\,s^{-2}}$.

(a) the tension in the cable when the lift is accelerating   **(3)**

....

....

....

....

(b) the magnitude of the force exerted by the lift on the man when the lift is decelerating.   **(3)**

....

....

....

....

Forces as vectors

Guided   **1**   Two forces, $(3\mathbf{i} - 6\mathbf{j})$ N and $(p\mathbf{i} + q\mathbf{j})$ N, act on a particle P of mass m kg. The resultant of the two forces is $\mathbf{R}$. Given that $\mathbf{R}$ acts in a direction which is parallel to the vector $(2\mathbf{i} - \mathbf{j})$:

(a) find the angle between $\mathbf{R}$ and the vector $\mathbf{j}$ **(3)**

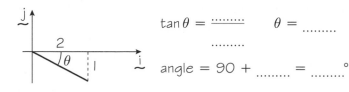

$\tan\theta = \dfrac{\text{.........}}{\text{.........}}$ $\theta = $ ....

angle $= 90 + $ .... $= $ ....°

> Draw a sketch to make sure you calculate the correct angle.

(b) show that $p + 2q = 9$ **(4)**

> To find the resultant, add the **i** components and the **j** components.

....

....

2   A particle is acted upon by two forces $\mathbf{F}_1$ and $\mathbf{F}_2$, given by

$\mathbf{F}_1 = (2\mathbf{i} - 4\mathbf{j})$ N

$\mathbf{F}_2 = (p\mathbf{i} + 2p\mathbf{j})$ N, where p is a positive constant.

(a) Find the angle between $\mathbf{F}_2$ and $\mathbf{i}$.   **(2)**

....

The resultant of $\mathbf{F}_1$ and $\mathbf{F}_2$ is $\mathbf{R}$. Given that $\mathbf{R}$ is parallel to $\mathbf{j}$:

(b) find the value of p, and the resultant force $\mathbf{R}$.   **(4)**

....

....

3   Three forces $\mathbf{F}_1$, $\mathbf{F}_2$ and $\mathbf{F}_3$ act on a particle P.

$\mathbf{F}_1 = (-3\mathbf{i} + 4\mathbf{j})$ N, $\mathbf{F}_2 = (p\mathbf{i} - 10\mathbf{j})$ N and $\mathbf{F}_3 = (7\mathbf{i} + q\mathbf{j})$ N, where p and q are constants.

(a) If particle P is in equilibrium, find the values of p and q.   **(3)**

....

....

....

....

(b) Force $\mathbf{F}_3$ is now removed. The resultant of $\mathbf{F}_1$ and $\mathbf{F}_2$ is $\mathbf{R}$. Find the magnitude of $\mathbf{R}$ and the angle it makes with the vector $\mathbf{i}$.   **(5)**

> Draw a sketch to make sure you calculate the correct angle.

....

....

....

....

....

Motion in 2D

1   A particle of mass 2.5 kg is moving under the action of a constant force of $(2\mathbf{i} - 3\mathbf{j})$ N.

(a) Find the magnitude of the acceleration of the particle.   **(3)**

....

....

(b) Find the angle that the acceleration of the particle makes with $\mathbf{j}$.   **(2)**

....

....

> **Guided**

2   A ball P of mass 0.5 kg is at rest when it is acted on by a constant force of $(4\mathbf{i} + 3\mathbf{j})$ N

(a) Find the total distance travelled by the ball in the first 5 seconds of its motion.   **(4)**

$$\underset{\sim}{F} = m\underset{\sim}{a}$$

$$4\underset{\sim}{i} + 3\underset{\sim}{j} = 0.5\underset{\sim}{a}$$

$$\underset{\sim}{a} = \text{...............}$$

$$|\underset{\sim}{a}| = \sqrt{\text{...............}^2 + \text{...............}^2} = \text{...............}\,m\,s^{-2}$$

$$s = ut + \frac{1}{2}at^2$$

$$= \text{...............}$$

$$= \text{...............}\,m$$

> The ball starts from rest and the force is acting in a straight line. The ball is moving with constant acceleration, so you can use $s = ut + \frac{1}{2}at^2$ to find the distance travelled.

At time $t = 5$ s, a second force of $(1.3\mathbf{i} - 0.5\mathbf{j})$N acts on the particle.

(b) Find the new acceleration of the particle.   **(4)**

....

....

....

3   A particle Q of mass 4 kg is at rest under the action of three forces $\mathbf{F}_1$, $\mathbf{F}_2$ and $\mathbf{F}_3$, where $\mathbf{F}_1 = (10\mathbf{i} + 3\mathbf{j})$ N.

Force $\mathbf{F}_2$ is removed and the particle accelerates at a rate of $(3\mathbf{i} - \mathbf{j})$ m s^{-2}.
Find force $\mathbf{F}_3$, giving your answer in the form $(p\mathbf{i} + q\mathbf{j})$ N   **(5)**

....

....

....

> **Problem solving** The particle is initially at rest so $\mathbf{F}_1 + \mathbf{F}_2 + \mathbf{F}_3 = 0$ and the force causing the acceleration is $\mathbf{F}_1 + \mathbf{F}_3$.

....

....

....

Pulleys

> **Guided**

1 The particles A and B have masses 4 kg and m kg respectively, where $m < 4$. They are attached to the ends of a light inextensible string. The string passes over a smooth pulley which is fixed. The particles are held in position with the string taut and the hanging parts of the string vertical, at a height of 3 m above the floor, as shown in the diagram. The particles are then released from rest and in the subsequent motion B does not reach the pulley. The initial acceleration of each particle has magnitude $\frac{4}{7}g$.

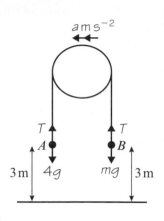

$a\,\mathrm{m\,s}^{-2}$

T ↑ A ● ↓ T ↑ ● B ↑
3 m $4g$ mg 3 m

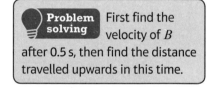

As $m < 4$, A will move down and B will move up. Apply $F = ma$ for each particle.

As the pulley is smooth, the tension in the string is the same for both particles.

(a) Find the tension in the string immediately after the particles are released, and the value of m. **(6)**

A: $4g - T = 4a$

....

....

....

....

When the particles have been moving for 0.5 s, the string breaks.

(b) Find the further time that elapses until B hits the floor. **(9)**

$R(\uparrow): v = u + at =$ .... $=$ ....

$R(\uparrow): s = ut + \frac{1}{2}at^2 =$ .... $=$ ....

$R(\downarrow): s = ut + \frac{1}{2}at^2$

> **Problem solving** First find the velocity of B after 0.5 s, then find the distance travelled upwards in this time.

> **Problem solving** Finally, find the time taken for B to fall from the height where the string broke to the floor.

....

....

....

....

....

2 Two particles of masses 7 kg and 3 kg are connected by a light inextensible string passing over a smooth pulley. The system moves freely with the strings taut and vertical. Find the acceleration of the particles and the tension in the string. **(6)**

....

....

....

....

....

....

Connected particles 1

Guided

1 A particle A, of mass 4.8 kg, rests on a smooth horizontal table. It is connected by a light inextensible string passing over a smooth pulley fixed at the edge of the table to a particle B, of mass 1.2 kg, which hangs freely.

The system is released from rest with B at a height of 3 m above the ground.

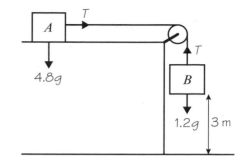

(a) Find the acceleration of the system when it is released from rest, and the tension in the string. **(7)**

$F = ma$ for A: $\qquad$ $T = 4.8a$

$F = ma$ for B: $\quad 1.2g - \ldots\ldots\ldots = \ldots\ldots\ldots$

Adding gives $\qquad \ldots\ldots\ldots = \ldots\ldots\ldots$ so $a = \ldots\ldots\ldots$ m s^{-2}

Substituting gives $T = 4.8 \times \ldots\ldots\ldots = \ldots\ldots\ldots$ N

(b) Find the speed with which **B** hits the ground, and the time taken for this to happen. **(6)**

$s = 3 \quad u = \ldots\ldots\ldots \quad v = \ldots\ldots\ldots \quad a = \ldots\ldots\ldots \quad t = \ldots\ldots\ldots$

> Choose *suvat* formulae to enable you to calculate *v* and *t*.

....

....

....

....

2 Two particles of masses 3 kg and 4 kg are connected by a light inextensible string passing over a smooth pulley. The system is released from rest with the strings taut and vertical.

After 3 seconds the 4 kg mass hits the ground.

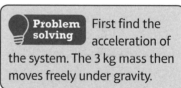
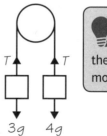

> 💡 **Problem solving** First find the acceleration of the system. The 3 kg mass then moves freely under gravity.

(a) Given that in the subsequent motion the 3 kg mass does not reach the pulley, find the further time that elapses before the 3 kg mass reaches its greatest height. **(7)**

....

....

....

....

....

....

(b) Find the **total** distance travelled by the 3 kg mass when it reaches its greatest height. **(6)**

....

....

....

....

Combining techniques

1   A ball *A*, of mass *m* kg, is held at rest on a rough horizontal table. It is attached to one end of a light inextensible string which passes over a smooth pulley at the edge of the table. The other end of the string is attached to a ball *B*, of mass 3 kg, hanging freely vertically below the pulley.

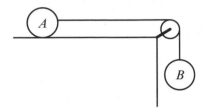

The system is released from rest with the string taut.

The resistance to the motion of *A* from the rough table is modelled as having constant magnitude 15.5 N.

(a) Given that ball *A* travels 1.8 m towards the pulley in 1.5 seconds and ball *B* does not reach the floor in this time, use the model to find the mass of ball *A*. **(8)**

....

....

....

....

....

....

....

> Label the diagram with all the forces acting on the balls

> Use a *suvat* formula to find the acceleration of the system

> Use $F = ma$ for both balls to find the value of *m*.

(b) Following the experiment, ball *A* is weighed and is found to have a mass of 5 kg. In light of this information

   (i) comment on the appropriateness of this model to find the mass of ball *A*,

   (ii) suggest one possible improvement to the model. **(2)**

....

....

....

....

....

Variable acceleration 1

Guided   **1**   A particle moves on the x-axis such that its distance from the origin, O, at time t seconds is given by

$$s = t^3 - 11t^2 + 24t, \ t \geqslant 0$$

(a) Sketch a distance–time graph for the particle.   **(3)**

> This is a cubic graph with a positive coefficient of t^3.

$s = t(t^2 - 11t + 24) = t(\text{............})(\text{............})$

$s = 0$ when $t = \text{............}$ and when $t = \text{............}$

Graph crosses t-axis at $t = 0$, $t = \text{............}$, $t = \text{............}$

(b) Describe the motion of the particle during the first 8 seconds.   **(3)**

> Consider changes of direction and times when the particle returns to O.

....

....

(c) Find the times when the particle is instantaneously at rest.   **(4)**

> Instantaneously at rest means the velocity will be zero. Differentiate the expression for s.

....

....

(d) Find the furthest distance of the particle from O during the first 8 seconds.   **(3)**

> Compare the values of s when the particle is instantaneously at rest.

....

....

2   A particle moves on the x-axis such that its distance from the origin, O, at time t seconds is given by

$$s = \frac{t^3 - 24t^2 + 144t}{9}, \ 0 \leqslant t \leqslant 12$$

(a) Sketch a distance–time graph for the particle.   **(3)**

(b) Find the initial velocity of the particle.   **(3)**

....

....

....

(c) Find the times when the particle is instantaneously at rest.   **(3)**

....

....

(d) Find the maximum distance of the particle from O in the interval $0 \leqslant t \leqslant 12$ **(2)**

....

....

Variable acceleration 2

Guided **1** A particle, P, moves on the x-axis. At time t seconds, the velocity of P is $v\,\text{ms}^{-1}$, in the direction of x increasing, where

$$v = t^2 - 8t + 12, \quad t \geq 0$$

(a) Find the times when P is instantaneously at rest. **(3)**

P is instantaneously at rest when $v = 0$

$t^2 - 8t + 12 = 0$,　$(\ldots\ldots\ldots)(\ldots\ldots\ldots) = 0$,　so $t = \ldots\ldots\ldots$ and $t = \ldots\ldots\ldots$

(b) Sketch the velocity–time graph of the particle and find its maximum speed in the first 4 seconds of the motion. **(4)**

> **Problem solving** Use the symmetry of the graph to find the value of t at the minimum point. Work out v and compare it with $12\,\text{m\,s}^{-1}$ at $t = 0$.

....

....

....

(c) Find the total distance travelled by P in the interval $0 \leq t \leq 5$ **(5)**

....

....

....

....

> Distance = area under a v–t graph. Use definite integration.

2 A particle, Q, moves on the x-axis such that its distance, in metres, from the origin, O, at time t seconds is given by $s = 8t - \frac{2}{3}t^3$, $t \geq 0$

(a) Find the initial velocity of the particle. **(2)**

....

(b) Show that Q changes direction between $t = 0$ and $t = 4$ **(3)**

....

....

....

> **Problem solving** A change of direction means that Q will be instantaneously at rest during this time.

(c) Find the total distance travelled by Q in the interval $0 \leq t \leq 4$ **(3)**

....

....

....

> **Problem solving** Q oscillates both sides of O, so you need to consider distances travelled in both directions.

Deriving *suvat* formulae

1 The diagram shows a velocity–time graph for a particle travelling in a straight line and accelerating uniformly from velocity U m s^{-1} to velocity V m s^{-1} in time T seconds. The acceleration of the particle, a m s^{-2}, is equal to the gradient of the graph.

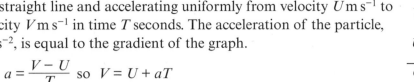

$$a = \frac{V - U}{T} \text{ so } V = U + aT$$

(a) Show that the distance travelled, s, is given by $\left(\dfrac{U + V}{2}\right)T$ **(4)**

Distance travelled = area under graph so $s = A_1 + A_2$

$A_1 = \frac{1}{2} \times \text{base} \times \text{height} = \frac{1}{2} \times T \times (V - U)$ and $A_2 = U \times T$

So $s = \frac{1}{2}T(V - U) + UT = \frac{1}{2}TV - \text{............} + \text{............} = \text{...................} = \text{...................}$

(b) Use the two *suvat* equations above to derive the equations

   (i) $s = UT + \frac{1}{2}aT^2$ **(3)**   (ii) $V^2 = U^2 + 2as$ **(3)**

> Use algebra, involving substitution.

....

....

....

....

....

2 Points A and B are 720 m apart along a straight line.

A particle, P, travels from A to B. Its displacement from A is given by $s = 16t - 0.3t^2$, $t \geqslant 0$

A particle, Q, travels along the same straight line but in the opposite direction.

Q passes point B at time $t = 0$ with an initial velocity, towards A, of 5 m s^{-1} and a constant acceleration of 0.8 m s^{-2}.

(a) Derive an expression, in terms of t, for the distance travelled towards A by particle Q. **(4)**

   Do **not** use the kinematics formulae to derive this expression.

....

....

....

> **Problem solving** Use calculus. For Q, $a = 0.8$. Integrate to find v, then s.

....

(b) Find the time taken for the particles to meet. **(4)**

....

....

> **Problem solving** Use total distance = 720 m.

....

(c) Find the distance from A when the particles meet. **(2)**

....

....

You are the examiner!

Checking through your work is a key skill for A Level Maths. Have a look at pages 162 and 163 of the *Revision Guide*, then practise with these questions. There are full worked solutions on page 220.

1 A train travels between two stations A and B which are 23.1 km apart. It starts from rest at A and takes $3\frac{1}{2}$ minutes to accelerate uniformly to a speed of 35 m s^{-1}.

It maintains this speed for a period of time and then decelerates uniformly to come to rest at B. The distance travelled when decelerating is 1575 m.

(a) Sketch a velocity–time graph to illustrate the motion of the train. **(3)**

(b) Find the time taken, in minutes, for the journey between the two stations. **(5)**

....

....

....

....

....

2 Three forces $\mathbf{F}_1$, $\mathbf{F}_2$ and $\mathbf{F}_3$ act on a particle P.

$\mathbf{F}_1 = (2p\mathbf{i} - \mathbf{j})$ N, $\mathbf{F}_2 = (q\mathbf{i} - 5p\mathbf{j})$ N and $\mathbf{F}_3 = (4\mathbf{i} - 7q\mathbf{j})$ N, where p and q are constants.

(a) If particle P is in equilibrium, find the values of p and q. **(5)**

....

....

....

....

....

Force $\mathbf{F}_3$ is now removed. The resultant of $\mathbf{F}_1$ and $\mathbf{F}_2$ is $\mathbf{R}$.

(b) Find the magnitude of $\mathbf{R}$ and the angle it makes with the vector $\mathbf{j}$. **(5)**

....

....

....

....

....

You are the examiner!

Checking through your work is a key skill for A Level Maths. Have a look at pages 162 and 163 of the *Revision Guide*, then practise with these questions. There are full worked solutions on page 220.

3 Two particles, A and B, of masses 4 kg and 6 kg respectively, are connected by a light inextensible string which passes over a smooth pulley.

The system is released from rest with the strings taut and vertical.

(a) Find the acceleration of the system when it is released from rest, and the tension in the string. **(6)**

A ☐ ☐ B

....

....

....

(b) Find the speed of the particles 1.5 seconds after the system is released from rest. **(2)**

....

After 1.5 seconds, the string breaks. Given that in the subsequent motion particle A does not reach the pulley,

(c) find the further time that elapses before particle A reaches its greatest height **(2)**

....

....

(d) find the **total** distance travelled by particle A when it reaches its greatest height. **(5)**

....

....

....

4 A particle moves along the x-axis.

The acceleration of the particle, in m s^{-2}, at time t seconds is given by $a = 4 - 2t$

The initial velocity of the particle as it passes the origin, O, is 5 m s^{-1} in the positive x direction.

(a) Find the velocity of the particle as a function of t. **(3)**

....

....

(b) Find the greatest speed of the particle. **(2)**

....

(c) Find the distance travelled by the particle from the time when it is travelling at its greatest speed to the time when it comes to instantaneous rest. **(7)**

....

....

....

Moments 1

1

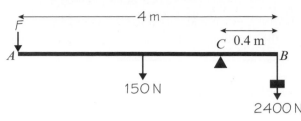

A lever consists of a uniform steel rod AB, of weight 150 N and length 4 m, which rests on a small smooth pivot at a point C of the rod. A load of weight 2400 N is suspended from the end B of the rod by a rope. The lever is held in equilibrium in a horizontal position by a vertical force applied at the end A, as shown in the diagram. The rope is modelled as a light string. Given that $BC = 0.4$ m:

(a) find the magnitude of the force applied at A.   **(4)**

↻ moment about C = 2400 × 0.4

↺ moment about C = 150 × .... + F × ....

....

....

> The lever is in equilibrium so $\sum\circlearrowleft$ moments = $\sum\circlearrowright$ moments. Remember, moment = force × distance.

> 💡 **Problem solving** Take moments about C so you can ignore the normal reaction.

The position of the pivot is changed so that the rod remains in equilibrium when the force at A has magnitude 150 N.

(b) Find, to the nearest cm, the new distance of the pivot from B.   **(5)**

> Let distance $BC = d$ and take moments about C.

↻ moment about C = 2400 × d

↺ moment about C = 150 × .... + 150 × ....

....

....

....

2   A uniform plank AB has mass 50 kg and length 5 m. It is supported in a horizontal position by two smooth pivots, one at the end A, the other at the point C of the plank where $AC = 3.5$ m, as shown in the diagram. A man of mass 80 kg stands on the plank, which remains in equilibrium.

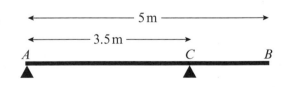

The magnitudes of the reactions at the two pivots are each equal to R newtons. By modelling the plank as a rod and the man as a particle, find:

(a) the value of R **(2)**

> The lever is in equilibrium so the resultant of the forces acting in a vertical direction must be zero.

....

....

(b) the distance of the man from A.   **(4)**

....

....

....

Moments 2

> **Guided** 1

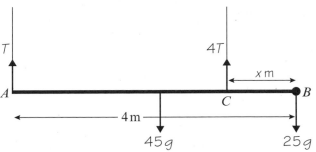

A plank AB has mass 45 kg and length 4 m. A load of mass 25 kg is attached to the plank at B. The loaded plank is held in equilibrium, with AB horizontal, by two vertical ropes attached at A and C, as shown in the diagram. The plank is modelled as a uniform rod and the load as a particle. Given that the tension in the rope at C is 4 times the tension in the rope at A, calculate:

(a) the tension in the rope at C **(2)**

$R(\uparrow)$: $T + 4T = $ ....

         $T = $ ....   so $4T = $ ....

(b) the distance CB to the nearest cm.   **(5)**

$\circlearrowleft$ moment about $C = $ ....

     $= $ ....

$\circlearrowright$ moment about $C = $ ....

     $= $ ....

....

....

> **Problem solving**   Let $BC = x$, then take moments about C, so you can ignore the component of the tension acting through C.

> **Start by labelling the diagram. Label the tensions T and $4T$ and resolve vertically for the whole system to find T.**

2   A heavy uniform steel girder AB has length 12 m. A load of weight 200 N is attached to the girder at A and a load of weight 300 N is attached to the girder at B. The loaded girder hangs in equilibrium in a horizontal position, held by two vertical steel cables attached to the girder at the points C and D, where $AC = 2$ m and $DB = 4$ m, as shown in the diagram.

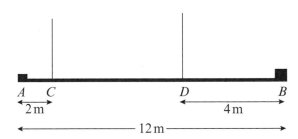

The girder is modelled as a uniform rod, the loads as particles and the cables as light inextensible strings. The tension in the cable at D is 3 times the tension in the cable at C. Find the tension in the cable at C and the weight of the girder.   **(7)**

....

....

....

....

....

....

....

Centres of mass

> **Guided** 1 A large log AB is 8 m long. It rests in a horizontal position on two smooth supports C and D, where $AC = 1.5$ m and $BD = 1.5$ m, as shown in the diagram. When a force of magnitude 1750 N is applied vertically upwards to the log at A, the log is about to tilt about D.

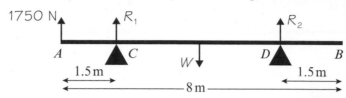

1750 N R_1 R_2

A C W D B

1.5 m 1.5 m

8 m

(a) Modelling the log as a uniform rod, estimate the weight of the log. **(3)**

> If the log is **uniform** the weight will act at the **midpoint**.

↻ moment about $D = 1750 \times$ ....

↺ moment about $D = W \times$ ....

> Take moments about D so you can ignore the reaction at D.

....

....

The log is now modelled as a non-uniform rod. When the force at A is removed and a new force of magnitude 1500 N is applied vertically upwards at B, the log is about to tilt about C.

(b) Find a new estimate for the weight of the log. **(6)**

> **Problem solving** Taking the distance of the centre of mass as x from C, take moments about D with the 1750 N force at A, then moments about C with the 1500 N force at B. Solve the equations simultaneously.

↻ moment about $D = 1750 \times$ ....   ↻ moment about $C = W \times$ ....

↺ moment about $D = W \times$ ....   ↺ moment about $C = 1500 \times$ ....

....

....

2 A non-uniform rod AB has length 8 m and weight 240 N. The rod rests horizontally in equilibrium on two smooth supports C and D, where

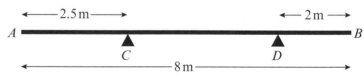

2.5 m 2 m

A C D B

8 m

$AC = 2.5$ m and $DB = 2$ m, as shown in the diagram. The centre of mass of AB is x metres from A. A particle of weight W newtons is placed on the rod at A. The rod remains in equilibrium and the magnitude of the reaction of C on the rod is 180 N.

(a) Show that $40x - W = 135$ **(5)**

....

....

The particle is now removed from A and placed on the rod at B. The rod remains in equilibrium and the reaction of C on the rod now has magnitude 60 N.

(b) Calculate the value of x and the value of W. **(6)**

....

....

....

Resolving forces

Guided **1** A truck of mass 1750 kg is towing a car of mass 750 kg along a straight horizontal road. The two vehicles are joined by a light tow-bar which is inclined at an angle θ to the road, as shown in the diagram. The vehicles are travelling at 20 m s^{-1} as they enter a zone where the speed limit is 14 m s^{-1}. The truck's brakes are applied to give a constant braking force on the truck. The distance travelled between the instant when the brakes are applied and the instant when the speed of each vehicle is 14 m s^{-1} is 100 m.

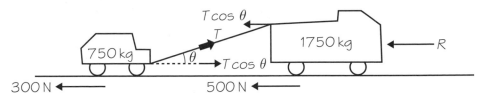

(a) Find the deceleration of the truck and the car. **(3)**

$v^2 = u^2 + 2as$: $14^2 =$ ....

$a =$ ....   Deceleration = ...

The constant braking force on the truck has magnitude R newtons. The truck and the car also experience constant resistances to motion of 500 N and 300 N respectively.

Given that $\cos\theta = 0.9$, find:

(b) the force in the tow-bar **(4)**

$T\cos\theta - 300 =$ ....

....

....

> Consider the forces acting on the car and apply $F = ma$ horizontally.

> The component of T in a horizontal direction is $T\cos\theta$.

(c) the value of R. **(4)**

$-T\cos\theta - 500 - R =$ ....

$R =$ .... N

> Consider the forces acting on the truck and apply $F = ma$ horizontally.

2 A body of mass 5 kg is sliding down a smooth plane inclined at 30° to the horizontal. Find:

(a) the acceleration of the mass **(3)**

....

....

....

> Consider the forces acting parallel to the plane and apply $F = ma$.

(b) the normal reaction exerted by the plane on the mass. **(2)**

....

....

....

....

....

> Consider the forces acting perpendicular to the plane. As there is no motion in this direction, the resultant force is 0.

Friction

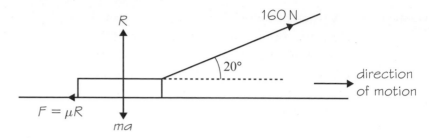

Guided 1 A sledge is pulled in a straight line with constant speed along horizontal ground by means of a rope. The rope makes an angle of 20° with the horizontal, as shown in the diagram.

The coefficient of friction between the sledge and the ground is 0.3. The sledge is modelled as a particle and the rope as a light inextensible string.
The tension in the rope is 160 N.
Find, to 3 significant figures:

(a) the normal reaction of the ground on the sledge **(3)**

R(→): $160 \cos 20° - F = 0$

$F =$ ....

but $F = \mu R = 0.3R$, so $R =$ .... N

> The sledge moves with constant speed, so the resultant force is 0.

> Friction (F) opposes motion. The sledge is moving so $F = \mu R$.

> First resolve forces horizontally.

(b) the mass of the sledge. **(3)**

R(↑): $R +$ .... $- mg = 0$

> Resolve forces vertically.

....

....

2 A heavy suitcase S of mass 45 kg is moving along a horizontal floor under the action of a force of magnitude P newtons. The force acts at 40° to the floor, as shown in the diagram, and S moves in a straight line at constant speed. The suitcase is modelled as a particle and the floor as a rough horizontal plane. The coefficient of friction between S and the floor is $\frac{2}{3}$.

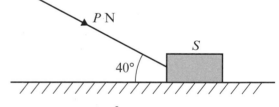

Calculate the value of P. **(6)**

....

....

....

....

....

....

....

Sloping planes

Guided　1　A box of mass 4 kg is pulled up a rough plane by means of a light rope. The plane is inclined at an angle of 30° to the horizontal, as shown in the diagram. The rope is parallel to a line of greatest slope of the plane. The tension in the rope is 40 N. The coefficient of friction between the box and the plane is 0.5. By modelling the box as a particle, find:

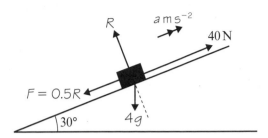

(a) the normal reaction of the plane on the box　**(3)**

$$R(\nwarrow): \quad R - 4g\cos 30° = 0$$

$$R = \dots\dots\dots\dots\dots$$

> Resolve the forces perpendicular to the plane. As there is no motion in this direction, the resultant force is 0.

(b) the acceleration of the box.　**(5)**

> Resolve the forces along the plane and apply $F = ma$.

$$R(\nearrow): \quad 40 - \dots\dots\dots\dots - F = 4a$$

$$F = \mu R = 0.5 \times \dots\dots = \dots\dots$$

> Friction (F) opposes motion. The box is moving so $F = \mu R$. Make sure you don't confuse friction with force due to gravity.

....

....

2　A particle of mass 1 kg is held at rest on a rough plane. The plane is inclined at an angle α to the horizontal, where $\tan \alpha = \frac{5}{12}$. The particle is released from rest and slides down a line of greatest slope of the plane. The particle moves 2.5 m during the first 2 seconds of its motion. Find:

(a) the acceleration of the particle　**(3)**

....

....

(b) the coefficient of friction between the particle and the plane.　**(5)**

....

....

> 5-12-13 is a right-angled triangle.

....

3　A particle P of mass 5 kg is moving up a fixed rough plane at constant speed under the action of a force of magnitude 40 N. The plane is inclined at 20° to the horizontal. The force acts in the vertical plane containing the line of greatest slope of the plane through P, and acts at 20° to the inclined plane, as shown in the diagram. The coefficient of friction between P and the plane is μ. Find:

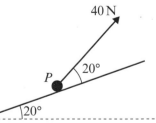

(a) the magnitude of the normal reaction between P and the plane　**(4)**

....

....

(b) the value of μ.　**(5)**

....

....

Projectiles

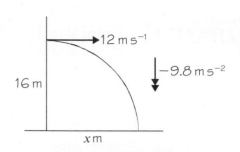

Guided 1 A ball is thrown horizontally at a speed of $12\,\mathrm{m\,s^{-1}}$ from a window 16 metres above level ground. Find:

(a) how long it takes to reach the ground   **(3)**

For the vertical motion: $s =$ ...., $u = 0$, $a = -9.8$, $t = ?$

Using $s = ut + \frac{1}{2}at^2$

.... $= 0 - \frac{1}{2} \times 9.8 \times t^2$, giving $t = \sqrt{\dfrac{.........}{4.9}} = $ ....

$\qquad\qquad\qquad = $ .... s (2 s.f.)

The ball lands after .... seconds.

> Always state which direction is positive. Upwards is positive, so $g = -9.8\,\mathrm{m\,s^{-2}}$.

(b) how far it is from the foot of the building when it hits the ground   **(2)**

For the horizontal motion: distance = speed × time

$x = 12 \times$ .... = ... = ... m (3 s.f.)

The ball lands .... m from the building.

> t is your answer from part (a). Always use the accurate value in your calculations.

(c) the speed with which it hits the ground and the angle at which it hits the ground.   **(6)**

Using $v = u + at$ for the vertical motion,

$v_y = 0 - 9.8 \times$ .... = ...

$v = \sqrt{12^2 + }$ ....^{2} giving $v =$ ....

$\qquad\qquad = $ .... $\mathrm{m\,s^{-1}}$ (3 s.f.)

$\tan\alpha = \dfrac{.........}{12}$ giving $\alpha =$ .... = ... (3 s.f.)

> **Problem solving** Draw a diagram showing the two speed components.
>
>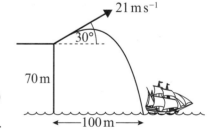

The ball lands with a speed of .... $\mathrm{m\,s^{-1}}$ at an angle of .... to the horizontal.

2 A cannonball is fired from the top of a vertical cliff, 70 metres high, at an angle of 30° to the horizontal and with a speed of $21\,\mathrm{m\,s^{-1}}$. The target is a pirate ship which is sailing 100 metres from the foot of the cliff. Find:

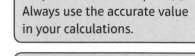

(a) the time taken for the cannonball to land at sea level   **(5)**

....

....

....

(b) the speed with which the cannonball reaches sea level   **(4)**

....

....

....

(c) whether or not the cannonball hits the pirate ship.   **(3)**

....

....

Projectile formulae

Guided   **1**   A particle is projected with speed $14\,\text{m s}^{-1}$ at an angle α to the horizontal. It just clears a wall 6 metres high and 10 metres from the point of projection.

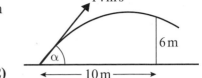

(a) Write down expressions for the horizontal and vertical distances travelled after time t seconds.   **(2)**

$x = 14$ .... and, using $s = ut + \frac{1}{2}at^2$, $y = 14$ .... − ....

(b) Show that the equation of the trajectory is $2.5\tan^2\alpha - 10\tan\alpha + 8.5 = 0$ **(5)**

$$t = \frac{x}{14............} = \frac{10}{14............}$$

Using $y = 14$ .... − .... ,

$$6 = 14 .... \times \frac{10}{14............} - 4.9\left(\frac{10}{14............}\right)^2$$

$$= 10 .... - \frac{4.9 \times 10^2}{14^2............}$$

$$= 10 .... - \frac{490............}{196} = 10 .... - 2.5(1 + ...)$$

$2.5\tan^2\alpha - 10\tan\alpha + 8.5 = 0$

> **Problem solving**   Use $x = 10$ and $y = 6$, and eliminate t from the two expressions for the horizontal and vertical distances in part (a) by substituting the value of t from $x = ...$ into the equation for $y = ...$, and using the identity $\sec^2\alpha = 1 + \tan^2\alpha$.

(c) Find the possible values of α so that the particle just clears the wall.   **(3)**

$$\tan\alpha = \frac{10 \pm \sqrt{100 - 4 \times .... \times ....}}{5} = \frac{10 \pm \sqrt{........}}{5} = ... \text{ or } ....$$

so $\alpha = ...$ or .... (3 s.f.)

> Use the quadratic formula.

2   Jonny is playing rugby for England against Australia. He takes what could be a winning penalty kick in the last minute of the game, from a distance of 45 metres. His kick hits the crossbar, which is 3 metres high, before going between the posts.

He kicks the ball with speed U at an angle α to the horizontal.

(a) Show that $3 = 45\tan\alpha - \dfrac{9922.5}{U^2\cos^2\alpha}$ **(6)**

> **Problem solving**   Draw a diagram and write expressions for x and y, the horizontal and vertical distances travelled at time t. Then use $x = 45$ and $y = 3$ and eliminate t to find the equation of the trajectory.

....

....

....

....

....

(b) Given that $\alpha = 32°$, find the value of U.   **(2)**

....

....

....

Static particles

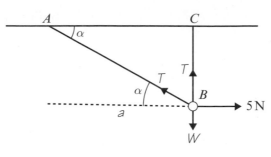

> **Guided** 1

> The bead is in equilibrium, so the **resultant force** in any direction will be **zero**.

> The bead is threaded on a **light inextensible string**, so tension is the **same** throughout the string.

A smooth bead B is threaded on a light inextensible string. The ends of the string are attached to two fixed points A and C on the same horizontal level. The bead is held in equilibrium by a horizontal force of magnitude 5 N acting parallel to AC. The bead B is vertically below C and $\angle BAC = \alpha$, as shown in the diagram. Given that $\tan \alpha = \frac{3}{4}$, find:

(a) the tension in the string   **(3)**

> To find T, resolve forces horizontally.

$R(\rightarrow)$: T.................... $= 5$

$T = $ ....

(b) the weight of the bead.   **(4)**

> To find W, resolve forces vertically.

$R(\uparrow)$: $T + T$.................... $= W$

....

2 A particle of mass m kg is attached at C to two light inextensible strings AC and BC. The other ends of the strings are attached to fixed points A and B on a horizontal ceiling. The particle hangs in equilibrium with AC and BC inclined to the horizontal at 20° and 70° respectively, as shown in the diagram. Given that the tension in AC is 15 N, find:

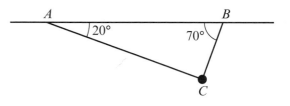

(a) the tension in BC **(4)**

....

....

(b) the value of m.   **(4)**

....

3 A particle P of mass 3 kg is held in equilibrium under gravity by two light inextensible strings. One string is horizontal and the other is inclined at an angle α to the horizontal, as shown in the diagram. The tension in the horizontal string is 20 N. The tension in the other string is T newtons.

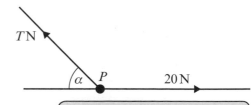

Find the size of the angle α and the value of T.   **(8)**

> **Problem solving** Resolve horizontally and vertically to find two equations to solve simultaneously.
> Remember that $\frac{\sin \alpha}{\cos \alpha} = \tan \alpha$.

....

....

....

....

Limiting equilibrium

Guided 1

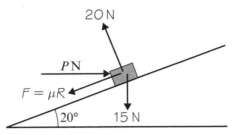

20 N

P N

$F = \mu R$

20°   15 N

> The parcel is on the point of slipping **up** the plane so $F = \mu R$ and acts down the plane.

A parcel of weight 15 N lies on a rough plane inclined at an angle of 40° to the horizontal. A horizontal force of magnitude P newtons acts on the parcel, as shown in the diagram. The parcel is in equilibrium and on the point of slipping up the plane. The normal reaction of the plane on the parcel is 20 N. The coefficient of friction between the parcel and the plane is μ. Find:

(a) the value of P **(4)**

> Resolve the forces **perpendicular** to the plane.

R(↖): $P\sin 20° + 15$ .... $= 20$

....

....

(b) the value of μ. **(5)**

> Resolve the forces **parallel** to the plane and substitute $F = \mu R$.

R(↗): $P\cos 20° = 15$ .... $+ F$

....

....

The horizontal force is removed.

(c) Determine whether or not the parcel moves. **(5)**

> **Problem solving** First find the **new value** of the **normal reaction** of the plane on the parcel.

$R =$ .... $=$ ....

$F_{max} =$ ....

Component of weight down plane = ...

....

....

> **Problem solving** Compare the component of weight down the plane with the new F_{max} to determine whether or not the parcel will move.

2 A sledge is held in equilibrium on a slope by a rope. The sledge is attached to one end of the rope, the other end being held by a man standing at the top of the slope. The sledge is modelled as a particle of mass 30 kg. The slope is modelled as a rough plane inclined at 50° to the horizontal and the rope as a light inextensible string. The string is assumed to be parallel to a line of greatest slope of the plane, as shown in the diagram. At the contact between the sledge and the slope, the coefficient of friction is 0.25. Find the minimum tension in the rope for the sledge to stay in equilibrium on the slope. **(8)**

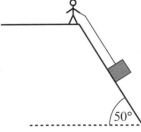

50°

....

....

....

....

Static rigid bodies

Guided ▷ **1** A uniform ladder AB, of length $2a$ and weight W, has its end A on rough horizontal ground and end B against a smooth vertical wall. The ladder makes an angle θ with the ground, where $\tan \theta = \frac{4}{3}$. The ladder rests in a vertical plane, perpendicular to the wall. When a man of weight $8W$ stands three-quarters of the way up the ladder, the ladder is on the point of slipping.

Find the value of μ, the coefficient of friction between the ladder and the ground. **(9)**

The ladder is on the point of slipping (limiting equilibrium),

so $F = \mu R$

$R(\rightarrow)$: $F (= \mu R) = S$

$R(\uparrow)$: $R = \text{........}$ which gives $S = \mu\text{.........}$

Taking moments about A:

$W \times a\cos\theta + 8W \times \dfrac{3a}{2} \text{...............} = S \times 2a \text{..............}$

$W \times a \times \frac{3}{5} + 8W \times \dfrac{3a}{2}\text{.........} = \mu\text{.........} \times 2a \times \text{.........}$

This simplifies to $\text{.........} + \text{.........} = \text{.........}\mu$

So $\mu = \dfrac{\text{.........}}{\text{.........}} = \dfrac{\text{.........}}{\text{.........}}$

> Draw a diagram showing all the forces acting on the ladder.

> Resolve horizontally and vertically and choose a point about which to take moments. In this case take moments about A, and remember:
> moment = force × perpendicular distance

> Use this right-angled triangle for the trigonometric ratios:

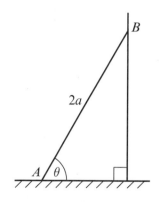

2 A ladder AB of weight W and length $2a$ has one end A resting on rough horizontal ground and the other end B resting on a rough vertical wall. The coefficient of friction between the ladder and the wall is 0.3, the coefficient of friction between the ladder and the ground is μ, and friction is limiting at both A and B. The ladder makes an angle θ with the ground, where $\tan \theta = \frac{7}{4}$. The ladder is modelled as a uniform rod lying in a vertical plane perpendicular to the wall.

Find the value of μ. **(9)**

....

....

....

....

....

....

....

....

....

> Draw a diagram showing all the forces acting on the ladder. Both surfaces are rough so include friction forces at both ends of the ladder.

> **Problem solving** Resolve horizontally and vertically and take moments about A or B. In your equations, substitute for the trig ratios and eliminate unknowns to leave an equation in μ.

Connected particles 2

1 The diagram shows two particles P and Q, of masses 4 kg and 5 kg respectively, connected by a light inextensible string. Initially P is held at rest on a rough fixed plane inclined at 40° to the horizontal. The coefficient of friction between P and the plane is 0.4. The string passes over a small smooth light pulley A fixed at the top of the plane. The part of the string from P to A is parallel to a line of greatest slope of the plane. The particle Q hangs freely below A. The system is released from rest with the string taut. Find:

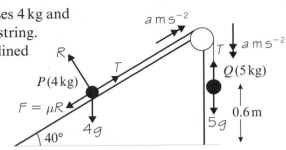

(a) the acceleration of the system   (8)

> **Problem solving** Write down the equations of motion for P and Q and solve the equations simultaneously.

Q: $5g - T = 5a$ ①

P: $R = 4g\cos 40° = $ .... N

   $T - F - 4g\sin 40° = 4a$ ②

....

....

....

(b) the tension in the string.   **(2)**

....

....

On release, Q is at a height of 0.6 m above the ground.

(c) Find the speed of Q as it reaches the ground.   **(2)**   Use the *suvat* formulae.

....

....

2 Two particles P and Q have masses $4m$ and $6m$ respectively. They are connected by a light inextensible string which passes over a small smooth light pulley fixed at the edge of a rough horizontal table. Particle P lies on the table and particle Q hangs freely below the pulley, as shown in the diagram. The coefficient of friction between P and the table is 0.5. The system is released from rest with the string taut. For the period before Q hits the floor or P reaches the pulley:

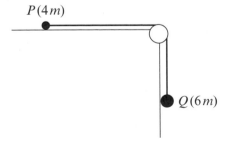

(a) find, in terms of g, the acceleration of Q **(4)**

....

....

....

(b) find, in terms of m and g, the tension in the string.   **(2)**

....

....

Vectors in kinematics

> **Guided** **1** A boat B is moving with constant velocity. At noon, B is at the point with position vector $(2\mathbf{i} - 5\mathbf{j})$ km with respect to a fixed origin O. At 1430 on the same day, B is at the point with position vector $(7\mathbf{i} + 10\mathbf{j})$ km.

(a) Find the speed of the boat. **(4)**

$\underline{r} = \underline{r_0} + \underline{v}t$

$7\underline{i} + 10\underline{j} = (2\underline{i} - 5\underline{j}) + \underline{v} \times \ ....$

....

....

....

> **Problem solving** Use $\mathbf{r} = \mathbf{r_0} + \mathbf{v}t$ and rearrange for $\mathbf{v}$. If the velocity $\mathbf{v} = (p\mathbf{i} + q\mathbf{j})$ m s^{-1}, then speed is $|\mathbf{v}| = \sqrt{p^2 + q^2}$. Alternatively, use the position vectors to calculate the change in displacement.

At time t hours after noon, the position vector of B is $\mathbf{b}$ km.

(b) Find, in terms of t, an expression for $\mathbf{b}$. **(3)** Use $\mathbf{r} = \mathbf{r_0} + \mathbf{v}t$.

....

....

2 A particle P is moving with constant velocity $(-4\mathbf{i} + 3\mathbf{j})$ m s^{-1}. At time $t = 5$ s, P is at the point with position vector $(-3\mathbf{i} - 6\mathbf{j})$ m.
Find the distance of P from the origin at time $t = 3$ s. **(5)**

....

....

....

....

> **Problem solving** Use $\mathbf{r} = \mathbf{r_0} + \mathbf{v}t$ and rearrange to find the starting point, $\mathbf{r_0}$. If the position vector $\mathbf{r} = (a\mathbf{i} + b\mathbf{j})$ m s^{-1}, then distance from origin is $|\mathbf{r}| = \sqrt{a^2 + b^2}$.

3 Two ships P and Q are travelling at night with constant velocities. At midnight, P is at the point with position vector $(12\mathbf{i} + 14\mathbf{j})$ km relative to a fixed origin O. At the same time, Q is at the point with position vector $(8\mathbf{i} - 4\mathbf{j})$ km. Three hours later, P is at the point with position vector $(24\mathbf{i} + 32\mathbf{j})$ km. The ship Q travels with velocity $10\mathbf{j}$ km h^{-1}. At time t hours after midnight, the position vectors of P and Q are $\mathbf{p}$ km and $\mathbf{q}$ km respectively. Find:

(a) the velocity of P, in terms of $\mathbf{i}$ and $\mathbf{j}$ **(2)**

....

....

(b) expressions for $\mathbf{p}$ and $\mathbf{q}$, in terms of t, $\mathbf{i}$ and $\mathbf{j}$. **(4)**

....

....

At time t hours after midnight, the distance between P and Q is d km.

(c) By finding an expression for $\overrightarrow{PQ}$ show that $d^2 = 32t^2 - 112t + 340$ **(5)** Use $\overrightarrow{PQ} = \mathbf{q} - \mathbf{p}$.

....

....

....

....

Vectors and bearings

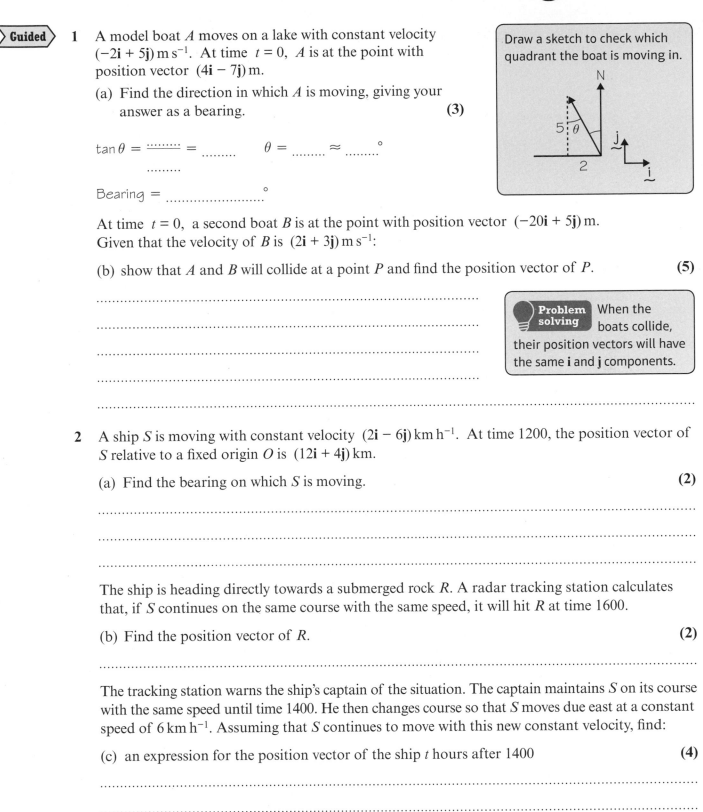

Guided **1** A model boat A moves on a lake with constant velocity $(-2\mathbf{i} + 5\mathbf{j})\,\text{m s}^{-1}$. At time $t = 0$, A is at the point with position vector $(4\mathbf{i} - 7\mathbf{j})\,\text{m}$.

(a) Find the direction in which A is moving, giving your answer as a bearing. **(3)**

> Draw a sketch to check which quadrant the boat is moving in.

$\tan\theta = \dfrac{\text{\dots\dots\dots}}{\text{\dots\dots}} = \text{\dots\dots}$ $\theta = \text{\dots\dots} \approx \text{\dots\dots}°$

Bearing = \dots\dots\dots\dots\dots°

At time $t = 0$, a second boat B is at the point with position vector $(-20\mathbf{i} + 5\mathbf{j})\,\text{m}$. Given that the velocity of B is $(2\mathbf{i} + 3\mathbf{j})\,\text{m s}^{-1}$:

(b) show that A and B will collide at a point P and find the position vector of P. **(5)**

....

....

....

....

....

> **Problem solving** When the boats collide, their position vectors will have the same **i** and **j** components.

2 A ship S is moving with constant velocity $(2\mathbf{i} - 6\mathbf{j})\,\text{km h}^{-1}$. At time 1200, the position vector of S relative to a fixed origin O is $(12\mathbf{i} + 4\mathbf{j})\,\text{km}$.

(a) Find the bearing on which S is moving. **(2)**

....

....

....

The ship is heading directly towards a submerged rock R. A radar tracking station calculates that, if S continues on the same course with the same speed, it will hit R at time 1600.

(b) Find the position vector of R. **(2)**

....

The tracking station warns the ship's captain of the situation. The captain maintains S on its course with the same speed until time 1400. He then changes course so that S moves due east at a constant speed of $6\,\text{km h}^{-1}$. Assuming that S continues to move with this new constant velocity, find:

(c) an expression for the position vector of the ship t hours after 1400 **(4)**

....

....

(d) the time when S will be due north of R. **(2)**

....

....

....

....

> **Problem solving** When S is north of R, the **i** components of their position vectors will be the same.

Variable acceleration 3

Guided 1 A particle is moving in a straight line with acceleration at time t given by $a = 2\cos\pi t\,\text{m s}^{-2}$, $t \geq 0$

The velocity of the particle at time $t = 0$ is $\dfrac{3}{\pi}\,\text{m s}^{-1}$. Find:

(a) an expression for the velocity at time t seconds (3)

$$v = \int a\,dt = \int 2\cos\pi t\,dt = \frac{2}{\pi}\,\text{..............} + c$$

When $t = 0$, $v = \dfrac{3}{\pi}$, so $\dfrac{3}{\pi} = \dfrac{2}{\pi}\,\text{..............} + c$, giving $c = \text{.........}$

so $v = \dfrac{2}{\pi}\,\text{..............} + \text{.........}$

(b) the maximum speed of the particle (2)

Since the maximum value of .... is 1, maximum velocity = ... + ... = ...

(c) the distance travelled by the particle in the first 4 seconds of its motion. (4)

$$s = \int v\,dt = \int_0^4\left(\frac{2}{\pi}\text{.........} + \text{.........}\right)dt = \left[\frac{-2}{\pi^2}\text{.........} + \text{.........}\right]_0^4$$

$$= \left(\frac{-2}{\pi^2}\text{.........} + \text{.........}\right) - \left(\frac{-2}{\pi^2}\text{.........} + \text{.........}\right)$$

$$= \text{.........} + \text{.........} + \text{.........} = \text{.........} \text{ m or } \text{.........} \text{ m (3 s.f.)}$$

2 A particle P moves along the x-axis. At time t seconds, the velocity of P is $v\,\text{m s}^{-1}$, in the direction of x increasing, where v is given by

$$v = 6t^{1.5} - 2t^2, \qquad 0 \leq t \leq 4$$
$$v = 12 + \frac{(t - 2)^3}{2}, \qquad t > 4$$

When $t = 0$, P is at the origin, O. Find:

(a) the greatest speed of P in the interval $0 \leq t \leq 4$ (3)

....

....

(b) the distance of P from O when $t = 4$ (4)

....

....

(c) the acceleration of P at 5 seconds (2)

....

....

(d) the total distance travelled by P in the first 6 seconds of its motion. (4)

....

....

....

....

Calculus with vectors

Guided   **1**   A particle moves in a horizontal plane under the action of a force **F** newtons. The unit vectors **i** and **j** are directed east and north respectively. At t seconds, the velocity of the particle is v m s^{-1}, where

$$v = (6t - t^3)\mathbf{i} + 4\sqrt{t}\,\mathbf{j}$$

(a) Find an expression for the acceleration of the particle at time t seconds.   **(2)**

$$\underset{\sim}{a} = \frac{dv}{dt} = (6 - 3t^2)\underset{\sim}{i} + \ldots\ldots\ldots\underset{\sim}{j}$$

The mass of the particle is 3 kg.

(b) Find:

   (i)   an expression for the force, **F**, acting on the particle at time t seconds   **(2)**

Using $\underset{\sim}{F} = m\underset{\sim}{a}$ when $m = 3$, $\underset{\sim}{F} = 3\underset{\sim}{a} = (18 - 9t^2)\underset{\sim}{i} + \ldots\ldots\ldots\underset{\sim}{j}$

   (ii)   the magnitude of **F** when $t = 1$ **(3)**

When $t = 1$, $\underset{\sim}{F} = 9\underset{\sim}{i} + \ldots\ldots\ldots\underset{\sim}{j}$, so magnitude of $\underset{\sim}{F} = \sqrt{9^2 + \ldots\ldots\ldots^2} = \ldots\ldots\ldots$ N

(c) Find the value of t when **F** acts due north.   **(2)**

> If **F** acts due north, the **i** component of the force will be zero.

$\ldots\ldots\ldots\ldots = 0$, $t^2 = \ldots\ldots\ldots$, $t = \ldots\ldots\ldots = \ldots\ldots\ldots$ s (2 s.f.)

(d) When $t = 0$, the particle is at the point with position vector $(\mathbf{i} - 2\mathbf{j})$ m.
Find an expression for the position vector of the particle after 4 seconds.   **(4)**

$$\underset{\sim}{r} = \int \underset{\sim}{v}\,dt = \int((6t - t^3)\underset{\sim}{i} + 4t^{0.5}\underset{\sim}{j})\,dt = (3t^2 - \ldots\ldots\ldots)\underset{\sim}{i} + \ldots\ldots\ldots\underset{\sim}{j} + \underset{\sim}{c}$$

When $t = 0$, $\underset{\sim}{r} = \underset{\sim}{i} - 2\underset{\sim}{j}$,

> **Problem solving**   Integrate to find the position vector, **r**, and put in the initial conditions to find **c**, the constant of integration vector.

so $\underset{\sim}{i} - 2\underset{\sim}{j} = \ldots\ldots\ldots + \ldots\ldots\ldots + \underset{\sim}{c}$, giving $\underset{\sim}{c} = \ldots\ldots\ldots$

so $\underset{\sim}{r} = (3t^2 - \ldots\ldots\ldots\ldots\ldots)\underset{\sim}{i} + (\ldots\ldots\ldots\ldots\ldots)\underset{\sim}{j}$

and when $t = 4$, $\underset{\sim}{r} = (48\ldots\ldots\ldots)\underset{\sim}{i} + (\ldots\ldots)\underset{\sim}{j} = \ldots\ldots\ldots\underset{\sim}{i} + \ldots\ldots\ldots\underset{\sim}{j} = \ldots\ldots\ldots\underset{\sim}{i} + \ldots\ldots\ldots\underset{\sim}{j}$ (3 s.f.)

2   A particle has a mass of 4 kg and is acted upon by a single force **F**, where $\mathbf{F} = (12e^{-2t}\mathbf{i} - 8t^3\mathbf{j})$ N

(a) Find the acceleration of the particle at time t seconds.   **(2)**

....

....

At time $t = 0$, the velocity of the particle is $(6.5\mathbf{i} - 5\mathbf{j})$ m s^{-1}.

(b) Find an expression for the velocity of the particle at time t seconds.   **(4)**

....

....

....

....

 Problem solving   Integrate the acceleration vector. Don't forget to include a constant of integration vector.

(c) Find the speed of the particle when $t = 2$.   **(4)**

....

....

....

 Problem solving   Don't leave your answer in vector form. Speed is the magnitude of the velocity vector when $t = 2$.

You are the examiner!

Checking through your work is a key skill for A Level Maths. Have a look at pages 180 and 181 of the *Revision Guide*, then practise with these questions. There are full worked solutions on page 223.

1　At time t seconds, where $t \geq 0$, a particle P moves so that its acceleration $\mathbf{a}$ m s^{-2} is given by

$$\mathbf{a} = 2t\mathbf{i} + \frac{3}{\sqrt{t}}\mathbf{j}$$

When $t = 4$, the velocity of P is $(17\mathbf{i} + 10\mathbf{j})$ m s^{-1}

(a) Find an expression for the velocity of P after t seconds.　**(4)**

....

....

....

....

....

At time $t = 0$, the position vector of P relative to the origin O is $(3\mathbf{i} - \mathbf{j})$ m

(b) Find the position vector of P when $t = 1$　**(5)**

....

....

....

....

....

....

2　A force of 35 N is pulling a box of mass 4 kg up a rough slope inclined at an angle of θ to the horizontal, where $\tan \theta = \frac{3}{4}$. The force acts parallel to the line of greatest slope and the box accelerates at 1.25 m s^{-2}

Find:

(a) the normal reaction of the plane on the box　**(2)**

....

....

(b) the coefficient of friction between the box and the plane.　**(6)**

....

....

....

....

You are the examiner!

Checking through your work is a key skill for A Level Maths. Have a look at pages 180 and 181 of the *Revision Guide*, then practise with these questions. There are full worked solutions on page 224.

3   A batsman hits a cricket ball with an initial speed of 30 m s^{-1} at an angle of 50° to the horizontal.

     (a) Find the greatest height of the cricket ball. Assume that it is hit from 1 m above ground level. **(3)**

....

....

     (b) Find the time taken for the cricket ball to reach its greatest height. **(3)**

....

....

     (c) Show that the cricket ball clears the roof of the cricket pavilion, which is 20 m high and at a distance of 65 m from the batsman. **(5)**

....

....

....

....

....

4   A uniform rod AB of weight W and length $6a$ rests with its end A on rough horizontal ground and with a point C of the rod, where $AC = 4a$, in contact with a smooth peg. The rod makes an angle θ with the ground, where $\tan \theta = \frac{4}{3}$.

     (a) Find the magnitude of the force exerted by the peg on the rod. **(3)**

....

....

....

....

     (b) Find the magnitudes of the normal reaction and the frictional force at A. **(4)**

....

....

....

     (c) μ is the coefficient of friction between the rod and the ground. Show that $\mu \geqslant \frac{4}{7}$ **(2)**

....

....

Pure Mathematics 1
Calculators may be used in this practice paper.
Time: 2 hours
Total marks: 100
You may use the Mathematical Formulae and Statistical Tables booklet which is available from the Edexcel website.

1 A curve, C, has equation $y = 2x^3 - 5x^2 - 4x + 3$

  (a) Find $\dfrac{dy}{dx}$ **(2)**

  (b) Find $\dfrac{d^2y}{dx^2}$ **(1)**

  (c) Verify that C has a stationary point when $x = 2$ **(2)**

  (d) Determine the nature of this stationary point, giving a reason for your answer. **(2)**

2 The function f is defined by $f : x \mapsto |3x + 2|, \ x \in \mathbb{R}$

  (a) By sketching the graph of $f(x)$ and the graph of $y = x + 3$ on the same axes, show that the equation $|3x + 2| = x + 3$ has two solutions. **(2)**

  (b) Solve $f(x) = x + 3$ **(3)**

3 Find the values of k for which the equation $(3k - 8)x^2 - kx + (3k - 5) = 0$ has equal roots. **(6)**

4 Use integration by parts to find

$$\int 2x^2 \ln 3x \, dx$$ **(4)**

5 Solve, for $0° \leqslant x \leqslant 360°$, $\cos^2(x - 70°) = 0.3$

giving your answers to 2 decimal places. **(7)**

6 The equation $2x^3 + 3x^2 - 12x + 4 = 0$ has three real roots.

  (a) Show that one of the roots lies between $x = 1$ and $x = 2$ **(2)**

  (b) Taking $x_1 = 2$, use the Newton–Raphson method to work out x_2 and x_3 **(4)**

  (c) Explain why the Newton–Raphson method fails if $x_1 = 1$ **(1)**

7 A geometric series has a positive common ratio.

Its first three terms are $20, k$ and 8.45

  (a) Find the value of k. **(3)**

  (b) Find the sum of the first 12 terms of the series. **(2)**

8 The diagram shows a sketch of triangle ABC.

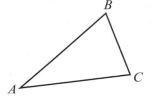

Given that

$$\overrightarrow{AB} = \mathbf{i} + 2\mathbf{j} - 5\mathbf{k}$$
$$\overrightarrow{BC} = -2\mathbf{i} - 3\mathbf{j} + \mathbf{k}$$

find the size of angle BAC. **(5)**

9 Prove, from first principles, that the derivative of $5x + 2x^3$ is $5 + 6x^2$ **(4)**

10 (a) Express $\dfrac{2x + 5}{(2 - x)(1 + x)}$ in partial fractions. **(3)**

   (b) Find the first three terms in the binomial expansion of $\dfrac{2x + 5}{(2 - x)(1 + x)}$, stating the values of x for which the expansion is valid. **(7)**

11 A cubic curve has equation $y = 2x^3 - 4x^2 + 1$

   (a) Find the coordinates of the stationary points on the curve and determine their nature. **(5)**

   (b) Show that the tangent to the curve at the point where $x = -\frac{2}{3}$ has gradient 8. **(2)**

   (c) Find the coordinates of the other point, P, on the curve where the gradient of the tangent is 8. **(2)**

   (d) Find the equation of the normal to the curve at P. **(2)**

12 A colony of bats is increasing. The population, P, is modelled by $P = a \times 10^{bt}$, where t is the time in years after 2010 and a and b are constants.

   (a) Show that the graph of $\log_{10} P$ against t will be a straight line of gradient b. **(2)**

   (b) Write down, in terms of a, the intercept of this graph on the vertical axis. **(1)**

   (c) This sketch shows the relationship between t and $\log_{10} P$.

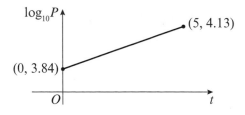

   Use the graph to work out the equation for P in terms of t. **(4)**

   (d) Predict the number of bats in the colony in 2018. **(2)**

13 The diagram shows a triangular prism, of length l cm, with a cross-section of a right-angled triangle, two sides of which are $3x$ cm and $4x$ cm.

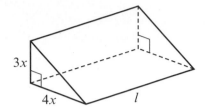

The volume of the triangular prism is 120 cm³.

(a) Show that the total length, L, of the nine edges of the prism is given by $L = 24x + \dfrac{60}{x^2}$ **(4)**

(b) Find the minimum value of L. **(5)**

(c) Justify that the value of L in part (b) is a minimum. **(2)**

14 The diagram shows a sketch of part of the curve, C, with equation $y = x\sqrt{1 + x^2}, \quad x > 0$

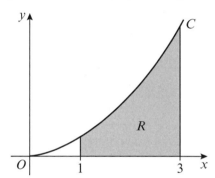

The finite region, R, is bounded by C, the x-axis and the lines $x = 1$ and $x = 3$

The table below shows corresponding values of x and y, given to 4 decimal places as appropriate.

x	1	1.5	2	2.5	3
y	1.4142	2.7042	4.4721	6.7315	9.4868

(a) Use the trapezium rule, with the values of y shown in the table, to obtain an estimate for the area of R, giving your answer to 3 decimal places. **(3)**

(b) Explain how the trapezium rule could be used to give a more accurate estimate for the area of R. **(1)**

(c) Using integration by substitution, or otherwise, find the exact value of the area of R, giving your answer to 3 decimal places. **(5)**

TOTAL FOR PAPER 1 IS 100 MARKS

Pure Mathematics 2
Calculators may be used in this practice paper.
Time: 2 hours
Total marks: 100
You may use the Mathematical Formulae and Statistical Tables booklet which is available from the Edexcel website.

1 Given that $y = 3x(5x - 2)^3$ show that

$$\frac{dy}{dx} = 6(5x - 2)^n(Ax + B)$$

where n, A and B are constants to be found. **(5)**

2 (a) Given that θ is small, use the small angle approximations for $\sin\theta$ and $\cos\theta$ to show that:

$$2\cos\theta - 3\sin\theta + 5\cos^2\theta \approx 7 - 3\theta - 6\theta^2$$ **(3)**

Sean uses $\theta = 5°$ to test the approximations in part (a). Here is his working:

Calculator: $2\cos\theta - 3\sin\theta + 5\cos^2\theta = 6.693$ (3 d.p.)

Approximations: $7 - 3\theta - 6\theta^2 = 7 - 3(5) - 6(5)^2 = -158$

So the approximations are not true for $\theta = 5°$.

   (b) Identify Sean's mistake and show that the approximations give an answer correct to 3 decimal places when $\theta = 5°$. **(2)**

3 The diagram shows the cross-section of a small building.
   AB is a straight line of length 2.6 m.
   BCD is a sector of a circle, centre B, of radius 3.2 m.
   The arc length, CD, is 1.12 m.
   Angle $ABC = \dfrac{\pi}{3}$ radians.
   AD is a straight line.

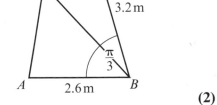

   (a) Find the size of angle CBD, in radians. **(2)**

   (b) Find the size of angle ABD, in radians. **(1)**

   (c) Find the area of cross-section $ABCD$. **(5)**

4 A curve, C, has equation $2y^2 - y = 6x - 3x^2$

   (a) Find $\dfrac{dy}{dx}$ in terms of x and y. **(2)**

   (b) Find the coordinates of the points on C at which $\dfrac{dy}{dx} = 0$ **(4)**

5 Show that there are no positive integer solutions of the equation $x^2 - y^2 = 18$ **(5)**

6 Solve, for $-180° \leqslant \theta \leqslant 180°$, the equation

$$3\cos 2\theta = 2 - \sin\theta$$

giving your answers to 2 decimal places where appropriate. **(6)**

7 In an arithmetic series, the first term is 14 and the common difference is 4. The sum of the first $2n$ terms is equal to the sum of the next n terms.

   Find the value of n. **(5)**

8 (a) Use the binomial expansion, in ascending powers of x, to show that

$$\sqrt[3]{8-x} \approx 2 - \frac{x}{12} + kx^2$$

where k is a rational constant to be found. **(4)**

(b) Give a reason why substituting $x = 2$ into both sides of this equation will give a valid approximation for $\sqrt[3]{6}$. **(1)**

(c) Show that substituting $x = 2$ gives a value for $\sqrt[3]{6}$ that is correct to 3 significant figures. **(2)**

9 A cup of liquid is cooling. Its initial temperature is $90\,°C$. After 2 minutes its temperature is $75\,°C$.

(a) Given that $T = 22 + me^{-kt}$ where T is the temperature in $°C$, t is the time in minutes, and m and k are constants, find the values of m and k. **(4)**

(b) What is the temperature of the liquid after 10 minutes? **(2)**

(c) Explain why the temperature of the liquid can never fall to $20\,°C$. **(1)**

10 In a geometric sequence the third term is 40 more than the second term and the fifth term is 30 more than the third term.

Find the two possible values of the common ratio, and the corresponding values of the first term. **(8)**

11 $f(x) = 2e^x - \frac{1}{2}\ln 2x - 4$

(a) Find $f'(x)$ **(2)**

The curve with equation $y = f(x)$ has a stationary point at P. The x-coordinate of P is α.

(b) Show that $\alpha = \frac{1}{4}e^{-\alpha}$ **(2)**

The iterative formula $x_{n+1} = \frac{1}{4}e^{-x_n}$ where $x_1 = 0.5$, is used to find an approximate value for α.

(c) Find the values of x_2, x_3, x_4 and x_5, giving your answers to 4 decimal places. **(2)**

(d) By considering a change of sign of $f(x)$ in a suitable interval, show that $\alpha = 0.2039$ to 4 decimal places. **(2)**

12 The path of a shot thrown by a shot putter can be modelled by the parametric equations

$$x = 11t \qquad y = -5t^2 + 8t + 2 \qquad 0 \leqslant t \leqslant k$$

where x is the horizontal distance, in metres, from the point of release and y is the height above the ground, in metres, after t seconds.

(a) Write down the height from which the shot is thrown. **(1)**

(b) Find the value of k and hence state the time taken for the shot to land. **(3)**

(c) Find the horizontal distance travelled by the shot. **(1)**

(d) Find the maximum height of the shot above the ground. **(3)**

13 The function f is defined by $f : \mapsto e^{2x} + 1, \; x \in \mathbb{R}$

    (a) State the range of f. **(1)**

    (b) Show that $x = \ln 3 - 2$ is an exact solution of the equation $f(x + 2) = 10$ **(3)**

    (c) Find f^{-1}, the inverse function of f, stating its domain. **(3)**

    (d) On the same axes, sketch the curves $y = f(x)$ and $y = f^{-1}(x)$, giving the coordinates of all points where the curves cross the axes and indicating any asymptotes. **(5)**

14 The diagram shows a sketch of the curve, C, with equation $y = 8x - 4x^{\frac{3}{2}} - 3$

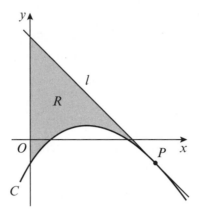

The point P (4, −3) lies on C and the line l is a tangent to C at the point P.

The shaded region, R, is bounded by the curve C, the line l and the y-axis.

Show that the area of R is 19.2, making your method clear.

(Solutions based entirely on graphical or numerical methods are not acceptable.) **(10)**

TOTAL FOR PAPER 2 IS 100 MARKS

Statistics and Mechanics
Calculators may be used in this practice paper.
Time: 2 hours
Total marks: 100
You may use the Mathematical Formulae and Statistical Tables booklet which is available from the Edexcel website.

Section A: Statistics
Answer ALL questions

1   A survey of 72 students recorded how many hours per week they spent texting or phoning their friends.

The results are summarised in the following table.

Hours	$0 < x \leqslant 10$	$10 < x \leqslant 15$	$15 < x \leqslant 20$	$20 < x \leqslant 30$	$30 < x \leqslant 50$
Frequency	24	18	12	15	3

A histogram was drawn to represent these data.

The $15 < x \leqslant 20$ group was represented by a bar of width 2 cm and height 8 cm.

   (a) Find the width and height of the bar representing the $20 < x \leqslant 30$ group. **(4)**

   (b) Use your calculator to estimate the mean and the standard deviation of the number of hours spent texting or phoning.

   Give your answers to 3 significant figures. **(3)**

   (c) Use linear interpolation to estimate the median time. **(2)**

2   The random variable Y is modelled as $Y \sim B(30, p)$.

A single observation of Y is taken and used to test $H_0 : p = 0.4$ against $H_1 : p \neq 0.4$

   (a) Using a 5% level of significance, find the critical region for this test. **(3)**

   (b) State the actual significance level of this test. **(1)**

   (c) The observed value of Y is 17. Comment on this observation in the light of your critical region. **(2)**

3   Comfy Cars have a fleet of taxis. They replace all the tyres on a taxi as soon as one tyre is down to 3 mm of tread. The lifetime of tyres is represented by the random variable, X, which is normally distributed with mean 26 500 miles and standard deviation 3500 miles.

   (a) Find $P(X > 24\,000)$ **(1)**

   (b) The tyres of 95% of the fleet of taxis last for more than k miles. Find the value of k. **(2)**

Comfy Cars are contacted by a different tyre supplier who claim that their tyres have a longer mean lifetime. A random sample of 12 taxis are fitted with these tyres and a hypothesis test is carried out to investigate the claim.

Given that the lifetime of this sample is represented by the random variable, Y, which is normally distributed with a standard deviation of 3300 miles,

   (c) write down the suitable null and alternative hypotheses for the test. **(2)**

   (d) The lifetime of the tyres for the sample of 12 taxis has a mean of 28 200 miles. Test, at the 5% significance level, whether there is evidence to show that the mean lifetime of the tyres is longer. **(5)**

4 The table shows the mean daily temperature, $t\,°C$, and the mean daily total rainfall, $h\,$mm, for the month of May 2017 for the seven places in the northern hemisphere recorded in the large data set.

	A	B	C	D	E	F	G
$t\,°C$	12.8	14.4	16.5	16.3	14.2	24.0	26.5
$h\,$mm	1.32	1.29	2.16	1.93	1.56	1.53	2.55

(a) Calculate the product moment correlation coefficient for these data. **(2)**

(b) Stating your hypothesis clearly, test, at the 5% level of significance, whether or not the product moment correlation coefficient for the data is greater than zero. **(3)**

(c) Using your knowledge of the large data set, suggest the names of the places labelled **F** and **G** in the above table. **(1)**

(d) Suggest how you could make better use of the large data set to investigate the relationship between daily mean temperature and daily total rainfall. **(1)**

5 Given that $P(A) = 0.5$ $P(B) = 0.6$ $P(A|B) = 0.4$

(a) find $P(A \cap B)$ **(2)**

(b) find $P(A' \cap B')$ **(3)**

(c) explain why A and B are not independent events. **(1)**

Event C has $P(C) = 0.15$

Events A and C are mutually exclusive.

Events B and C are statistically independent.

(d) Draw a Venn diagram to illustrate the events A, B and C, giving the probabilities for each region. **(5)**

6 A particular plant produces pink flowers 42% of the time and also comes in other colours. A garden centre sells this plant in containers of 10 plants.

A container of 10 plants is selected at random.

(a) Write down a binomial model for X, the number of plants that will produce pink flowers. **(1)**

(b) Find the probability that the container will have more plants that will produce pink flowers than plants that will produce any other colour. **(2)**

(c) If 80 of these plants are planted, use a suitable approximation to find the probability that at least 30 of them will produce pink flowers. **(4)**

TOTAL FOR SECTION A IS 50 MARKS

Section B: Mechanics
Answer ALL questions

Unless otherwise indicated, whenever a numerical value of g is required, take $g = 9.8\,\mathrm{m\,s^{-2}}$ and give your answer to either 2 significant figures or 3 significant figures.

7 A particle moves along the x-axis in a positive direction. At time $t = 0$, the particle passes the origin with a speed of $5\,\mathrm{m\,s^{-1}}$.

The acceleration of the particle at time t seconds is $(2t^3 - 7t)\,\mathrm{m\,s^{-2}}$, $t \geqslant 0$.

Find

(a) the velocity of the particle at time t seconds **(3)**

(b) the times when the particle is instantaneously at rest. **(3)**

8 A uniform rod, AB, of mass 15 kg and length 2 m, rests with one end, A, on rough horizontal ground. The rod is held in limiting equilibrium at an angle of 30° to the horizontal by a force, P newtons, acting at B. The line of action of P is in the vertical plane that contains the rod. The coefficient of friction between the ground and the rod is $\frac{2}{5}$.

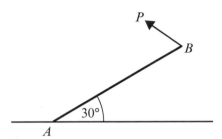

Find the magnitude of the normal reaction of the ground on the rod at A. **(7)**

9 At time t seconds, the velocity of a car, P, is given by $[(6t - 5)\mathbf{i} + 4\mathbf{j}]\,\mathrm{m\,s^{-1}}$. When $t = 0$, the position vector of P is $(2\mathbf{i} + \mathbf{j})\,\mathrm{m}$ relative to a fixed point, O.

(a) Find an expression for the position vector of P at time t seconds. **(4)**

Another car, Q, moves with constant velocity $(3\mathbf{i} + w\mathbf{j})\,\mathrm{m\,s^{-1}}$. When $t = 0$, the position vector of Q is $(5\mathbf{i} + 7\mathbf{j})$ relative to O.

Cars P and Q meet after T seconds.

(b) Find the value of T. **(4)**

(c) Find the value of w. **(2)**

10 A particle, P, of mass 3 kg, is projected from a point A up a line of greatest slope of a fixed inclined plane. The plane is inclined at an angle α to the horizontal, where $\tan \alpha = \frac{3}{4}$. The plane is smooth from A to B, a distance of 2.5 m.

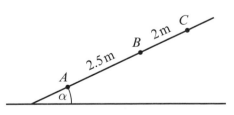

(a) Given that the particle passes through B with a speed of $6\,\mathrm{m\,s^{-1}}$, find the speed of projection from A. **(4)**

The plane is rough from B to C, a distance of 2 m, and the coefficient of friction between P and the plane is μ. The particle comes to instantaneous rest at C.

(b) Find the value of μ. **(7)**

(c) Determine whether the particle will remain at C, carefully justifying your answer. **(2)**

11 A golfer hits his tee shot from an elevated position 11 m above the level of the green. The ball is hit at a speed of 40 m s⁻¹ and at an angle of 25° to the horizontal. The ball lands on the green, bounces and runs into the hole for a hole-in-one.

Modelling the golf ball as a particle and using a value of $g = 10\,\text{m s}^{-2}$, find

(a) the time taken for the ball to land on the green (5)

(b) the speed of the ball as it lands on the green (5)

(c) the angle at which the ball lands on the green. (2)

(d) Suggest two improvements that could be made to the model. (2)

TOTAL FOR SECTION B IS 50 MARKS

TOTAL FOR PAPER 3 IS 100 MARKS

Answers

Worked solutions have been provided for all Guided questions. These are marked with a ⯈**G**⯈. Short answers have been provided for all other questions.

PURE MATHEMATICS
1. Index laws

1   5^{-3}

⯈**G** 2 $\sqrt{3}\left(27^{\frac{2}{3}}\right) = 3^{\frac{1}{2}} \times \left(27^{\frac{1}{3}}\right)^2 = 3^{\frac{1}{2}} \times 3^2 = 3^{\frac{5}{2}}$

3   $6x^{\frac{1}{4}}$

4   $5x^{\frac{2}{3}}$

⯈**G** 5 $\dfrac{\left(3x^{\frac{1}{2}}\right)^3}{9x^3} = \dfrac{27x^{\frac{3}{2}}}{9x^3} = 3x^{-\frac{3}{2}} = \dfrac{3}{x^{\frac{3}{2}}}$

6   $3x^{-\frac{1}{2}} - x;\ p = -\frac{1}{2},\ q = 1$

7   $x = \frac{1}{2}$

8   $x = \frac{1}{2}$

9   $3x^{-\frac{5}{2}} + 2x^{-\frac{9}{2}};\ p = -\frac{5}{2},\ q = -\frac{9}{2}$

2. Expanding and factorising

⯈**G** 1 $(x - 1)(x + 2)^2 = (x - 1)(x^2 + 4x + 4)$
$= x^3 + 4x^2 + 4x - x^2 - 4x - 4 = x^3 + 3x^2 - 4$

⯈**G** 2 $x^3 - 9x = x(x^2 - 9) = x(x + 3)(x - 3)$

3   $x^3 - 3x^2 - 6x + 8$

4   $x(x + 5)(x - 1)$

5   $(2 - 3\sqrt{x})(2 - 3\sqrt{x}) = 4 - 6\sqrt{x} - 6\sqrt{x} + 9x$
$= 4 - 12\sqrt{x} + 9x$

6   (a) $x(x^2 - x - 6)$
(b) $x(x - 3)(x + 2)$

3. Surds

1   $6\sqrt{2}$

⯈**G** 2 $\sqrt{18} + \sqrt{50} = \sqrt{9 \times 2} + \sqrt{25 \times 2}$
$= 3 \times \sqrt{2} + 5 \times \sqrt{2} = 8\sqrt{2}$

⯈**G** 3 $\dfrac{\sqrt{5} + 3}{\sqrt{5} - 2} = \dfrac{(\sqrt{5} + 3)(\sqrt{5} + 2)}{(\sqrt{5} - 2)(\sqrt{5} + 2)}$
$= \dfrac{5 + 5\sqrt{5} + 6}{5 - 4} = \dfrac{11 + 5\sqrt{5}}{1} = 11 + 5\sqrt{5}$

4   $12\sqrt{3}$

5   $a = 2, b = 3$

6   $c = 7, d = 52$

7   $12\sqrt{5} - 27$

4. Quadratic equations

1   $x = -2,\ x = \frac{4}{3}$

⯈**G** 2   (a) $x^2 - 10x + 15 = (x - 5)^2 - 25 + 15 = (x - 5)^2 - 10$
(b) $(x - 5)^2 - 10 = 0$
$(x - 5)^2 = 10$
$x - 5 = \pm\sqrt{10}$
$x = 5 \pm \sqrt{10}$
$c = 5, d = 1$

3   $p = -4, q = 10$

4   $a = 3, b = 1, c = 2$

5. Functions and roots

⯈**G** 1   Let $u = x^2$, then $2u^2 - u - 28 = 0$, $(2u + 7)(u - 4) = 0$
so $2u + 7 = 0$ or $u - 4 = 0$, giving $u = -\frac{7}{2}$ or $u = 4$
So, using $u = x^2$, $x^2 = -\frac{7}{2}$, but x^2 cannot be negative
so $x^2 = 4$, giving $x = 2$ or $x = -2$

2   $x = \frac{1}{2}, x = -2$

3   $x = \frac{9}{4}, x = 25$

4   $x = 64$

5   $4x^4 + 5x^2 - 6 = 0$
$(4x^2 - 3)(x^2 + 2) = 0$
$4x^2 = 3, x^2 = \frac{3}{4}, x = -\frac{\sqrt{3}}{2}$ since $x < 0$
$x^2 = -2$ is inadmissible

6   $x = 9 - 4\sqrt{2}$

6. Sketching quadratics

⯈**G** 1   When $x = 0, y = (0 - 3)(0 + 2) = -6$
When $y = 0, 0 = (x - 3)(x + 2)$
so $x = 3$ or $x = -2$

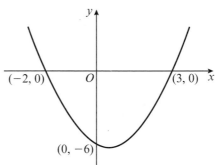

⯈**G** 2   The coordinates of the vertex are $(-3, 4)$
When $x = 0, y = (0 + 3)^2 + 4 = 13$

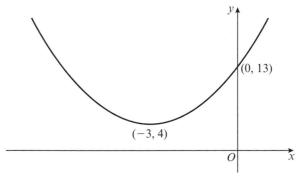

3

4 (a) $3(x - 2)^2 + 5$

(b)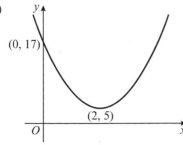

(c) No points of intersection with the x-axis

7. The discriminant

 1 $a = 1, b = -2p, c = p$

$b^2 - 4ac = (-2p)^2 - 4 \times 1 \times p = 4p^2 - 4p$

$4p^2 - 4p = 0$

$4p(p - 1) = 0$

$p(p - 1) = 0$

$p = 1$ (as $p \neq 0$)

 2 $3x^2 + kx - 5 - k = 0$

$a = 3, b = k, c = -5 - k$

$b^2 - 4ac = (k)^2 - 4 \times 3 \times (-5 - k) = k^2 + 12k + 60$

For no real roots, $b^2 - 4ac < 0$ so $k^2 + 12k + 60 < 0$

3 -19

4 (a) $p^2 + 4p + 16$

(b) $p^2 + 4p + 16 = (p + 2)^2 + 12$, giving $a = 2, b = 12$

(c) $(p + 2)^2 \geqslant 0$ for all values of p,
so $(p + 2)^2 + 12 > 0$,
so there are real different roots for all values of p

8. Modelling with quadratics

 1 (a) Relative speed upstream
= speed of boat − speed of current = $(u - 5.5)$ km/h

Time to travel upstream, $t_1 = \dfrac{\text{distance}}{\text{relative speed}}$

$= \dfrac{30}{u - 5.5}$ hours

Relative speed downstream = $(u + 5.5)$ km/h

so $t_2 = \dfrac{\text{distance}}{\text{relative speed}} = \dfrac{30}{u + 5.5}$ hours

(b) $\dfrac{30}{u - 5.5} + \dfrac{30}{u + 5.5} = 3$

$10(u + 5.5) + 10(u - 5.5) = (u + 5.5)(u - 5.5)$

$10u + 55 + 10u - 55 = u^2 - 30.25$

so $u^2 - 20u - 30.25 = 0$

(c) $u = 21.4127 \text{ m s}^{-1}$, $t_1 = 113$ minutes, $t_2 = 67$ minutes

2 (a) 2.86 seconds

(b) Maximum height = 10.22... metres

9. Simultaneous equations

 1 $y = x - 3$ ③

$x^2 - 2(x - 3) = 6$

$x^2 - 2x + 6 = 6$

$x^2 - 2x = 0$

$x(x - 2) = 0$

$x = 0, y = -3$ or $x = 2, y = -1$

2 (a) $x(x + 8) + 3x^2 = 16$ gives $4x^2 + 8x - 16 = 0$

so $x^2 + 2x - 4 = 0$

(b) $x = -1 \pm \sqrt{5}, y = 7 \pm \sqrt{5}$

3 (a) $(4, -3)$

(b)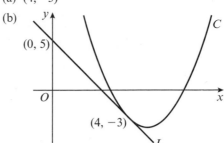

Curve crosses x-axis at 3 and 7. L is a tangent to the curve at the point $(4, -3)$

10. Inequalities

 1 (a) $2x - 6 < 4 - 3x$

$5x < 10$ so $x < 2$

(b) $(2x - 5)(2 + x) = 0$

So $x = -2$ or $x = \frac{5}{2}$

For $y < 0$, $-2 < x < \frac{5}{2}$

(c) $-2 < x < 2$

2 (a) $x < 3$ and $x > 5$

(b)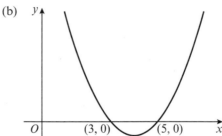

The regions $x < 3$ and $x > 5$ are where the curve is above the x-axis

3 (a) $(2k)^2 - 4(3 - 2k) > 0$ gives $k^2 + 2k - 3 > 0$

(b) $k < -3$ and $k > 1$

4 $-3 < p < 2$

11. Inequalities on graphs

 1 (a) $2x^2 + 3x - 5 = 0$, $(2x + 5)(x - 1) = 0$, $x = -2.5$ and $x = 1$

When $x = 0$, $y = -5$

For $y = 2x + 1$,
graph crosses y-axis when $x = 0$, so $y = 1$
graph crosses x-axis when $y = 0$, so $x = -0.5$

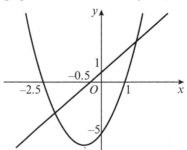

(b) $2x^2 + 3x - 5 = 2x + 1$, $2x^2 + x - 6 = 0$

$(2x - 3)(x + 2) = 0$, $x = 1.5$ and $x = -2$

When $x = 1.5$, $y = 4$ and when $x = -2$, $y = -3$

(c) $x \leqslant -2$ and $x \geqslant 1.5$

2 (a) $(-5, 6)$ and $(2, -8)$

(b)

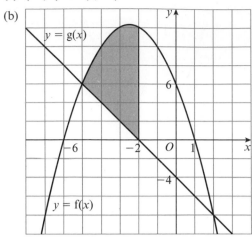

(c) $-5 < x < 2$

(d) See shaded area on graph above.

12. Cubic and quartic graphs

G 1 When $y = 0$, $0 = x(x + 2)(x - 5)$

so $x = -2$ or $x = 0$ or $x = 5$

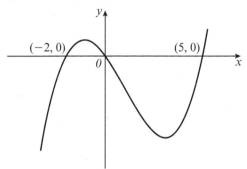

G 2 When $y = 0$, $0 = (x + 1)^2(3 - x)$ so $x = -1$ or $x = 3$

When $x = 0$, $y = (0 + 1)^2(3 - 0) = 3$

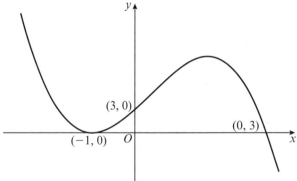

3

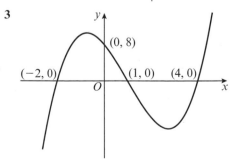

4

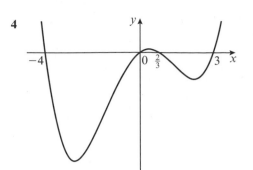

13. Transformations 1

1

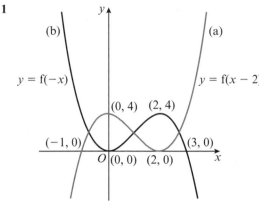

2 (a)

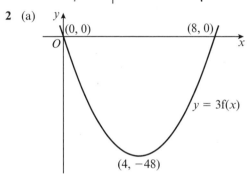

(b)

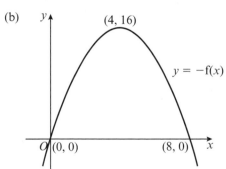

(c)

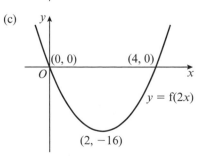

(d) $k = 4$

14. Transformations 2

1 (a)

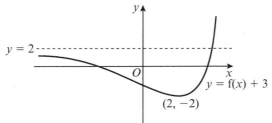

(b)

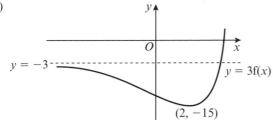

(c)

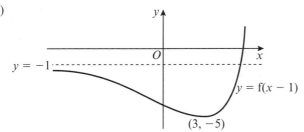

2 (a)

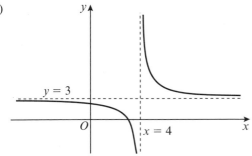

(b) $f(x - 3) = \dfrac{3(x-3)}{(x-3)-1} = \dfrac{3(x-3)}{x-4}$

$(0, 2.25)$ and $(3, 0)$

15. Reciprocal graphs

1 (a)

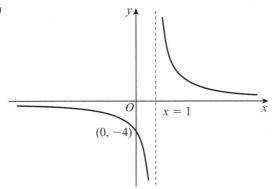

(b) $x = 1$ and $y = 0$

2 (a)

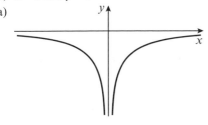

(b)

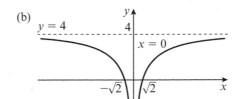

(c)

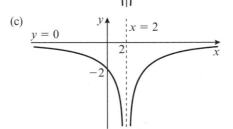

16. Points of intersection

G 1 (a)

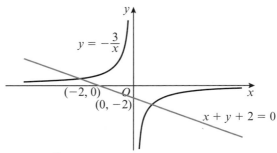

(b) $y = -x - 2$

$-\dfrac{3}{x} = -x - 2$ so $-3 = -x^2 - 2x$

$x^2 + 2x - 3 = 0$

$(x + 3)(x - 1) = 0$

$(-3, 1)$ and $(1, -3)$

2 (a)

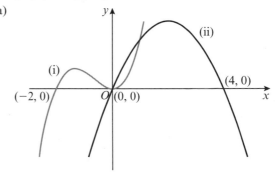

(b) $(0, 0)$ and $(1, 3)$ and $(-4, -32)$

17. Equations of lines

1 When $x = 3$, $y = 7 - 3 \times 3 = -2$ so $(3, -2)$ lies on L

G 2 $7y = 3 - 2x$

$y = \dfrac{3}{7} - \dfrac{2}{7}x$

Gradient $= -\dfrac{2}{7}$

G 3 $x_1 = 3$, $y_1 = -2$, $m = -\dfrac{1}{3}$

$y - (-2) = -\dfrac{1}{3}(x - 3)$

$3(y + 2) = -1(x - 3)$

$3y + 6 = -x + 3$

$y = -\dfrac{1}{3}x - 1$

G 4 (a) $x_1 = -2$, $y_1 = 1$, $x_2 = 6$, $y_2 = -2$

$m = \dfrac{y_2 - y_1}{x_2 - x_1} = \dfrac{-2 - 1}{6 + 2} = \dfrac{-3}{8}$

(b) $y - 1 = -\dfrac{3}{8}(x + 2)$

$8(y - 1) = -3(x + 2)$

$8y - 8 = -3x - 6$

$3x + 8y - 2 = 0$

5 (a) $p = 1$ (b) $4x + 3y - 17 = 0$

Answers

18. Parallel and perpendicular

G 1 (a) When $x = 3$, $y = 4 - 3 \times 3 = -5$, so $(3, -5)$ lies on L

   (b) Gradient of $L = -3$

      Gradient of perpendicular line $= \frac{1}{3}$

      Equation of perpendicular line through $(3, -5)$ is

      $y + 5 = \frac{1}{3}(x - 3)$

      $3y + 15 = x - 3$

      $x - 3y - 18 = 0$

G 2 (a) Coordinates of midpoint are $\left(\dfrac{-2 + 6}{2}, \dfrac{5 + 3}{2}\right) = (2, 4)$

   (b) $4x - y - 4 = 0$

3 $y = \frac{4}{3}x + \frac{5}{3}$

19. Lengths and areas

1 $p = 4$

G 2 (a) $x + 3(x + 1) - 15 = 0$

      $x + 3x + 3 - 15 = 0$

      $4x = 12$

      $x = 3$

      Coordinates are $(3, 4)$

   (b) 32

3 l_2 has equation $2x + 3y = 14$

   Point of intersection is $(-2, 6)$

   Area $= 39$

20. Equation of a circle

1 $(x - 4)^2 + (y + 1)^2 = 6^2$

G 2 (a) $r = \sqrt{(-1 - 2)^2 + (7 - 3)^2} = 5$

      $(x - 2)^2 + (y - 3)^2 = r^2$

      $(x - 2)^2 + (y - 3)^2 = 25$

   (b) $(5 - 2)^2 + (7 - 3)^2 = 3^2 + 4^2 = 9 + 16 = 25$

      so $(5, 7)$ lies on C.

3 $(x - 1)^2 + (y - 8)^2 = 25$

4 (a) Centre $(-1, 3)$, radius 4

   (b) $(-1 + \sqrt{7}, 0)$, $(-1 - \sqrt{7}, 0)$, $(0, 3 + \sqrt{15})$, $(0, 3 - \sqrt{15})$

21. Circle properties

1 Equation is $(x + 2)^2 + (y - 3)^2 = 25$;

   centre $(-2, 3)$, radius 5

   Midpoint of PQ is $(-2, 3)$ so PQ is diameter.

G 2 (a) Gradient of tangent $= \frac{3}{5}$

      Gradient of line through P and $Q = -\frac{5}{3}$

      Equation of line is $y - y_1 = m(x - x_1)$

      $y - 7 = -\frac{5}{3}(x - 1)$

      $3y - 21 = -5x + 5$

      $5x + 3y - 26 = 0$

   (b) $Q\,(4, 2)$

3 (a) $P\,(22, 0)$, $Q\,(0, 11)$

   (b) 165

22. Solving circle problems

G 1 Substitute $y = 2x - 3$ into the equation of the circle.

   $(x + 3)^2 + (2x - 3 + 2)^2 = 26 \Rightarrow (x + 3)^2 + (2x - 1)^2 = 26$

   $x^2 + 6x + 9 + 4x^2 - 4x + 1 = 26$

   $5x^2 + 2x - 16 = 0$

   $(5x - 8)(x + 2) = 0$, so $x = 1.6$ and $x = -2$

   When $x = 1.6$, $y = 2 \times 1.6 - 3 = 0.2$

   and when $x = -2$, $y = 2(-2) - 3 = -7$

   $(-2, -7)$ and $(\frac{8}{5}, \frac{1}{5})$

2 $k < -2\sqrt{5}$ and $k > 2\sqrt{5}$

3 $k = 10\sqrt{2}$

23. The factor theorem

G 1 (a) $f(x) = 2x^3 - 3x^2 - 11x + 6$

      $f(-2) = 2(-2)^3 - 3(-2)^2 - 11(-2) + 6$

      $= -16 - 12 + 22 + 6$

      $= 0$

      So $(x + 2)$ is a factor.

   (b) $f(x) = (x + 2)(2x^2 - 7x + 3)$

      $= (x + 2)(2x - 1)(x - 3)$

2 (a) $(x + 6)(2x + 1)(x - 2)$

   (b) $(x - 4)(3x - 4)(x + 2)$

   (c) $(x - 3)(3x - 1)(2x - 3)$

3 (a) $c = -24$

   (b) $(x - 4)(2x + 3)(x + 2)$

4 (a) $(x - 2)(3x - 1)(x + 5)$

   (b) $x = 2$, $x = \frac{1}{3}$, $x = -5$

24. Binomial expansion 1

G 1 $a = 3 \qquad b = -2x \qquad n = 5$

   $(3 - 2x)^5 = (3)^5 + \binom{5}{1}(3)^4(-2x) + \binom{5}{2}(3)^3(-2x)^2 + \ldots$

   $= 243 + [5 \times 81 \times (-2x)] + [10 \times 27 \times 4x^2] + \ldots$

   $\approx 243 - 810x + 1080x^2$

G 2 (a) $a = 1 \qquad b = px \qquad n = 9$

      $(1 + px)^9 = 1^9 + \binom{9}{1}1^8 px + \binom{9}{2}1^7(px)^2 + \ldots$

      $\approx 1 + 9px + 36p^2 x^2$

   (b) $(1 + px)^9 = 1 + 9px + 36p^2 x^2 + \ldots$

      $9p = q \qquad 36p^2 = 20q$

      $36p^2 = 20 \times 9p$

      $p^2 = 5p$

      $p = 5, q = 45$

3 $16\,384 - 86\,016x + 193\,536x^2$

4 (a) $64 + 576x + 2160x^2$

   (b) $64 + 560x + 2016x^2$

25. Solving binomial problems

G 1 $n = 12 \qquad r = 7 \qquad a = 4 \qquad b = -\frac{x}{2}$

   $\binom{12}{7}4^5\left(-\frac{x}{2}\right)^7 = 792 \times 1024 \times \left(-\frac{x^7}{128}\right) = -6336x^7$

   Coefficient $= -6336$

G 2 $1 + \frac{x}{2} = 1.005$, $\frac{x}{2} = 0.005$, $x = 0.01$

   $(1.005)^8 = 1 + 4(0.01) + 7(0.01)^2 + 7(0.01)^3 + \ldots\ldots\ldots$

      $\approx 1.040\,71$ (5 d.p.)

3 (a) $1 + \dfrac{9x}{4} + \dfrac{9x^2}{4} + \dfrac{21x^3}{16}$

   (b) 1.2488

4 (a) $1 - 14x + 84x^2 - 280x^3$

   (b) 0.8681

   (c) $\left(1 - \frac{x}{2}\right)(1 - 14x + 84x^2)$

      $= 1 - 14x + 84x^2 - \frac{x}{2} + 7x^2$

      $= 1 - \frac{29}{2}x + 91x^2$

26. Proof

G 1 (a) $\dfrac{n + 1}{n + 2}$

   (b) Difference $= \dfrac{n + 1}{n + 2} - \dfrac{n}{n + 1} = \dfrac{(n + 1)^2 - n(n + 2)}{(n + 2)(n + 1)}$

      $= \dfrac{\cancel{n^2} + \cancel{2n} + 1 - \cancel{n^2} - \cancel{2n}}{(n + 2)(n + 1)}$

      $= \dfrac{1}{(n + 2)(n + 1)}$ as required.

   (c) 11th and 12th terms

2 $(2n + 1)^3 - (2n - 1)^3 = (8n^3 + 12n^2 + 6n + 1)$
$\qquad\qquad\qquad\qquad - (8n^3 - 12n^2 + 6n - 1)$
$\qquad\qquad\qquad\qquad = 24n^2 + 2$

Mean of $(2n + 1)$ and $(2n - 1) = 2n$
$(2n)^2 = 4n^2$, $6 \times 4n^2 = 24n^2$ as required

3 (a)

n	1	2	3	4	5	6	7
$2n^2 - n + 1$	2	7	16	29	46	67	92

i.e. never divisible by 11

(b) Trying $n = 2, 3, 5$ and 7 gives a prime number, but $n = 11$ gives 155, which is divisible by 5.

4 $3n^2 + 6n = 3n(n + 2)$. If n is even then both n and $(n + 2)$ are divisible by 2, so $3n^2 + 6n$ will have factors of 3, 2 and 2 i.e. a factor of 12

27. Cosine rule

G 1 $a^2 = b^2 + c^2 - 2bc \cos A$
$a^2 = 5^2 + 8^2 - 2 \times 5 \times 8 \cos 2.1 = 129.387$
$a = 11.4\,\text{cm}$ (3 s.f.)

G 2 $\cos B = \dfrac{a^2 + c^2 - b^2}{2ac}$
$= \dfrac{9^2 + 6^2 - 12^2}{2 \times 6 \times 9} = -\dfrac{1}{4}$
$B = \cos^{-1}(-0.25) = 104°$

3 $17.4\,\text{km}$

4 2.09 radians

28. Sine rule

G 1 $\angle ABC = \pi - 0.85 - 1.05 = 1.2415\ldots$ radians
$\dfrac{b}{\sin B} = \dfrac{c}{\sin C}, \dfrac{9}{\sin 1.2415} = \dfrac{c}{\sin 1.05}$
so $c = \dfrac{9 \sin 1.05}{\sin 1.2415} = 8.25\,\text{cm}$ (3 s.f.)

G 2 (a) $\dfrac{\sin x}{14} = \dfrac{\sin 0.3}{8}$, $\sin x = \dfrac{14 \sin 0.3}{8} = 0.517$ (3 d.p.)

(b) $x = \sin^{-1}(0.517) = 0.54$ (2 d.p.)
or $x = \pi - 0.54 = 2.60$ radians (2 d.p.)

3 (a) $17.8\,\text{cm}$ \qquad (b) $59.2°$ \qquad (c) $212\,\text{cm}^2$

29. Trigonometric graphs

1 (a)

(b) $(0, 3), (180°, -3), (360°, 3)$

G 2 (a)

(b) When $x = 0$: $y = \sin\left(0 - \dfrac{\pi}{3}\right) = -\sin\left(\dfrac{\pi}{3}\right) = -\dfrac{\sqrt{3}}{2}$

Meets y-axis at $\left(0, -\dfrac{\sqrt{3}}{2}\right)$

When $y = 0$: $x = \dfrac{\pi}{3}$ and $x = \dfrac{4\pi}{3}$

Meets x-axis at $\left(\dfrac{\pi}{3}, 0\right), \left(\dfrac{4\pi}{3}, 0\right)$

3 $a = 1.5, b = 30°$

30. Trigonometric equations 1

G 1 $\sin x = \dfrac{2}{5} = 0.4$
$x = \sin^{-1}(0.4) = 23.6°$ or $x = 180° - 23.6° = 156.4°$

G 2 $\tan x = 3$
$x = \tan^{-1}(3) = 71.6°$
or $x = 180° + 71.6° = 251.6°$

3 (a)

(b) $x = 1.772$ radians and 4.511 radians

4 (a) $x = -0.644$ radians or -2.498 radians

(b) $x = -0.841$ radians and 0.841 radians

31. Trigonometric identities 1

G 1 (a) $3 \sin x = 2 \cos^2 x$
$\sin^2 x + \cos^2 x = 1$ so $\cos^2 x = 1 - \sin^2 x$
$3 \sin x = 2(1 - \sin^2 x)$
so $\quad 2 \sin^2 x + 3 \sin x - 2 = 0$

(b) $2 \sin^2 x + 3 \sin x - 2 = 0$
$(2 \sin x - 1)(\sin x + 2) = 0$
$\sin x = \dfrac{1}{2}$ $\quad (\sin x \neq -2)$
$x = 30°$ or $x = 150°$

G 2 (a) $\dfrac{\sin \theta}{\cos \theta} = \dfrac{2}{3}$
so $\tan \theta = \dfrac{2}{3}$

(b) $\theta = \tan^{-1}\left(\dfrac{2}{3}\right)$
$\theta = 33.7°$ or $\theta = 213.7°$

3 $45°, 225°, 210°$ and $330°$

4 $1.047, 1.982, 4.301$ and 5.236 radians

32. Trigonometric equations 2

G 1 (a) $0 \leqslant 2x \leqslant 360°$. Let $Z = 2x$
$Z = \sin^{-1}\left(\dfrac{1}{2}\right) = 30°$
or $Z = 180° - 30° = 150°$
$2x = 30°$ or $150°$
$x = 15°$ or $x = 75°$

(b) $-50° \leqslant x - 50° \leqslant 130°$. Let $Z = X - 50°$
$Z = \cos^{-1}(0.3) = 72.5°$
or $Z = 360° - 72.5° = 287.5°$ (outside range)
$x - 50° = 72.5°$
so $x = 122.5°$

2 $23.2°, -156.8°$

3 $\theta = 38.6°, 121.4°$

4 $\dfrac{\pi}{12}, \dfrac{3\pi}{4}, \dfrac{13\pi}{12}, \dfrac{21\pi}{12}$

33. Vectors

G 1 (a) $\left|\overrightarrow{OP}\right| = \sqrt{1^2 + 7^2} = \sqrt{1 + 49} = \sqrt{50} = 5\sqrt{2}$

(b) $\overrightarrow{QP} = \overrightarrow{QO} + \overrightarrow{OP}$
$= \overrightarrow{OP} - \overrightarrow{OQ}$
$= \mathbf{i} + 7\mathbf{j} - (3\mathbf{i} + 2\mathbf{j}) = -2\mathbf{i} + 5\mathbf{j}$

(c) $\sqrt{29}$

Answers

2 (a) $\frac{1}{10}(8\mathbf{i} - 6\mathbf{j})$ (b) $\frac{1}{17}(8\mathbf{i} + 15\mathbf{j})$ (c) $\frac{1}{9}(8\mathbf{i} - 4\mathbf{j} - \mathbf{k})$

3 (a) (i) $\overrightarrow{PQ} = -3\mathbf{i} - 5\mathbf{j} + \mathbf{k}$ (ii) $|\overrightarrow{PQ}| = \sqrt{35}$

     (b) (i) $\overrightarrow{PQ} = -6\mathbf{i} - 2\mathbf{j} + 9\mathbf{k}$ (ii) $|\overrightarrow{PQ}| = 11$

4 $\lambda = \pm\sqrt{20}$ or $\pm 2\sqrt{5}$

5 $\mu = \frac{-5}{12}$ and $\mu = 2$

34. Solving vector problems

1 (a) $\overrightarrow{AB} = \overrightarrow{AO} + \overrightarrow{OB} = \overrightarrow{OB} - \overrightarrow{OA} = \binom{4}{2} - \binom{-2}{5} = \binom{6}{-3}$

            $\overrightarrow{BC} = \overrightarrow{BO} + \overrightarrow{OC} = \overrightarrow{OC} - \overrightarrow{OB} = \binom{6}{4} - \binom{4}{2} = \binom{2}{2}$

            $\overrightarrow{AC} = \overrightarrow{AO} + \overrightarrow{OC} = \overrightarrow{OC} - \overrightarrow{OA} = \binom{6}{4} - \binom{-2}{5} = \binom{8}{-1}$

     (b) $|\overrightarrow{AB}| = \sqrt{36+9} = \sqrt{45}$, $|\overrightarrow{BC}| = \sqrt{4+4} = \sqrt{8}$,

         $|\overrightarrow{AC}| = \sqrt{64+1} = \sqrt{65}$

         $\cos C = \frac{65+8-45}{2\times\sqrt{65}\times\sqrt{8}} = \frac{14}{\sqrt{65}\sqrt{8}}$, $C = 52.125\ldots°$

         Area $= \frac{1}{2} \times \sqrt{8} \times \sqrt{65} \times \sin 52.125\ldots° = 9$

     (c) 18

     (d) $\binom{0}{7}$

2 $\overrightarrow{AC} = \overrightarrow{AB} + \overrightarrow{BC} = 5\mathbf{i} + 8\mathbf{j} - 3\mathbf{k}$

    $|\overrightarrow{AB}| = \sqrt{45}$, $|\overrightarrow{BC}| = \sqrt{29}$, $|\overrightarrow{AC}| = \sqrt{98}$

    $\cos ABC = \dfrac{45+29-98}{2\sqrt{45}\sqrt{29}}$

    $\angle ABC = 109.401\ldots° = 109.4°$ (1 d.p.)

35. Differentiating from first principles

1 $f'(x) = \lim_{h\to 0} \dfrac{f(x+h) - f(x)}{h}$

   $= \lim_{h\to 0} \dfrac{(x+h)^3 + 5(x+h)^2 - x^3 - 5x^2}{h}$

   $= \lim_{h\to 0} \dfrac{x^3 + 3x^2h + 3xh^2 + h^3 + 5x^2 + 10xh + 5h^2 - x^3 - 5x^2}{h}$

   $= \lim_{h\to 0} \dfrac{3x^2h + 3xh^2 + h^3 + 10xh + 5h^2}{h}$

   $= \lim_{h\to 0} (3x^2 + 3xh + h^2 + 10x + 5h)$

   As $h \to 0$, $3xh \to 0$, $h^2 \to 0$ and $5h \to 0$,

   so $f'(x) = 3x^2 + 10x$ as required.

2 $f'(3) = \lim_{h\to 0} \dfrac{f(3+h) - f(3)}{h}$

   $= \lim_{h\to 0} \dfrac{2(3+h)^2 - 7(3+h) + 1 - [2(3)^2 - 7(3) + 1]}{h}$

   $= \lim_{h\to 0} \dfrac{18 + 12h + 2h^2 - 21 - 7h + 1 - 18 + 21 - 1}{h}$

   $= \lim_{h\to 0} \dfrac{5h + 2h^2}{h}$

   $= \lim_{h\to 0} (5 + 2h)$

   As $h \to 0$, $2h \to 0$ so $f'(3) = 5$

3 $f(x) = ax^2 + 3bx$

   $f'(x) = \lim_{h\to 0} \dfrac{f(x+h) - f(x)}{h}$

   $= \lim_{h\to 0} \dfrac{a(x+h)^2 + 3b(x+h) - ax^2 - 3bx}{h}$

   $= \lim_{h\to 0} \dfrac{\cancel{ax^2} + 2ahx + ah^2 + \cancel{3bx} + 3bh - \cancel{ax^2} - \cancel{3bx}}{h}$

   $= \lim_{h\to 0} (2ax + ah + 3b)$

   $= 2ax + 3b$

36. Differentiation 1

1 $5 - \frac{9}{2}x^{\frac{1}{2}} + 12x^2$

2 $y = 5x^2 + 2x^{-1} - 3x^{-2}$

   $\dfrac{dy}{dx} = 10x - 2x^{-2} + 6x^{-3}$

3 $f(x) = \dfrac{3x - 2\sqrt{x}}{x} = \dfrac{3x}{x} - \dfrac{2\sqrt{x}}{x} = 3 - 2x^{-\frac{1}{2}}$

   $f'(x) = x^{-\frac{3}{2}}$

4 (a) $5x^{-\frac{2}{3}} - 2x^{-1}$

     (b) $\dfrac{dy}{dx} = 4 - \dfrac{10}{3}x^{-\frac{5}{3}} + 2x^{-2}$

5 $f'(x) = -16x^{-2} - 4x^{-\frac{3}{2}}$

37. Differentiation 2

1 (a) $\dfrac{dy}{dx} = 12x^2 - 3$

     (b) $\dfrac{d^2y}{dx^2} = 24x$

2 (a) When $x = 1$, $y = 5 \times 1 - \frac{2}{1^2} = 5 - 2 = 3$, so P lies on C

     (b) $y = 5x - \frac{2}{x^2} = 5x - 2x^{-2}$

        $\dfrac{dy}{dx} = 5 + 4x^{-3} = 5 + \dfrac{4}{x^3}$

        When $x = 1$, $\dfrac{dy}{dx} = 5 + \dfrac{4}{1^3} = 9$

        Gradient at $P = 9$

3 (a) $f'(x) = 3 + 4x^{-2}$ (b) $x = \pm\frac{2}{3}$

4 (a)

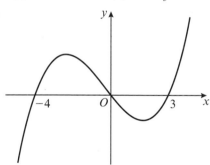

     (b) $3x^2 + 2x - 12$

     (c) At $x = -4$, gradient $= 28$

        At $x = 0$, gradient $= -12$

        At $x = 3$, gradient $= 21$

38. Tangents and normals

1 $y = \frac{1}{3}x^3 + 2x^2 - 8x + 4$

   $\dfrac{dy}{dx} = x^2 + 4x - 8$

   When $x = 3$, $\dfrac{dy}{dx} = 3^2 + 4 \times 3 - 8 = 13$

   Equation of tangent: $y - 7 = 13(x - 3)$ giving $y = 13x - 32$

2 (a) When $x = 4$, $y = 8 \times 4 + 2 \times 4^{\frac{3}{2}} - 3 \times 4^2 = 32 + 16 - 48 = 0$,

        so $P(4, 0)$ lies on C

     (b) $\dfrac{dy}{dx} = 8 + 3x^{\frac{1}{2}} - 6x$

     (c) $\dfrac{dy}{dx} = 8 + 3x^{\frac{1}{2}} - 6x$

        When $x = 4$, $\dfrac{dy}{dx} = 8 + 6 - 24 = -10$

        Gradient of tangent $= -\frac{10}{1}$ so gradient of normal $= \frac{1}{10}$

        Equation of normal: $y - 0 = \frac{1}{10}(x - 4)$

        giving $x - 10y - 4 = 0$

3 (a) $y = x^3 + 2x^2 - 9x - 18$

        $\dfrac{dy}{dx} = 3x^2 + 4x - 9$

(b) When $x = -3$, $\dfrac{dy}{dx} = 6$

$y - 0 = 6(x + 3)$

$y = 6x + 18$

(c) $3x^2 + 4x - 9 = 6$

$3x^2 + 4x - 15 = 0$

$(x + 3)(3x - 5) = 0$

$x = \frac{5}{3}$

39. Stationary points 1

G 1 $\dfrac{dy}{dx} = 6x - 18$

$6x - 18 = 0$

$x = 3 \Rightarrow y = -27$

Coordinates are $(3, -27)$

G 2 $\dfrac{dy}{dx} = -5 + 40x^{-3} = -5 + \dfrac{40}{x^3}$

If $x > 2$, then $x^3 > 8$, and $\dfrac{40}{x^3} < 5$

$\dfrac{40}{x^3} - 5 < 0$

So $\dfrac{dy}{dx} < 0$ and hence y is decreasing.

3 $(2, -3)$

4 $\left(-\frac{1}{3}, \frac{185}{27}\right)$ and $(5, -69)$

5 $k = -\frac{2}{3}$

40. Stationary points 2

G 1 (a) $\dfrac{dy}{dx} = 3x^2 + 6x - 24$, $\dfrac{dy}{dx} = 0$ when $3x^2 + 6x - 24 = 0$

$3(x^2 + 2x - 8) = 0$, $3(x + 4)(x - 2) = 0$

$x = -4$ and $x = 2$

When $x = -4$, $y = 80$, and when $x = 2$, $y = -28$

(b) $\dfrac{d^2y}{dx^2} = 6x + 6$

When $x = -4$, $\dfrac{d^2y}{dx^2} = -18$, so we have a maximum

When $x = 2$, $\dfrac{d^2y}{dx^2} = 18$, so we have a minimum

2 (a) $x = \sqrt{3}$ or $-\sqrt{3}$

(b) $\dfrac{d^2y}{dx^2} = -72x^{-5}$

When $x = \sqrt{3}$, $\dfrac{d^2y}{dx^2} = -\dfrac{8\sqrt{3}}{3} < 0$ so maximum

When $x = -\sqrt{3}$, $\dfrac{d^2y}{dx^2} = \dfrac{8\sqrt{3}}{3} > 0$ so minimum

3 (a)

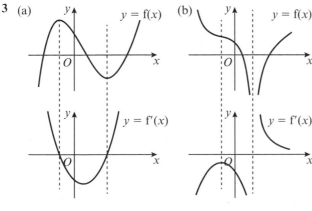

41. Modelling with calculus

G 1 (a) Volume $= 2x^2y = 8000$

$y = \dfrac{8000}{2x^2} = \dfrac{4000}{x^2}$

$A = 2xy + 4xy + 2x^2 = 6xy + 2x^2 = 6x\left(\dfrac{4000}{x^2}\right) + 2x^2$

$= \dfrac{24\,000}{x} + 2x^2$

(b) $A = 24\,000x^{-1} + 2x^2$

$\dfrac{dA}{dx} - 24\,000x^{-2} + 4x = 0$ for a stationary point

$4x = 24\,000x^{-2}$

$4x^3 = 24\,000$

$x^3 = 6000$

$x = 18.2\,\text{cm}$

(c) $\dfrac{d^2A}{dx^2} = 48\,000x^{-3} + 4 = \dfrac{48\,000}{x^3} + 4$

$= \dfrac{48\,000}{6000} + 4 = 12 > 0$

so minimum

(d) Minimum amount of cardboard $= \dfrac{24\,000}{18.2} + 2(18.2)^2$

$= 1981.2\,\text{cm}^2$

2 (a) $V = \pi r^2h$

$A = 2\pi r^2 + 2\pi rh = 900$

$2\pi rh = 900 - 2\pi r^2$

$h = \dfrac{450}{\pi r} - r$

$V = \pi r^2\left(\dfrac{450}{\pi r} - r\right) = 450r - \pi r^3$

(b) $V = 2073\,\text{cm}^3$

(c) $r = 6.9\,\text{cm}$

$\dfrac{d^2V}{dr^2} = -6\pi r = -130 < 0$ so maximum

42. Integration

G 1 $y = 4x - 3x^{-2}$

$\displaystyle\int y\,dx = \dfrac{4x^2}{2} - \dfrac{3x^{-1}}{-1} + c = 2x^2 + \dfrac{3}{x} + c$

G 2 $\displaystyle\int (3x^2 - 5 + x^{-\frac{1}{2}})\,dx = \dfrac{3x^3}{3} - 5x + 2x^{\frac{1}{2}} + c$

$= x^3 - 5x + 2x^{\frac{1}{2}} + c$

3 $-3x^{-1} + \dfrac{3x^{-2}}{4} + c = \dfrac{-3}{x} + \dfrac{3}{4x^2} + c$

4 (a) $(3 - 2\sqrt{x})^2 = (3 - 2\sqrt{x})(3 - 2\sqrt{x}) = 9 - 12\sqrt{x} + 4x$

$k = 12$

(b) $9x - 8x^{\frac{3}{2}} + 2x^2 + c$

5 (a) $p = \frac{3}{2}$, $q = 2$

(b) $\dfrac{8x^{\frac{5}{2}}}{5} - \dfrac{2x^3}{3} + c$

43. Finding the constant

G 1 (a) $f(x) = \displaystyle\int\left(3x + \dfrac{2}{x^2}\right)dx$

$= \displaystyle\int (3x + 2x^{-2})\,dx$

$= \dfrac{3x^2}{2} - 2x^{-1} + c = \dfrac{3x^2}{2} - \dfrac{2}{x} + c$

$10 = \dfrac{3 \times 4}{2} - \dfrac{2}{2} + c$

$c = 5$

$f(x) = \dfrac{3x^2}{2} - \dfrac{2}{x} + 5$

(b) $f(x) = \dfrac{3x^2}{2} - \dfrac{2}{x} + 5$

$f(-1) = \frac{3}{2} + 2 + 5 = 8.5$

G 2 $\dfrac{dy}{dx} = \dfrac{x-3}{\sqrt{x}} = x^{\frac{1}{2}} - 3x^{-\frac{1}{2}}$

$y = \int (x^{\frac{1}{2}} - 3x^{-\frac{1}{2}})\, dx = \dfrac{2x^{\frac{3}{2}}}{3} - 6x^{\frac{1}{2}} + c$

$\dfrac{1}{3} = \dfrac{2 \times 8}{3} - 6 \times 2 + c = \dfrac{16}{3} - 12 + c$

$c = 7$

$y = \dfrac{2x^{\frac{3}{2}}}{3} - 6x^{\frac{1}{2}} + 7$

3 (a) $\dfrac{dy}{dx} = \dfrac{(x^2 - 2)^2}{x^2} = \dfrac{(x^2 - 2)(x^2 - 2)}{x^2} = \dfrac{x^4 - 4x^2 + 4}{x^2}$

$\qquad = x^2 - 4 + 4x^{-2}$

(b) $y = \dfrac{x^3}{3} - 4x - 4x^{-1} + 5$

44. Definite integration

G 1 $\int_1^2 (x^3 - 3x^2 + 5x - 7)\, dx = \left[\dfrac{x^4}{4} - x^3 + \dfrac{5x^2}{2} - 7x\right]_1^2$

$= (4 - 8 + 10 - 14) - \left(\dfrac{1}{4} - 1 + \dfrac{5}{2} - 7\right) = -8 - \left(-\dfrac{21}{4}\right) = -\dfrac{11}{4}$

G 2 $\int_1^2 \left(2x^2 + 3 - \dfrac{5}{x^2}\right) dx = \int_1^2 (2x^2 + 3 - 5x^{-2})\, dx$

$= \left[\dfrac{2x^3}{3} + 3x + 5x^{-1}\right]_1^2 = \left[\dfrac{2x^3}{3} + 3x + \dfrac{5}{x}\right]_1^2$

$= \left(\dfrac{16}{3} + 6 + \dfrac{5}{2}\right) - \left(\dfrac{2}{3} + 3 + 5\right) = \dfrac{83}{6} - \dfrac{26}{3} = \dfrac{31}{6}$

3 $\dfrac{47}{2}$

4 $30 + 4\sqrt{2}$

5 $\dfrac{41}{8}$

45. Area under a curve

G 1 Graph crosses x-axis at $x = -1$ and $x = 3$

$y = 3 + 2x - x^2$

$\int_{-1}^3 (3 + 2x - x^2)\, dx = \left[3x + \dfrac{2x^2}{2} - \dfrac{x^3}{3}\right]_{-1}^3 = \left[3x + x^2 - \dfrac{x^3}{3}\right]_{-1}^3$

$= (9 + 9 - 9) - \left(-3 + 1 + \dfrac{1}{3}\right) = 9 - \left(-\dfrac{5}{3}\right) = \dfrac{32}{3}$

Area $= \dfrac{32}{3}$

G 2 Graph crosses x-axis at $x = -2$ and $x = 4$

$y = x^2 - 2x - 8$

$\int_{-2}^4 (x^2 - 2x - 8)\, dx = \left[\dfrac{x^3}{3} - \dfrac{2x^2}{2} - 8x\right]_{-2}^4 = \left[\dfrac{x^3}{3} - x^2 - 8x\right]_{-2}^4$

$= \left(\dfrac{64}{3} - 16 - 32\right) - \left(-\dfrac{8}{3} - 4 + 16\right) = -\dfrac{80}{3} - \dfrac{28}{3} = -36$

Area $= 36$

3 24

46. More areas

G 1 $L\,(2, 0)$; $M\,(4, 0)$ At N: $x = 6$, $y = 6^2 - 6 \times 6 + 8 = 8$

Area of triangle $= \dfrac{1}{2} \times$ base $\times$ height $= \dfrac{1}{2} \times 4 \times 8 = 16$

$\int_4^6 (x^2 - 6x + 8)\, dx = \left[\dfrac{x^3}{3} - \dfrac{6x^2}{2} + 8x\right]_4^6 = \left[\dfrac{x^3}{3} - 3x^2 + 8x\right]_4^6$

$\qquad = (72 - 108 + 48) - \left(\dfrac{64}{3} - 48 + 32\right)$

$\qquad = 12 - \dfrac{16}{3} = \dfrac{20}{3}$

Area of $R = 16 - \dfrac{20}{3} = \dfrac{28}{3}$

2 (a) $A\,(-6, 38)$, $B\,(1, 17)$ (b) Area of $S = \dfrac{385}{2} - 135\dfrac{1}{3} = \dfrac{343}{6}$

47. Exponential functions

1 (a) D   (b) C   (c) A   (d) B

G 2 (b)   (c)

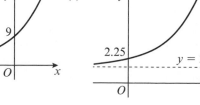

(d)

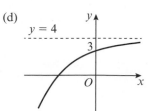

3 (a) $6e^{6x}$ (b) $-3e^{-3x}$ (c) $2e^{\frac{x}{2}}$

(d) $1.2e^{0.2x}$ (e) $-7e^{-x} + 8e^{-4x}$ (f) $9e^{3x} + 2e^{-2x}$

(g) $\dfrac{5}{4}e^{\frac{5x}{4}} + \dfrac{9}{2}e^{\frac{9x}{4}}$

48. Logarithms

G 1 (a) $8^2 = 64$ so $\log_8 64 = 2$

(b) $3\log_a 2 = \log_a 2^3 = \log_a 8$

$\log_a 8 + \log_a 7 = \log_a(8 \times 7) = \log_a 56$

2 (a) $p = \dfrac{1}{16}$ (b) $y = 5$

3 (a) $\log_a 200$ (b) $\log_a \dfrac{27}{4}$

G 4 $\log_4 y = \log_4 4x^3$

$\qquad = \log_4 4 + \log_4 x^3$

$\qquad = 1 + 3\log_4 x$

5 $y^2 = 9x^4$

$\log_3 y^2 = \log_3 9x^4$

$2\log_3 y = \log_3 9 + \log_3 x^4$

$2\log_3 y = \log_3 3^2 + 4\log_3 x$

$2\log_3 y = 2\log_3 3 + 4\log_3 x$

$2\log_3 y = 2 + 4\log_3 x$

$\log_3 y = 1 + 2\log_3 x$

6 $3\log_a x + \dfrac{1}{2}\log_a y - 4\log_a z$

49. Equations with logs

G 1 $\log_3 \dfrac{2x - 1}{x} = 1$

$\dfrac{2x - 1}{x} = 3^1$

$2x - 1 = 3x$

$x = -1$

2 $x = \dfrac{1}{2}$

G 3 $a = 4b$ ①

$\log_2 a + \log_2 b = 3$ ②

$\log_2 4b + \log_2 b = 3$

$\log_2 4b^2 = 3$

$4b^2 = 2^3$

$4b^2 = 8$

$b^2 = 2$

$b = \sqrt{2}$ and $a = 4\sqrt{2}$ (a and b both positive)

4 (a) $2\log_2(x - 2) - \log_2(6 - x) = 1$

$\log_2 \dfrac{(x - 2)^2}{(6 - x)} = 1$

$\dfrac{(x - 2)^2}{(6 - x)} = 2^1$

$x^2 - 4x + 4 = 2(6 - x)$

$x^2 - 2x - 8 = 0$

(b) $x = 4$ ($x \neq -2$)

5 $x = 27$ or $\dfrac{1}{27}$

50. Exponential equations

G 1 (a) $3^x = 5$

$\log 3^x = \log 5$

$x\log 3 = \log 5$

$x = \dfrac{\log 5}{\log 3} = 1.46$

(b) Let $Y = 3^x$ so $3^{2x} = (3^x)^2 = Y^2$
$Y^2 - 8Y + 15 = 0$
$(Y - 3)(Y - 5) = 0$
$Y = 3$ or 5, so $Y = 3^x = 3$ or $3^x = 5$
$x = 1$ or $x = \dfrac{\log 5}{\log 3} = 1.46$

2 $x = 0.43$

3 $x = 0$, $x = 0.936$

4 (a) 7.638 (b) 1.723

5 The quadratic is $0.5 x^2 \log 3 - x \log 9 + \log 9 = 0$
Discriminant $= (\log 9)^2 - 4 \times 0.5 \log 3 \times \log 9$
$= (\log 9)^2 - 2 \log 3 \times \log 9$
$= (\log 9)^2 - \log 3^2 \times \log 9$
$= (\log 9)^2 - (\log 9)^2$
$= 0$ so the curves just touch

51. Natural logarithms

1 $\ln(5x + 24) = \ln(x + 2)^2$
$5x + 24 = (x + 2)^2$
$5x + 24 = x^2 + 4x + 4$
$0 = x^2 - x - 20$
$0 = (x - 5)(x + 4)$
$x = 5$
($x = -4$ is inadmissible since $\ln x$ is only defined for $x > 0$)

2 $x = 9$
($x = -2$ is inadmissible since $\ln x$ is only defined for $x > 0$)

3 $x = 0$, $x = \ln 2$

4 $x = \dfrac{\ln 5 + 1}{\ln 3 + 2}$

5 (a) $\dfrac{5x^2 - 13x - 6}{x^2 - 9} = \dfrac{(5x + 2)(x - 3)}{(x - 3)(x + 3)} = \dfrac{5x + 2}{x + 3}$

(b) $x = \dfrac{3e^2 - 2}{5 - e^2}$

52. Exponential modelling

1 (a) $370\,°C$

(b) $280 = 350e^{-0.08t} + 20$
so $\dfrac{260}{350} = e^{-0.08t}$ so $\ln\left(\dfrac{260}{350}\right) = -0.08t$
$t = 3.72$ minutes (3 s.f.)

(c) $1.14\,°C$/minute

(d) $e^{-0.08t} > 0$ for all values of t and $e^{-0.08t} \to 0$ as $t \to \infty$
So $T > 20$, i.e. the temperature can never fall to $18\,°C$

2 (a) $60\,g$

(b) $k = 0.00788$ (3 s.f.)

(c) $23.3\,g$ (3 s.f.)

(d) $0.319\,g$/year

(e)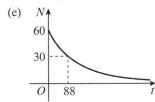

53. Modelling with logs

1 (a) $\log_{10} P = \log_{10}(at^n) = \log_{10} a + \log_{10} t^n = \log_{10} a + n\log_{10} t$

(b) Intercept $= \log_{10} a$

(c) $n = $ gradient $= \dfrac{1.67 - 1.48}{0.8} = 0.2375$
Intercept $= 1.48 = \log_{10} a$, so $a = 30.2$
So the equation is $P = 30.2\,t^{0.2375}$

(d) 66.6%

2 (a) $\log_{10} y = \log_{10} k + t\log_{10} b$ (b) $\log_{10} k$

(c) $y = 288(1.16)^t$ (d) £288 million

(e) 5.5 years

54. You are the examiner!

1 L is $y = -\frac{1}{2}x + \frac{5}{2}$ so gradient of line perpendicular to L is 2
Equation is $y - 4 = 2(x + 1)$
$\Rightarrow y - 4 = 2x + 2 \Rightarrow 2x - y + 6 = 0$

2 $y = 3x^2 - 2x + 4x^{-1}$ so $\dfrac{dy}{dx} = 6x - 2 - \dfrac{4}{x^2}$
When $x = 2$, $y = 12 - 4 + 2 = 10$ and $\dfrac{dy}{dx} = 12 - 2 - 1 = 9$
Equation of tangent is $y - 10 = 9(x - 2)$
$\Rightarrow y - 10 = 9x - 18 \Rightarrow y = 9x - 8$

3 From 1st equation, $y = 2x - 9$
Substituting for y in the 2nd equation gives $x^2 - x(2x - 9) = 20$
$x^2 - 2x^2 + 9x = 20 \Rightarrow x^2 - 9x + 20 = 0$
$\Rightarrow (x - 4)(x - 5) = 0 \Rightarrow x = 4$ and $x = 5$
When $x = 4$, $y = -1$ and when $x = 5$, $y = 1$

4 Range for $(x + 40°)$ is
$40° \leqslant (x + 40°) \leqslant 400°$
$\cos^{-1}(0.85) = 31.8°$ (1 d.p.),
which is not in the range
for $(x + 40°)$.
$(x + 40°) = 360° - 31.8°$
or $360 + 31.8°$
$(x + 40°) = 328.2°$ or $391.8°$
$x = 288.2°$ or $351.8°$

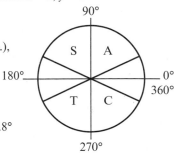

55. You are the examiner!

5 (a) $2e^{3x} - 9e^{2x} + 10e^x = 0$
$\Rightarrow e^x(2e^{2x} - 9e^x + 10) = 0 \Rightarrow e^x[2(e^x)^2 - 9e^x + 10] = 0$
$e^x(2e^x - 5)(e^x - 2) = 0$ so $e^x = 0$ (which is not possible)
or $e^x = 2$ or $e^x = \frac{5}{2}$
so $x = \ln 2$ or $x = \ln \frac{5}{2}$

(b) $\ln(4^x e^{3x + 2}) = \ln 5 \Rightarrow \ln 4^x + \ln e^{3x + 2} = \ln 5$
$x\ln 4 + (3x + 2)\ln e = \ln 5$
$\Rightarrow x\ln 4 + (3x + 2) = \ln 5$ (since $\ln e = 1$)
$x(\ln 4 + 3) = \ln 5 - 2$, so $x = \dfrac{\ln 5 - 2}{\ln 4 + 3}$

6 (a) $x^2 - 3x + 4 = 10 - 2x$
$x^2 - x - 6 = 0$
$(x + 2)(x - 3) = 0$
$x = -2$ or $x = 3$
When $x = -2$, $y = 14$, so A is $(-2, 14)$
and when $x = 3$, $y = 4$, so B is $(3, 4)$

(b) Area of trapezium formed by straight line and x-axis
between $x = -2$ and $x = 3$ is
$\frac{1}{2} \times 5 \times (14 + 4) = 45$
Area under curve between $x = -2$ and $x = 3$ is
$\displaystyle\int_{-2}^{3} (x^2 - 3x + 4)\,dx = \left[\dfrac{x^3}{3} - \dfrac{3x^2}{2} + 4x\right]_{-2}^{3}$
$= \left(9 - \dfrac{27}{2} + 12\right) - \left(-\dfrac{8}{3} - 6 - 8\right)$
$= 7\frac{1}{2} + 16\frac{2}{3} = 24\frac{1}{6}$
Shaded area $S = 45 - 24\frac{1}{6} = 20\frac{5}{6}$

56. Proof by contradiction

1 Assume that n is even, say $n = 2k$, then $3n + 7 = 3(2k) + 7$
$= 6k + 7 = 6(k + 1) + 1$
But $6(k + 1) + 1 = 2(3k + 3) + 1$ which is of the form
$2m + 1$ and so is odd.

This contradicts the original assumption, so if $3n + 7$ is
even then n must be odd.

G 2 Assume that x and y are different positive integers and $x^2 - y^2 = 10$ which means $(x + y)(x - y) = 10$

$(x + y)$ and $(x - y)$ must both be integers and since $(x + y)$ must be positive, the only factors of 10 to consider are 1 and 10 or 2 and 5

Suppose $x + y = 10$ and $x - y = 1$, solving simultaneously gives $x = 5.5$ and $y = 4.5$

Suppose $x + y = 5$ and $x - y = 2$, solving simultaneously gives $x = 3.5$ and $y = 1.5$

This contradicts the assumption that x and y are positive integers, so the original assumption is incorrect.

So there are no positive integer solutions of the equation $x^2 - y^2 = 10$

3 Assume that the arithmetic mean is less than the geometric mean.

$$\frac{m + n}{2} < \sqrt{mn}$$

$$\frac{(m + n)^2}{4} < mn \text{ hence } (m + n)^2 < 4mn$$

$m^2 + 2mn + n^2 < 4mn$, $m^2 - 2mn + n^2 < 0$, $(m - n)^2 < 0$

But $(m - n)^2$ is a perfect square, so cannot be negative.

So there is a contradiction, which means that the original assumption must be incorrect.

So the arithmetic mean is greater than the geometric mean.

4 Assume $\sin\theta + \cos\theta < 1$, then $(\sin\theta + \cos\theta)^2 < 1^2$ so $\sin^2\theta + \cos^2\theta + 2\sin\theta\cos\theta < 1$

But $\sin^2\theta + \cos^2\theta = 1$, so $2\sin\theta\cos\theta < 0$

But in the range $0 \leq \theta \leq \frac{\pi}{2}$, both $\sin\theta$ and $\cos\theta$ are positive, taking on values between 0 and 1

So $2\sin\theta\cos\theta$ cannot be < 0, which is a contradiction, so the original assumption is incorrect.

So if θ is such that $0 \leq \theta \leq \frac{\pi}{2}$, then $\sin\theta + \cos\theta \geq 1$

57. Algebraic fractions

G 1 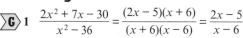 $\dfrac{2x^2 + 7x - 30}{x^2 - 36} = \dfrac{(2x - 5)(x + 6)}{(x + 6)(x - 6)} = \dfrac{2x - 5}{x - 6}$

2 $\dfrac{3x + 2}{x - 1}$

3 $\dfrac{2(x - 4)}{5x - 3}$

4 $\dfrac{2x + 1}{x(x - 1)}$

5 $\dfrac{3x - 5}{x - 5}$

6 $\dfrac{3(2x - 5)}{(3x + 2)(x - 3)}$

58. Partial fractions

G 1 $\dfrac{3x - 10}{(x - 2)(x - 4)} = \dfrac{A}{x - 2} + \dfrac{B}{x - 4}$

Let $x = 2$ and work out $\dfrac{3x - 10}{x - 4}$: $A = \dfrac{3(2) - 10}{2 - 4} = \dfrac{-4}{-2} = 2$

Let $x = 4$ and work out $\dfrac{3x - 10}{x - 2}$: $B = \dfrac{3(4) - 10}{4 - 2} = \dfrac{2}{2} = 1$

So $\dfrac{3x - 10}{(x - 2)(x - 4)} \equiv \dfrac{2}{x - 2} + \dfrac{1}{x - 4}$

2 $\dfrac{2}{2x + 1} + \dfrac{1}{4x - 1}$

3 $-\dfrac{1}{x} + \dfrac{4}{5(x + 2)} + \dfrac{1}{5(x - 3)}$

G 4 $x^2 - 13 = A(x - 1)(x + 2) + B(x + 2) + C(x - 1)^2$

When $x = -2$, $-9 = 9C$, so $C = -1$

When $x = 1$, $-12 = 3B$, so $B = -4$

Comparing coefficients of x^2, $1 = A + C$, so $A = 2$

5 $A = 1$, $B = -2$, $C = 1$, $D = -1$

59. Algebraic division

G 1

$$
\begin{array}{r}
2x^2 - 7x - 4 \\
x^2 + 0x - 3 \overline{\smash{\big)}\, 2x^4 - 7x^3 - 10x^2 + 24x + 10} \\
\underline{2x^4 + 0x^3 - 6x^2} \\
-7x^3 - 4x^2 + 24x + 10 \\
\underline{-7x^3 + 0x^2 + 21x} \\
-4x^2 + 3x + 10 \\
\underline{-4x^2 + 0x + 12} \\
3x - 2
\end{array}
$$

Answer: $2x^2 - 7x - 4 + \dfrac{3x - 2}{x^2 - 3}$

2 $a = 2$, $b = -5$, $c = 4$, $d = -11$, $e = 14$

3 $a = 5$, $b = 3$, $c = 10$, $d = 16$, $e = 12$

60. Domain and range

G 1 (a) $gf(x) = 2 + \dfrac{3}{x^2 - 2} = \dfrac{2(x^2 - 2) + 3}{x^2 - 2} = \dfrac{2x^2 - 1}{x^2 - 2}$

(b) $\frac{2}{7}$

(c) $x = \dfrac{1}{\sqrt{2}}$ and $x = -\dfrac{1}{\sqrt{2}}$

2 (a) $gf(x) = \dfrac{2(1 - 5x)}{(1 - 5x) + 3} = \dfrac{2 - 10x}{4 - 5x}$

(b) 1.75

(c) $gg(x) = \dfrac{4x}{5x + 9}$

(d) -1

(e) $x = \frac{1}{5}$ and $x = \frac{2}{5}$

61. Graphs and range

G 1 (a) Range of f is $-8 < f(x) < 6$

(b) $ff(6) = f(-4) = -6$

2 (a) $5 < f(x) < 11$

(b) $-12 \leq g(x) < 24$

3 (a) $\dfrac{5x + 14}{x^2 + 4x - 12} - \dfrac{3}{x - 2} = \dfrac{5x + 14}{(x + 6)(x - 2)} - \dfrac{3}{x - 2}$

$= \dfrac{5x + 14 - 3(x + 6)}{(x + 6)(x - 2)}$

$= \dfrac{2x - 4}{(x + 6)(x - 2)}$

$= \dfrac{2(x - 2)}{(x + 6)(x - 2)}$

$= \dfrac{2}{x + 6}$

(b) $\frac{1}{4} < f(x) < 2$

62. Inverse functions

G 1 (a) $y = \dfrac{2x}{3} - 4$, $3y = 2x - 12$, $x = \frac{1}{2}(3y + 12)$ so the inverse function f^{-1} is $x \mapsto \frac{1}{2}(3x + 12)$

(b) Domain of f^{-1} is $-6 < x < 2$

2 (a) $g^{-1}(x) = \dfrac{6x + 5}{x - 2}$

(b) Domain of g^{-1} is $2 < x < 10.5$

3 (a) $h^{-1}(x) = \dfrac{4 - x}{3x - 1}$

(b) Domain of h^{-1} is $\frac{1}{3} < x < 4$

63. Inverse graphs

G 1

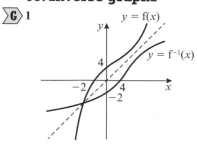

2

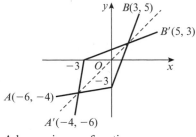

$B(3, 5)$
$B'(5, 3)$
$A(-6, -4)$
$A'(-4, -6)$

3 A has an inverse function.
B does not have an inverse function.
C does not have an inverse function.
D has an inverse function.

Those that do not have an inverse function are not one-to-one mappings – a line drawn horizontally cuts the graph more than once.

64. Modulus

1 (a)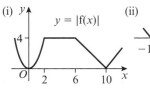
$y = |f(x)|$

(b)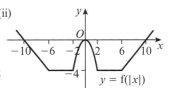
$y = f(|x|)$

2 (a) (i)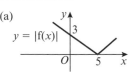
$y = |f(x)|$

(ii)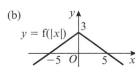
$y = f(|x|)$

(b) (i)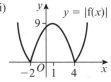
$y = |f(x)|$

(ii)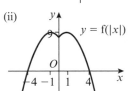
$y = f(|x|)$

(c) (i)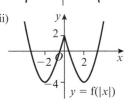
$y = |f(x)|$

(ii)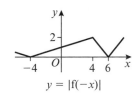
$y = f(|x|)$

65. Modulus transformations

1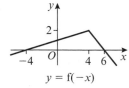
$y = f(-x)$ $y = |f(-x)|$

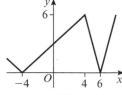
$y = 3|f(-x)|$

2 (a)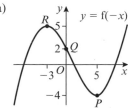
$y = f(-x)$

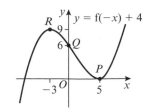
$y = f(-x) + 4$

(b)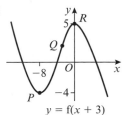
$y = f(x + 3)$

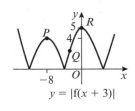
$y = |f(x + 3)|$

66. Modulus equations

1 (a)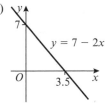
$y = 7 - 2x$

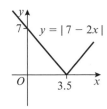
$y = |7 - 2x|$

(b) $7 - 2x = x + 3$
$x = \frac{4}{3}$

$-(7 - 2x) = x + 3$
$x = 10$

2 $x = 4$ and $x = \frac{4}{9}$

3 (a)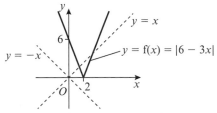
$y = x$
$y = -x$
$y = f(x) = |6 - 3x|$

(b) The graph of $y = -x$ does not intersect the graph of $y = f(x)$.

(c) $x = 1.5$ and $x = 3$

67. Arithmetic sequences

1 (a) First term $n = 1$ $3 \times 1 - 2 = 1$
Second term $n = 2$ $3 \times 2 - 2 = 4$
Third term $n = 3$ $3 \times 3 - 2 = 7$

(b) $d = 3$

2 (a) $a = 40, d = -2.5$
20th term $= a + (20 - 1)d = 40 + 19 \times -2.5 = -7.5$

(b) $r = 17$

3 (a) $a + 14d = 9$ and $a + 19d = 16.5$

(b) $a = -12, d = 1.5$

4 $3 + 2\sqrt{6}$

68. Arithmetic series

1 $a = -8, d = 3$
$a + (n - 1)d = 19$
$-8 + (n - 1) \times 3 = 19$
$3n - 11 = 19$
$n = 10$
$S_{10} = \frac{1}{2} \times 10[2 \times -8 + (10 - 1) \times 3] = 55$

2 Sum $= 2500$

3 (a) $S_{10} = \frac{10}{2}[2a + (10 - 1)d] = 150$
$5[2a + 9d] = 150$
$2a + 9d = 30$

(b) $a + 4d = 14$

(c) $a = 6, d = 2$

4 (a) $S_n = \frac{1}{2}n[2 \times 149 + (n - 1) \times (-2)] = 5000$
$n[149 + (n - 1) \times (-1)] = 5000$
$149n - n^2 + n = 5000$
$n^2 - 150n + 5000 = 0$

(b) $(n - 50)(n - 100) = 0$
$n = 50$ or $n = 100$

Answers

69. Geometric sequences

1 15th term = 0.888 (3 s.f.)

G 2 (a) Fourth term: $ar^3 = 72$ ①

Seventh term: $ar^6 = 9$ ②

② ÷ ①: $\dfrac{ar^6}{ar^3} = r^3 = \dfrac{9}{72} = \dfrac{1}{8}$

$r = \dfrac{1}{2}$

(b) $ar^3 = 72$ so $a = 576$

G 3 $\dfrac{15}{k} = \dfrac{k + 40}{15}$

$225 = k^2 + 40k$

$k^2 + 40k - 225 = 0$

$(k + 45)(k - 5) = 0$

$k = 5, k = -45$

4 (a) $\dfrac{k}{k + 6} = \dfrac{2k - 16}{k}$

$k^2 = (k + 6)(2k - 16)$ gives $k^2 - 4k - 96 = 0$

(b) $(k - 12)(k + 8) = 0$ so $k = 12$ (or $k = -8$, which is not possible as k is positive)

(c) $r = \dfrac{2}{3}$

70. Geometric series

G 1 $S_{20} = \dfrac{150\left(1 - \frac{2^{20}}{3}\right)}{1 - \frac{2}{3}} = 449.9$ (1 d.p.)

G 2 $\sum_{k=1}^{8} 10(3^k) = 30 + 90 + 270 + 810 + \ldots$

$a = 30, \quad r = 3$

$S_8 = \dfrac{30(1 - 3^8)}{1 - 3} = \dfrac{-196\,800}{-2} = 98\,400$

3 $S_{50} = -33\,088.9$

4 $S_n = \dfrac{3^n - 1}{2}$

5 (a) £41 500

(b) £593 000

71. Infinite series

G 1 $a = \dfrac{2}{3} \qquad r = \dfrac{1}{2} \div \dfrac{2}{3} = \dfrac{3}{4}$

$S_\infty = \dfrac{a}{1 - r} = \dfrac{\frac{2}{3}}{1 - \frac{3}{4}} = \dfrac{8}{3}$

G 2 $a = 150 \qquad S_\infty = \dfrac{a}{1 - r} = \dfrac{150}{1 - r} = 375$

$150 = 375(1 - r)$ so $r = \dfrac{3}{5}$

3 (a) $S_\infty = 150$

(b) $-1 < r < 1$

(c) 0.773

4 (a) $ar = 12$, so $a = \dfrac{12}{r}$

$\dfrac{12}{r(1 - r)} = 50$ gives $25r^2 - 25r + 6 = 0$

(b) $r = \dfrac{3}{5}$ and $a = 20$, or $r = \dfrac{2}{5}$ and $a = 30$

72. Recurrence relations

G 1 (a) $a_1 = 2$

$a_2 = 2a_1 - 3 = 4 - 3 = 1$

$a_3 = 2a_2 - 3 = 2 - 3 = -1$

(b) $a_4 = -5 \qquad a_5 = -13$

$a_1 + a_2 + a_3 + a_4 + a_5 = 2 + 1 - 1 - 5 - 13 = -16$

2 (a) $a_2 = 3k - 2$ (b) $a_3 = 3(3k - 2) - 2 = 9k - 8$

(c) $k = 2$ (d) Increasing

3 (a) $x_2 = p + 3$ (b) $x_3 = p(p + 3) + 3 = p^2 + 3p + 3$

(c) $p = -7, p = 4$

73. Modelling with series

G 1 (a) $a = 600, d = 100$

25th year: $u_n = 600 + 24 \times 100 = £3000$

(b) $S_{25} = \dfrac{1}{2} \times 25[2 \times 600 + (25 - 1) \times 100]$

$= \dfrac{25}{2}[1200 + 2400]$

$= £45\,000$

G 2 $a = 50, d = 10$

$S_w = \dfrac{1}{2}w(50 \times 2 + (w - 1) \times 10) = 12\,150$

$w(100 + 10w - 10) = 24\,300$

$10w(w + 9) = 24\,300$

$w(w + 9) = 2430 = 45 \times 54$

$w(w + 9) = 45 \times (45 + 9)$

$w = 45$

3 (a) $N = 36$ (b) 19 700

74. Series and logs

G 1 $a = 12 \qquad r = 2.5 \qquad S_n = \dfrac{a(1 - r^n)}{1 - r}$

$\dfrac{12(1 - 2.5^n)}{1 - 2.5} > 20\,000$

$12(1 - 2.5^n) < -30\,000$

$1 - 2.5^n < -2500$

$2501 < 2.5^n$

$2.5^n > 2501$

$n \log 2.5 > \log 2501$

$n > 8.539$

$n = 9$

G 2 $a = 25\,000 \qquad r = 0.85 \qquad n\text{th term} = ar^{n-1}$

$25\,000 \times 0.85^{n-1} < 1500$

$0.85^{n-1} < 0.06$

$n - 1 > \dfrac{\log 0.06}{\log 0.85}$

$n - 1 > 17.31$

$n > 18.31$

$n = 19$

so $m = 19 - 1 = 18$

($m = n - 1$ because first term is $a = 25\,000$)

3 $n = 5$

4 (a) $a = 250\,000 \qquad r = 1.04$

$250\,000 \times 1.04^{N-1} > 500\,000$

$1.04^{N-1} > 2$

$(N - 1) \log 1.04 > \log 2$

(b) $N = 19$

75. Binomial expansion 2

G 1 $(1 + 4x)^{\frac{3}{2}} = 1 + \left(\frac{3}{2}\right)(4x) + \dfrac{\left(\frac{3}{2}\right)\left(\frac{1}{2}\right)(4x)^2}{1 \times 2} + \dfrac{\left(\frac{3}{2}\right)\left(\frac{1}{2}\right)\left(-\frac{1}{2}\right)(4x)^3}{1 \times 2 \times 3} \cdots$

$= 1 + 6x + 6x^2 - 4x^3 \ldots$

G 2 $\sqrt{4 - x} = (4 - x)^{\frac{1}{2}} = \left[4\left(1 - \dfrac{x}{4}\right)\right]^{\frac{1}{2}} = 4^{\frac{1}{2}}\left(1 - \dfrac{x}{4}\right)^{\frac{1}{2}} = 2\left(1 - \dfrac{x}{4}\right)^{\frac{1}{2}}$

$2\left(1 - \dfrac{x}{4}\right)^{\frac{1}{2}} = 2\left[1 + \left(\frac{1}{2}\right)\left(\dfrac{-x}{4}\right) + \dfrac{\left(\frac{1}{2}\right)\left(-\frac{1}{2}\right)\left(\frac{-x}{4}\right)^2}{1 \times 2}\right.$

$\left. + \dfrac{\left(\frac{1}{2}\right)\left(\frac{-1}{2}\right)\left(\frac{-3}{2}\right)\left(\frac{-x}{4}\right)^3}{1 \times 2 \times 3} + \ldots\right]$

$= 2\left(1 - \dfrac{x}{8} - \dfrac{x^2}{128} - \dfrac{x^3}{1024} \ldots\right)$

$= 1 - \dfrac{x}{4} - \dfrac{x^2}{64} - \dfrac{x^3}{512} \cdots$

3 (a) $\dfrac{1}{2} - \dfrac{5x}{16} + \dfrac{75x^2}{256} - \dfrac{625x^3}{2048} \ldots, |x| < 0.8$

(b) 0.50637 (5 d.p.) (using $x = -0.02$)

(c) $2 - \dfrac{3x}{4} + \dfrac{55x^2}{64}$

76. Radians, arcs and sectors

G 1 (a) $9 = 6\theta$, $\theta = \frac{9}{6} = 1.5$ rad

(b) Area $= \frac{1}{2}r^2\theta = \frac{1}{2} \times 6^2 \times 1.5 = 27\,\text{cm}^2$

G 2 (a) Arc length $= r\theta = 10 \times 0.65 = 6.5\,\text{cm}$

Perimeter $= 6.5 + 10 + 10 = 26.5\,\text{cm}$

(b) Area $= \frac{1}{2}r^2\theta = \frac{1}{2} \times 10^2 \times 0.65 = 32.5\,\text{cm}^2$

3 (a) Arc length $PR = \frac{14\pi}{3}\,\text{cm}$

(b) Area of sector $= \frac{49\pi}{3}\,\text{cm}^2$

4 (a) 1.41 rad

(b) 27.3 cm

77. Areas of triangles

G 1 (a) $\cos Q = \dfrac{PQ^2 + QR^2 - PR^2}{2 \times PQ \times QR}$

$= \dfrac{(5\sqrt{2})^2 + (5\sqrt{2})^2 - (10)^2}{2 \times 5\sqrt{2} \times 5\sqrt{2}} = \dfrac{100 - 100}{100} = 0$

$Q = \dfrac{\pi}{2}$

(b) Area of sector $= \frac{1}{2}r^2\theta = \frac{1}{2} \times (5\sqrt{2})^2 \times \frac{\pi}{2} = \frac{50\pi}{4}$

Area $= \dfrac{25\pi}{2}\,\text{cm}^2$

(c) Area of triangle $= \frac{1}{2}ab\sin\theta$

$= \frac{1}{2} \times 5\sqrt{2} \times 5\sqrt{2} \times \sin\frac{\pi}{2}$

$= 25$

Area $= 25\,\text{cm}^2$

G 2 Area of $ABC = \frac{1}{2} \times 9 \times 12 \times \sin 0.8 = 38.737...\,\text{cm}^2$

Area of $ABD = \frac{1}{2} \times 9^2 \times 0.8 = 32.4\,\text{cm}^2$

Area of $R = 38.737 - 32.4 = 6.34\,\text{cm}^2$

3 Area of $R = 10.8\,\text{cm}^2$

78. Sec, cosec and cot

G 1

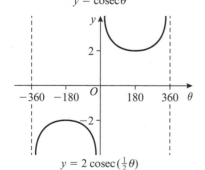

$y = \text{cosec}\,\theta$

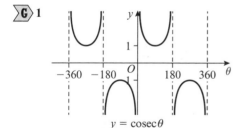

$y = 2\,\text{cosec}\left(\frac{1}{2}\theta\right)$

2

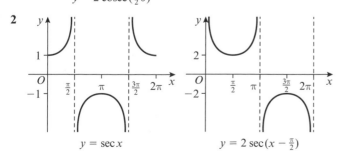

$y = \sec x$ $y = 2\sec\left(x - \frac{\pi}{2}\right)$

3

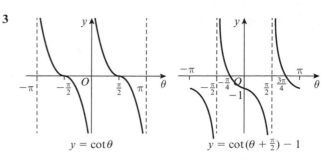

$y = \cot\theta$ $y = \cot\left(\theta + \frac{\pi}{2}\right) - 1$

79. Trigonometric equations 3

G 1 $\text{cosec}\,2x = \dfrac{2}{\sqrt{3}}$, $\dfrac{1}{\sin 2x} = \dfrac{2}{\sqrt{3}}$, $\sin 2x = \dfrac{\sqrt{3}}{2}$

$-180° \leqslant x \leqslant 180°$ so $-360° \leqslant 2x \leqslant 360°$

$2x = -300°, -240°, 60°, 120°$

$x = -150°, -120°, 30°, 60°$

2 $\theta = \dfrac{\pi}{12}$ and $\theta = \dfrac{7\pi}{12}$

3 $x = 78.5°, 281.5°$

4 $\theta = 23.6°, 156.4°, 270.0°$

80. Trigonometric identities 2

G 1 $\text{cosec}\,\theta - \sin\theta \equiv \dfrac{1}{\sin\theta} - \sin\theta \equiv \dfrac{1 - \sin^2\theta}{\sin\theta} \equiv \dfrac{\cos^2\theta}{\sin\theta}$

$\equiv \dfrac{\cos\theta}{\sin\theta} \times \cos\theta \equiv \cot\theta\cos\theta$

2 $\theta = 0, \dfrac{3\pi}{4}, \pi, \dfrac{7\pi}{4}, 2\pi$

3 $\sec^2\theta + \text{cosec}^2\theta \equiv \dfrac{1}{\cos^2\theta} + \dfrac{1}{\sin^2\theta} \equiv \dfrac{\sin^2\theta + \cos^2\theta}{\cos^2\theta\sin^2\theta}$

$\equiv \dfrac{1}{\cos^2\theta\sin^2\theta} \equiv \sec^2\theta\,\text{cosec}^2\theta$

4 $\theta = 22.5°, 38.0°, 112.5°, 128.0°$

5 $\theta = 18.4°, 135.0°, 198.4°, 315.0°$

81. Arcsin, arccos and arctan

1 (a) $\dfrac{\pi}{6}$ (b) $\dfrac{5\pi}{6}$ (c) $\dfrac{-\pi}{4}$

G 2 (a) $f\left(\dfrac{\sqrt{3}}{2}\right) = \arccos\left(\dfrac{\sqrt{3}}{2}\right) + \dfrac{\pi}{4} = \dfrac{\pi}{6} + \dfrac{\pi}{4} = \dfrac{5\pi}{12}$

(b) $x = \frac{1}{2}$

(c) Let $y = \arccos x + \dfrac{\pi}{4}$, $y - \dfrac{\pi}{4} = \arccos x$, $\cos\left(y - \dfrac{\pi}{4}\right) = x$

So $f^{-1}(x) = \cos\left(x - \dfrac{\pi}{4}\right)$

Domain of f^{-1} = range of f, so $\dfrac{\pi}{4} \leqslant x \leqslant \dfrac{5\pi}{4}$

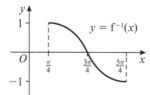

$y = f^{-1}(x)$

3 $g^{-1}(x) = \sin\left(\dfrac{x}{2} - \dfrac{\pi}{4}\right)$

Domain is $-\dfrac{\pi}{2} \leqslant x \leqslant \dfrac{3\pi}{2}$

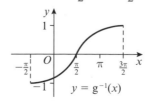

$y = g^{-1}(x)$

Answers

82. Addition formulae

G 1 $\tan 105° = \tan(60° + 45°) = \dfrac{\tan 60° + \tan 45°}{1 - \tan 60° \tan 45°}$

$= \dfrac{\sqrt{3} + 1}{1 - (\sqrt{3})(1)} = \dfrac{(\sqrt{3} + 1)(1 + \sqrt{3})}{(1 - \sqrt{3})(1 + \sqrt{3})}$

$= \dfrac{4 + 2\sqrt{3}}{1 - 3} = -2 - \sqrt{3}$

2   (a) $\theta = 30°, 210°$

    (b) $\theta = 26.6°, 108.4°, 206.6°, 288.4°$

3   (a) $\dfrac{-29}{35}$

    (b) $\dfrac{-4\sqrt{24}}{35}$ or $\dfrac{-8\sqrt{6}}{35}$

83. Double angle formulae

G 1

$1 = 2\sin\theta + 4(1 - 2\sin^2\theta)$

$8\sin^2\theta - 2\sin\theta - 3 = 0$

$(4\sin\theta - 3)(2\sin\theta + 1) = 0$

$\sin\theta = \tfrac{3}{4}$ or $\sin\theta = -\tfrac{1}{2}$

$\theta = 48.6°, 131.4°, \theta = -30°, -150°$

2   (a) $\dfrac{-4\sqrt{5}}{9}$ (b) $\tfrac{1}{9}$ (c) $-4\sqrt{5}$

3   $\dfrac{\sin 3A}{\sin A} + \dfrac{\cos 3A}{\cos A} = \dfrac{\sin 3A \cos A + \cos 3A \sin A}{\sin A \cos A}$

$= \dfrac{\sin 4A}{\tfrac{1}{2}\sin 2A} = \dfrac{2\sin 2A \cos 2A}{\tfrac{1}{2}\sin 2A} = 4\cos 2A$

4   $x = 129.6°, 230.4°$ (1 d.p.)

84. $a\cos\theta \pm b\sin\theta$

G 1   (a) $4\cos\theta + 2\sin\theta \equiv R(\cos\theta \cos\alpha + \sin\theta \sin\alpha)$

       $R\cos\alpha = 4, R\sin\alpha = 2, \tan\alpha = \tfrac{1}{2}, \alpha = 26.6°$

       $R = \sqrt{4^2 + 2^2} = \sqrt{20}$

       So $4\cos\theta + 2\sin\theta \equiv \sqrt{20}\cos(\theta - 26.6°)$

    (b) $\theta = 103.6°, 309.5°$

    (c)   Maximum $= \sqrt{20}$, minimum $= -\sqrt{20}$

2   (a) $\sqrt{89}\sin(x - 1.01219...)$

    (b) $x = 1.70, 3.46$ (2 d.p.)

85. Trig modelling

G 1   (a) $6\cos\theta + 8\sin\theta \equiv R(\cos\theta \cos\alpha + \sin\theta \sin\alpha)$

       $R\cos\alpha = 6, R\sin\alpha = 8, \tan\alpha = \tfrac{8}{6}, \alpha = 0.92729...$

       $R = \sqrt{6^2 + 8^2} = \sqrt{100} = 10$

       So $6\cos\theta + 8\sin\theta \equiv 10\cos(\theta - 0.92729...)$

    (b)   (i)   Maximum value $= 10$ (ii) $\theta = 0.92729...$

    (c)   Maximum temp. of 24°C at $t = 3.7$ hours

       Minimum temp. of 4°C at $t = 16.3$ hours

    (d)   Temp. of 12°C when $t = 10.797...$, i.e. at 10.48 hours

       i.e. 10.48 pm

       and when $t = 21.753...$ i.e. at 21.45 hours, i.e. 9.45 am

       (the next day)

    (e)

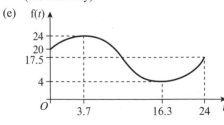

86. Parametric equations 1

G 1 $t = 1 - x$, so $t^2 = (1 - x)^2 = 1 - 2x + x^2$

      $y = t^2 - 4 = 1 - 2x + x^2 - 4$ so $y = x^2 - 2x - 3$

2   (a) $xy^2 = 9$

    (b) $y = x^2 + 2x + 2$

    (c) $25x^2 - y^2 = 25$

    (d) $4x^2 + y^2 - 8x - 2y + 1 = 0$

3   $(-\tfrac{4}{3}, -3)$ and $(1, \tfrac{1}{2})$

4   $2x^2 - 2xy + 5y^2 = 9$

87. Differentiating $\sin x$ and $\cos x$

G 1   Let $f(x) = \sin 2x$

$f'(x) = \lim\limits_{h \to 0} \dfrac{f(x + h) - f(x)}{h} = \lim\limits_{h \to 0} \dfrac{\sin 2(x + h) - \sin 2x}{h}$

$= \lim\limits_{h \to 0} \dfrac{\sin(2x + 2h) - \sin 2x}{h}$

$= \lim\limits_{h \to 0} \dfrac{\sin 2x \cos 2h + \cos 2x \sin 2h - \sin 2x}{h}$

$= \lim\limits_{h \to 0} \left[2\sin 2x \dfrac{(\cos 2h - 1)}{2h} + 2\cos 2x \dfrac{\sin 2h}{2h} \right]$

$= \lim\limits_{h \to 0} 2\sin 2x \dfrac{(\cos 2h - 1)}{2h} + \lim\limits_{h \to 0} 2\cos 2x \dfrac{\sin 2h}{2h}$

Since $\lim\limits_{h \to 0} \dfrac{\cos 2h - 1}{2h} = 0$ and $= \lim\limits_{h \to 0} \dfrac{\sin 2h}{2h} = 1$

$f'(x) = 2\cos 2x$

2   (a) $\tfrac{3}{2}$ (b)   2   (c)   2

    (d) $\tfrac{4}{9}$ (e) $\tfrac{2}{3}$ (f) $\tfrac{1}{3}$

88. The chain rule

G 1   (a) $u = 5 - 3x$ $y = u^7$

       $\dfrac{du}{dx} = -3$ $\dfrac{dy}{du} = 7u^6$

       $\dfrac{dy}{dx} = \dfrac{dy}{du} \times \dfrac{du}{dx} = 7u^6 \times -3 = -21(5 - 3x)^6$

    (b) $\dfrac{dy}{dx} = -4 \times (4 - x^2)^{-5} \times (-2x) = 8x(4 - x^2)^{-5}$

    (c) $9(1 + 6x)^{\frac{1}{2}}$ (d) $2(4x + 5)^{-\frac{1}{2}}$

    (e) $2x(3 - 2x^2)^{-\frac{3}{2}}$ (f) $-4x(3x^2 + 4)^{-\frac{4}{3}}$

2   (a) $\dfrac{1}{3y^2 + 6y - 4}$ (b) $-\tfrac{1}{4}$

3   $f'(x) = \dfrac{6(4\sqrt{x} + 3)^2}{\sqrt{x}}$

89. Differentiating standard functions

G 1   (a) $u = \sin x$ $y = u^3$

       $\dfrac{du}{dx} = \cos x$ $\dfrac{dy}{du} = 3u^2$

       $\dfrac{dy}{dx} = \dfrac{dy}{du} \times \dfrac{du}{dx} = 3u^2 \times \cos x = 3\sin^2 x \cos x$

    (b) $4\sin(5 - 4x)$

    (c) $2x\,e^{x^2+1}$

    (d) $\dfrac{3x^2}{x^3 + 2}$

2   (a) $-4\cos^3 x \sin x$ (b) $2\cos 2x - 3\sin 3x$

    (c) $6x^2 + 3\,e^{5 - 3x}$ (d) $-2\tan 2x$

3   (a) $y = \csc x = (\sin x)^{-1}$

       $\dfrac{dy}{dx} = -1(\sin x)^{-2}(\cos x) = \dfrac{-\cos x}{\sin^2 x} = \dfrac{-\cos x}{\sin x} \times \dfrac{1}{\sin x}$

                $= -\cot x \csc x$

    (b) $-\cot x$

90. The product rule

1 (a) $u = x^2 + 3$ $\qquad v = 2x^3 - 1$

$\dfrac{du}{dx} = 2x$ $\qquad \dfrac{dv}{dx} = 6x^2$

$\dfrac{dy}{dx} = u\dfrac{dv}{dx} + v\dfrac{du}{dx} = (x^2 + 3)(6x^2) + (2x^3 - 1)(2x)$

$\qquad = 6x^4 + 18x^2 + 4x^4 - 2x$

$\qquad = 10x^4 + 18x^2 - 2x$

(b) $u = x^4$ $\qquad v = \sin x$

$\dfrac{du}{dx} = 4x^3$ $\qquad \dfrac{dv}{dx} = \cos x$

$\dfrac{dy}{dx} = x^4(\cos x) + \sin x (4x^3)$

(c) $4x\,e^{2x}(x + 1)$

(d) $x^2 - 4 + (3x^2 - 4)\ln 2x$

2 (a) $h'(x) = e^{4x}\sec x\,(4 + \tan x)$

(b) $x = -1.33$ (3 s.f.)

3 $y = x^2(1 + x^2)^{\frac{1}{2}}$

$\dfrac{dy}{dx} = x^2\left[\frac{1}{2}(1 + x^2)^{-\frac{1}{2}}(2x)\right] + (1 + x^2)^{\frac{1}{2}}(2x)$

$\qquad = \dfrac{x^3}{(1 + x^2)^{\frac{1}{2}}} + 2x(1 + x^2)^{\frac{1}{2}}$

$\qquad = \dfrac{x^3 + 2x(1 + x^2)}{(1 + x^2)^{\frac{1}{2}}}$

$\qquad = \dfrac{3x^3 + 2x}{\sqrt{1 + x^2}}$

4 $(-1, 2e^{-2})$ and $(2, -e^4)$

91. The quotient rule

1 (a) $u = x^2$ $\qquad v = 2x + 1$

$\dfrac{du}{dx} = 2x$ $\qquad \dfrac{dv}{dx} = 2$

$\dfrac{dy}{dx} = \dfrac{v\dfrac{du}{dx} - u\dfrac{dv}{dx}}{v^2} = \dfrac{(2x + 1)(2x) - (x^2)(2)}{(2x + 1)^2} = \dfrac{2x^2 + 2x}{(2x + 1)^2}$

(b) $u = x^3$ $\qquad v = (1 - 2x^2)^{\frac{1}{2}}$

$\dfrac{du}{dx} = 3x^2$ $\qquad \dfrac{dv}{dx} = \frac{1}{2}(1 - 2x^2)^{-\frac{1}{2}}(-4x)$

$\qquad\qquad\qquad\qquad = (-2x)(1 - 2x^2)^{-\frac{1}{2}}$

$\dfrac{dy}{dx} = \dfrac{(1 - 2x^2)^{\frac{1}{2}}(3x^2) - (x^3)(-2x)(1 - 2x^2)^{-\frac{1}{2}}}{1 - 2x^2}$

$\qquad = \dfrac{(1 - 2x^2)(3x^2) - (x^3)(-2x)}{(1 - 2x^2)^{\frac{3}{2}}} = \dfrac{3x^2 - 4x^4}{(1 - 2x^2)^{\frac{3}{2}}}$

2 (a) $\dfrac{x^2 + 1}{(1 - x^2)^2}$

(b) $\dfrac{4}{(3x^2 + 1)^{\frac{3}{2}}}$

3 (a) $\dfrac{1 - \ln 2x}{3x^2}$

(b) $\dfrac{-3}{1 + \sin 3x}$

(c) $\dfrac{8\cos x - \sin x}{e^{2x}}$

92. Differentiation and graphs

1 (a) $\dfrac{dy}{dx} = (3x^2)\left(\dfrac{1}{x}\right) + (\ln x)(6x) = 3x + 6x\ln x$

(b) When $x = e$, $y = 3e^2\ln e = 3e^2$

When $x = e$, $\dfrac{dy}{dx} = 3e + 6e\ln e = 3e + 6e = 9e$

Equation of tangent is $y - 3e^2 = 9e(x - e)$,

i.e. $y = 9ex - 6e^2$

(c) $\left(\dfrac{2e}{3}, 0\right)$

2 (a) $y = e^{2x}\cos 3x$

$\dfrac{dy}{dx} = e^{2x}(-3\sin 3x) + \cos 3x\,(2e^{2x})$

$\qquad = e^{2x}(2\cos 3x - 3\sin 3x)$

Turnings points occur when $\dfrac{dy}{dx} = 0$,

i.e. $2\cos 3x = 3\sin 3x$, i.e. $\tan 3x = \frac{2}{3}$ (since $e^{2x} \neq 0$)

(b) $x + 2y = 2$

3 (a) Maximum at $(2, 1)$, minimum at $(-2, -1)$

(b) $12x - 25y + 8 = 0$

93. Parametric differentiation

1 (a) $\dfrac{dx}{dt} = -4\sin t$, $\dfrac{dy}{dt} = 3\cos t$, $\dfrac{dy}{dx} = \dfrac{dy}{dt} \div \dfrac{dx}{dt}$

$\qquad = \dfrac{3\cos t}{-4\sin t} = \dfrac{-3}{4\tan t}$ or $-\frac{3}{4}\cot t$

(b) $\sqrt{3}x + 4y = 8\sqrt{3}$ or $3x + 4\sqrt{3}y = 24$

2 (a) $-\frac{1}{2}e^{4t}$

(b) -8

(c) $(-2, 3)$

(d) $(-26, 0)$

(e) $xy + 3y + 5x = -7$

94. Implicit differentiation

1 Differentiating implicitly, $2x + 4\dfrac{dy}{dx} - 2y\dfrac{dy}{dx} = 0$

$2x = (2y - 4)\dfrac{dy}{dx}$, $\quad \dfrac{dy}{dx} = \dfrac{2x}{2y - 4} = \dfrac{x}{y - 2}$

When $x = -2$ and $y = 3$, $\dfrac{dy}{dx} = -2$

So gradient of normal $= \frac{1}{2}$

Equation of normal is $y - 3 = \frac{1}{2}(x - -2)$, i.e. $x - 2y + 8 = 0$

2 $(2, -4)$ and $(-2, 4)$

3 (a) $\dfrac{2y\,e^{2x}}{2\sin 2y - e^{2x}}$

(b) $-\pi$

(c) $\ln 2 + \frac{1}{4}$

95. Differentiating a^x

1 Let $u = 2x$, $\dfrac{du}{dx} = 2$, $y = 4^u$, $\dfrac{dy}{du} = 4^u\ln 4$

$\dfrac{dy}{dx} = \dfrac{dy}{du} \times \dfrac{du}{dx} = 4^u\ln 4 \times 2 = 2 \times 4^{2x} \times \ln 4$

(simplifies to $2^{4x+1}\ln 4$ or $4^{2x+1}\ln 2$)

2 (a) $3^{\tan x}\ln 3\,\sec^2 x$

(b) $6^{2x}x^2(3 + 2x\ln 6)$

(c) $\dfrac{5^{x^2}}{x} + 2x\,5^{x^2}\ln 5\ln 2x$

3 $y = \left(\frac{9}{4}\ln 3\right)x + 2$

4 (a) $(2, -4)$ and $\left(2, \frac{4}{3}\right)$

(b) At $(2, -4)$, $\dfrac{dy}{dx} = -\ln 4 - 1$

At $\left(2, \frac{4}{3}\right)$, $\dfrac{dy}{dx} = \ln 4 - \frac{1}{3}$

96. Points of inflexion

1 (a) $y = x^3 - 6x^2 + 9x - 1$

$\dfrac{dy}{dx} = 3x^2 - 12x + 9$, $\dfrac{d^2y}{dx^2} = 6x - 12$

Answers

(b) Stationary points occur when $\dfrac{dy}{dx} = 0$, $3x^2 - 12x + 9 = 0$,

$x^2 - 4x + 3 = 0$

$(x - 1)(x - 3) = 0$, $x = 1$ and $x = 3$

When $x = 1$, $y = 1 - 6 + 9 - 1 = 3$

When $x = 3$, $y = 27 - 54 + 27 - 1 = -1$

When $x = 1$, $\dfrac{d^2y}{dx^2} = 6 - 12 = -6$, so there is a maximum

point at $(1, 3)$

When $x = 3$, $\dfrac{d^2y}{dx^2} = 18 - 12 = 6$, so there is a minimum

point at $(3, -1)$

(c) A point of inflexion occurs when $\dfrac{d^2y}{dx^2} = 0$ and $\dfrac{d^2y}{dx^2}$

changes sign either side of this point.

$\dfrac{d^2y}{dx^2} = 0$, $6x - 12 = 0$, $x = 2$ and $y = 8 - 24 + 18 - 1 = 1$

When $x < 2$, $\dfrac{d^2y}{dx^2} < 0$, when $x > 2$, $\dfrac{d^2y}{dx^2} > 0$, so point of

inflexion at $(2, 1)$

2 (a) Maximum point at $\left(\frac{1}{3}, 3e^{\frac{1}{3}}\right)$

(b) Point of inflexion at $\left(-\frac{2}{3}, 6e^{-\frac{2}{3}}\right)$

(c) Concave in $[1, 2]$ since $\dfrac{d^2y}{dx^2} < 0$ in this interval.

97. Rates of change

1 $\dfrac{dV}{dt} = 8$, $V = \frac{2}{9}\pi x^3$, so $\dfrac{dV}{dx} = \frac{2}{3}\pi x^2$

Rate required $= \dfrac{dx}{dt} = \dfrac{dx}{dV} \times \dfrac{dV}{dt} = \dfrac{dV}{dt} \div \dfrac{dV}{dx}$

$= 8 \div \frac{2}{3}\pi x^2 = \dfrac{12}{\pi x^2}$

When $x = 6$, $\dfrac{dx}{dt} = \dfrac{1}{3\pi}$ cm s^{-1}

2 0.0249 cm s^{-1}

3 (a) Volume of water = cross-sectional area × length

$= \frac{1}{2}xh \times 4 = 2xh$

Using similar triangles, $\dfrac{1.5}{1} = \dfrac{x}{h}$, i.e. $x = 1.5h$

so volume of water, $V = 2 \times 1.5h \times h = 3h^2$

(b) 0.01 m s^{-1}

98. Iteration

1 (a) $f(2) = e^{-2} - 3 + 2\sqrt{2} = -0.0362\ldots$

$f(3) = e^{-3} - 3 + 2\sqrt{3} = 0.5138\ldots$

Hence there is a root between 2 and 3 because there is a change of sign.

(b) $e^{-x} - 3 + 2\sqrt{x} = 0$

$2\sqrt{x} = 3 - e^{-x}$

$\sqrt{x} = \frac{1}{2}(3 - e^{-x})$

$x = \frac{1}{4}(3 - e^{-x})^2$

(c) $x_1 = \frac{1}{4}(3 - e^{-2.1})^2 = 2.0701$, $x_2 = 2.0647$, $x_3 = 2.0637$

(all to 4 d.p.)

(d) $f(2.0635) = -0.000\,013\,790$, $f(2.0645) = 0.000\,555\,323$

Change of sign, so $2.0635 < \alpha < 2.0645$

i.e. $\alpha = 2.064$ (3 d.p.)

2 (a) $f(1) = -2$ and $f(2) = 10$

Change of sign, so root between 1 and 2

(b) $x^3 + 3x^2 - 4x - 2 = 0$

$x^2(x + 3) = 4x + 2$

$x^2 = \dfrac{4x + 2}{x + 3}$

$x = \sqrt{\dfrac{4x + 2}{x + 3}}$

(c) $x_1 = 1.3333$, $x_2 = 1.3009$, $x_3 = 1.2942$ (all to 4 d.p.)

(d) $f(1.292\,35) = -0.000\,452\,142$, $f(1.292\,45) = 0.000\,424\,387$

Change of sign, so $1.292\,35 < \alpha < 1.292\,45$

i.e. $\alpha = 1.2924$ (4 d.p.)

99. The Newton–Raphson method

1 (a) $(x) = x^3 - 3x^2 + 1$

$f(2) = 8 - 12 + 1 = -3$, $f(3) = 27 - 27 + 1 = 1$

so the graph crosses the x-axis between $x = 2$ and $x = 3$

(b) $f'(x) = 3x^2 - 6x$

(c) $f'(x) = 3x^2 - 6x = 3x(x - 2)$ so there are stationary points at $x = 0$ and $x = 2$ and the tangent at $x = 2$ would be horizontal and never intersect the x-axis.

(d) $x_{n+1} = x_n - \dfrac{f(x_n)}{f'(x_n)} = x_n - \dfrac{x_n^3 - 3x_n^2 + 1}{3x_n^2 - 6x_n}$

$x_1 = 3 - \dfrac{27 - 27 + 1}{27 - 18} = 2.8888\ldots = 2.889$ (3 d.p.)

$x_2 = 2.8888\ldots - \dfrac{(2.8888\ldots)^3 - 3(2.8888\ldots)^2 + 1}{3(2.8888\ldots)^2 - 6(2.8888\ldots)}$

$= 2.87945\ldots = 2.879$ (3 d.p.)

(e) $f(2.8785) = -0.006\,7201\ldots$, $f(2.8795) = 0.000\,871\,80\ldots$ so the change of sign means that 2.879 is correct to 3 d.p.

2 (a) $f(1) = -1.6209\ldots$, $f(2) = 1.9415\ldots$, so there is a root in the interval $[1, 2]$

(b) $f'(x) = \dfrac{1}{x} + 3 \sin x$ (c) $x = 1.447$ (3 d.p.)

(d) $f(1.4465) = -0.002\,78\ldots$, $f(1.4475) = 0.000\,885\ldots$, change of sign, so $x = 1.447$ is correct to 3 d.p.

100. Integrating standard functions

1 (a) $\int 6 \cos 2x \, dx = 3 \sin 2x + c$

(b) $2 \tan \dfrac{x}{2} + c$

(c) $-\frac{1}{6} \cos 3x + c$

(d) $-\frac{1}{2} \operatorname{cosec} 2\theta + c$

2 (a) $3 \cos 4x + c$ (b) $8 \sin \dfrac{\theta}{2} + c$

(c) $-\frac{1}{2} \cos 10x + c$ (d) $\frac{1}{6} \sin (3x + 5) + c$

3 (a) $\frac{2}{3}e^{3x} + c$ (b) $\frac{12}{5} e^{\frac{\theta}{4}} + c$

(c) $\frac{5}{2} \ln (2x - 1) + c$ (d) $\frac{1}{4} \ln (1 + 8x) + c$

4 (a) $\frac{2}{3}(x + 6)^{\frac{3}{2}} + c$ (b) $\frac{1}{6}(2x - 3)^{\frac{3}{2}} + c$

(c) $-\frac{2}{15}(4 - 3x)^{\frac{5}{2}} + c$ (d) $\frac{3}{16}(1 + 4x)^{\frac{4}{3}} + c$

5 $\int_2^6 \dfrac{1}{\sqrt{5x + 2}} dx = \int_2^6 (5x + 2)^{-\frac{1}{2}} dx = \frac{2}{5}\left[(5x + 2)^{\frac{1}{2}}\right]_2^6$

$= \frac{2}{5}(\sqrt{32} - \sqrt{12}) = \frac{2}{5}(4\sqrt{2} - 2\sqrt{3})$

$= \frac{4}{5}(2\sqrt{2} - \sqrt{3})$

6 $\frac{9}{14}$

101. Reverse chain rule

1. (a) $\int \dfrac{3x - 4}{3x^2 - 8x} dx = \frac{1}{2} \ln (3x^2 - 8x) + c$

(b) $\int 6x^2 (7 - 4x^3)^6 \, dx = -\frac{1}{14}(7 - 4x^3)^7 + c$

2 (a) $\frac{1}{72}(6x^2 - 2)^6 + c$

(b) $-\frac{3}{2} \ln (\cos 2\theta) + c$

3 (a) $-\frac{3}{4}\cos^4 x + c$

   (b) $\frac{1}{6}\sin(x^2) + c$

4 (a) $\frac{1}{2}\tan^4\theta + c$

   (b) $-\frac{3}{5}\operatorname{cosec}^5 x + c$

5 (a) $\frac{4}{9}(3x^2 - 2)^{\frac{3}{2}} + c$

   (b) $\frac{2}{3}(2x^3 - 6x^2 + 5)^{\frac{1}{2}} + c$

6 $\ln 3$

7 $\ln(1.5)$

8 0.576 (3 d.p.)

102. Identities in integration

G 1 $\cos 2A = 2\cos^2 A - 1$

   When $A = \frac{x}{2}$, $\cos x = 2\cos^2\left(\frac{x}{2}\right) - 1$

   So $\cos^2\left(\frac{x}{2}\right) = \frac{1}{2}(\cos x + 1)$

   $\int_{\frac{\pi}{6}}^{\frac{\pi}{2}} \cos^2\left(\frac{x}{2}\right)dx = \int_{\frac{\pi}{6}}^{\frac{\pi}{2}} \frac{1}{2}(\cos x + 1)\,dx = \frac{1}{2}\left[\sin x + x\right]_{\frac{\pi}{6}}^{\frac{\pi}{2}}$

                $= \frac{1}{2}\left[\left(1 + \frac{\pi}{2}\right) - \left(\frac{1}{2} + \frac{\pi}{6}\right)\right] = \frac{1}{4} + \frac{\pi}{6}$

2 $\frac{1}{8}$

3 (a) $\cos 5x = \cos(3x + 2x) = \cos 3x\cos 2x - \sin 3x\sin 2x$

    $\cos x = \cos(3x - 2x) = \cos 3x\cos 2x + \sin 3x\sin 2x$

    So $\cos 5x + \cos x = 2\cos 3x\cos 2x$

   (b) $\frac{3}{10}$

4 $\frac{\pi}{8} - \frac{1}{4}$

5 $\frac{1}{\sqrt{3}} - \frac{\pi}{6}$ $\left(\text{can also be written as } \frac{\sqrt{3}}{3} - \frac{\pi}{6} \text{ or } \frac{2\sqrt{3} - \pi}{6}\right)$

103. Integration by substitution

G 1 $u = \sin 2x, \dfrac{du}{dx} = 2\cos 2x$ so $\dfrac{du}{2} = \cos 2x\,dx$

   When $x = \frac{\pi}{12}$, $u = \sin\frac{\pi}{6} = 0.5$

   When $x = \frac{\pi}{4}$, $u = \sin\frac{\pi}{2} = 1$

   $\int_{\frac{\pi}{12}}^{\frac{\pi}{4}} \sin^3 2x\cos 2x\,dx = \int_{0.5}^{1} \frac{1}{2}u^3\,du = \left[\frac{1}{8}u^4\right]_{0.5}^{1} = \frac{1}{8} - \frac{1}{128} = \frac{15}{128}$

2 $\dfrac{2\sqrt{3}}{27}$

3 $\dfrac{e - 1}{2(1 + e)}$

4 π

104. Integration by parts

G 1 $u = x, \dfrac{du}{dx} = 1, \dfrac{dv}{dx} = e^{-x}, v = -e^{-x}$

   $\int x\,e^{-x}\,dx = x\,(-e^{-x}) - \int(-e^{-x})(1)\,dx$

            $= -x\,e^{-x} + \int(e^{-x})\,dx = -x\,e^{-x} - e^{-x} + c$

            $= -e^{-x}(x + 1) + c$

2 $u = \ln x, \dfrac{du}{dx} = \dfrac{1}{x}, \dfrac{dv}{dx} = x^3, v = \dfrac{x^4}{4}$

   $\int x^3\ln x\,dx = \dfrac{x^4}{4}\ln x - \int\dfrac{x^4}{4}\dfrac{1}{x}\,dx$

            $= \dfrac{x^4}{4}\ln x - \int\dfrac{x^3}{4}\,dx$

            $= \dfrac{x^4}{4}\ln x - \dfrac{x^4}{16} + c$

            $= \dfrac{x^4}{16}(4\ln x - 1) + c$

3 (a) $-2x\cos x + 2\sin x + c$

   (b) $(x^2 - 2)\sin x + 2x\cos x + c$

4 $\frac{1}{4}e^2(5e^2 - 1)$

105. Integrating partial fractions

G 1 (a) $\dfrac{5 - 8x}{(2 + x)(1 - 3x)} = \dfrac{A}{2 + x} + \dfrac{B}{1 - 3x}$

     so $5 - 8x = A(1 - 3x) + B(2 + x)$

    When $x = -2$, $21 = 7A$, so $A = 3$

    When $x = \frac{1}{3}$, $\frac{7}{3} = \frac{7}{3}B$, so $B = 1$

    So $\dfrac{5 - 8x}{(2 + x)(1 - 3x)} \equiv \dfrac{3}{2 + x} + \dfrac{1}{1 - 3x}$

   (b) $\int_{-1}^{0} \dfrac{5 - 8x}{(2 + x)(1 - 3x)}\,dx = \int_{-1}^{0}\left(\dfrac{3}{2 + x} + \dfrac{1}{1 - 3x}\right)dx$

              $= \left[3\ln(2 + x) - \frac{1}{3}\ln(1 - 3x)\right]_{-1}^{0}$

              $= (3\ln 2 - 0) - (0 - \frac{1}{3}\ln 4)$

              $= 3\ln 2 + \frac{2}{3}\ln 2 = \frac{11}{3}\ln 2$

2. (a) $-\dfrac{1}{2x + 3} + \dfrac{2}{2x - 3}$

   (b) $\dfrac{12x^3 - 31x - 18}{4x^2 - 9} = \dfrac{3x(4x^2 - 9) - 4x - 18}{4x^2 - 9}$

               $= 3x - \dfrac{4x + 18}{4x^2 - 9}$

               $= 3x - \dfrac{2(2x + 9)}{4x^2 - 9}$

   (c) $\frac{3}{2} + \ln 15$

106. Area between two curves

G 1 $0 = 2x^2 - 8 = 2(x^2 - 4) = 2(x + 2)(x - 2)$

   so $x = -2$ and $x = 2$

   Area $= \int_{-2}^{2}\left((4 + 2x - x^2) - (x^2 + 2x - 4)\right)dx$

       $= \int_{-2}^{2}(8 - 2x^2)\,dx = \left[8x - \frac{2}{3}x^3\right]_{-2}^{2}$

       $= (16 - \frac{16}{3}) - (-16 - \frac{16}{3}) = 21\frac{1}{3}$

2 (a) $P = (-2, -6)$, $Q = (1, 0)$, $R = (3, 14)$

   (b) $15\frac{3}{4} + 5\frac{1}{3} = 21\frac{1}{12}$

3 (a) $P = \left(\dfrac{\pi}{6}, \dfrac{3}{2}\right)$, $Q = \left(\dfrac{7\pi}{6}, -\dfrac{3}{2}\right)$

   (b) $4\sqrt{3}$

107. Areas and parametric curves

G 1 $x = 2t - \sin t, \dfrac{dx}{dt} = 2 - \cos t, y = 1 - \cos t$

   When $y = 0$, $\cos t = 1$, so $t = 0$ or 2π

   Area $= \int_{x=0}^{x=4\pi} y\,dx = \int_{t=0}^{t=2\pi} y\dfrac{dx}{dt}\,dt = \int_{0}^{2\pi}(1 - \cos t)(2 - \cos t)\,dt$

       $= \int_{0}^{2\pi}(2 - 3\cos t + \cos^2 t)\,dt$

       $= \int_{0}^{2\pi}(2 - 3\cos t + \frac{1}{2} + \frac{1}{2}\cos 2t)\,dt$

       $= \int_{0}^{2\pi}(-3\cos t + \frac{5}{2} + \frac{1}{2}\cos 2t)\,dt$

       $= \left[-3\sin t + \frac{5t}{2} + \frac{1}{4}\sin 2t\right]_{0}^{2\pi}$

       $= (0 + 5\pi + 0) - (0) = 5\pi$

2 $\frac{16}{3}$

3 $3e - 6$

108. The trapezium rule

G 1 (a)

x	0	0.8	1.6	2.4	3.2	4
y	0	0.303 03	0.350 88	0.309 28	0.261 44	0.222 22

   (b) $\int_{0}^{4} \dfrac{x}{x^2 + 2}\,dx \approx \dfrac{0.8}{2}[0 + 0.222\,22 + 2(0.303\,03 + 0.350\,88$

              $+ 0.309\,28 + 0.261\,44)] = 1.0686$ (4 d.p.)

   (c) $\ln 3$

   (d) 2.73% (3 s.f.)

Answers

2 (a)

x	1	1.5	2	2.5	3
y	0	0.810 93	2.079 44	3.665 16	5.493 06

(b) 4.6510 (4 d.p.)

(c) Let $A = \int_1^3 (2x - 1)\ln x\,dx = \int_1^3 2x \ln x\,dx - \int_1^3 1 \ln x\,dx$

$\int_1^3 2x \ln x\,dx = [x^2 \ln x]_1^3 - \int_1^3 x^2 \frac{1}{x}\,dx = \left[x^2 \ln x - \frac{x^2}{2}\right]_1^3$

$\int_1^3 1 \ln x\,dx = [x \ln x]_1^3 - \int_1^3 x \frac{1}{x}\,dx = [x \ln x - x]_1^3$

So $A = \left[x^2 \ln x - \frac{x^2}{2} - x \ln x + x\right]_1^3$

$= (9 \ln 3 - 4.5 - 3 \ln 3 + 3) - (0 - 0.5 - 0 + 1)$

$= 6 \ln 3 - 2$

109. Solving differential equations

1 (a) $\dfrac{10}{(x - 3)(3x + 1)} = \dfrac{A}{x - 3} + \dfrac{B}{3x + 1}$

i.e. $10 = A(3x + 1) + B(x - 3)$

When $x = 3$, $10 = 10A$, so $A = 1$

When $x = -\frac{1}{3}$, $10 = -\frac{10}{3}B$, so $B = -3$

Hence $\dfrac{10}{(x - 3)(3x + 1)} = \dfrac{1}{x - 3} - \dfrac{3}{3x + 1}$

(b) $\int \dfrac{10}{(x - 3)(3x + 1)}\,dx = \int \left(\dfrac{1}{x - 3} - \dfrac{3}{3x + 1}\right) dx$

$= \ln(x - 3) - \ln(3x + 1) + c = \ln\left(\dfrac{x - 3}{3x + 1}\right) + c$

(c) $y = \dfrac{32(x - 3)}{3x + 1}$ (obtained using $\ln k$ as a constant of integration)

2 $h = 4.10\,\text{m}$

110. You are the examiner!

1 $f(x) = \dfrac{x^2 + 2}{2x^2 - x - 1} = A + \dfrac{B}{x - 1} + \dfrac{C}{2x + 1}$

Multiplying through by $(2x + 1)(x - 1)$ gives

$x^2 + 2 = A(2x + 1)(x - 1) + B(2x + 1) + C(x - 1)$

Put $x = 1$: $3 = 3B$, so $B = 1$

Put $x = -\frac{1}{2}$: $\frac{9}{4} = -\frac{3}{2}C$, so $C = -\frac{3}{2}$

Put $x = 0$: $2 = -A + B - C$, so $A = B - C - 2 = 1 + \frac{3}{2} - 2 = \frac{1}{2}$

So $f(x) = \dfrac{x^2 + 2}{2x^2 - x - 1} = \dfrac{1}{2} + \dfrac{1}{x - 1} - \dfrac{3}{2(2x + 1)}$

2 Volume of cone $V = \frac{1}{3}\pi r^2 h$, so when $h = 4$, $V = \frac{4}{3}\pi r^2$

and $\dfrac{dV}{dr} = \dfrac{8}{3}\pi r$

$\dfrac{dr}{dt} = 0.5$, and since $\dfrac{dV}{dt} = \dfrac{dV}{dr} \times \dfrac{dr}{dt}$, $\dfrac{dV}{dt} = \dfrac{8}{3}\pi r \times 0.5 = \dfrac{4}{3}\pi r$

So when $r = 3$, $\dfrac{dV}{dt} = 4\pi\,\text{cm}^3\,\text{s}^{-1}$

3 (a) $y = \cos^3 x \sin 3x$

$\dfrac{dy}{dx} = \cos^3 x(3\cos 3x) + \sin 3x(3\cos^2 x(-\sin x))$

$= 3\cos^2 x(\cos x \cos 3x - \sin x \sin 3x)$

$= 3\cos^2 x \cos(x + 3x) = 3\cos^2 x \cos 4x$

(b) $\dfrac{d}{dx}(\tan 2x) = \dfrac{\cos 2x(2\cos 2x) - \sin 2x(-2\sin 2x)}{\cos^2 2x}$

$= \dfrac{2(\cos^2 2x + \sin^2 2x)}{\cos^2 2x} = \dfrac{2}{\cos^2 2x} = 2\sec^2 2x$

4 (a) $6\left(1 - \dfrac{\theta^2}{2}\right)^2 - \left(1 - \dfrac{\theta^2}{2}\right) - 2 = 6\left(1 - \theta^2 + \dfrac{\theta^4}{4}\right) - 1 + \dfrac{\theta^2}{2} - 2$

$= 3 - \dfrac{11}{2}\theta^2$

(b) $4° = 4 \times \dfrac{\pi}{180}$ radians, which must be used.

$3 - \dfrac{11}{2}\theta^2 = 3 - \dfrac{11}{2}\left(\dfrac{\pi}{45}\right)^2 = 2.97319... = 2.973$ (3 d.p.)

111. You are the examiner!

5 (a) $\int x \cos x\,dx = x \sin x - \int (\sin x . 1)\,dx = x \sin x + \cos x + c$

(b) $\int_0^{\frac{\pi}{2}} x^2 \sin x\,dx = [x^2(-\cos x)]_0^{\frac{\pi}{2}} - \int_0^{\frac{\pi}{2}} (-\cos x)\,2x\,dx$

$= [-(x^2 \cos x)]_0^{\frac{\pi}{2}} + 2\int_0^{\frac{\pi}{2}} x \cos x\,dx$

$= [-(x^2 \cos x)]_0^{\frac{\pi}{2}} + 2\left[x \sin x + \cos x\right]_0^{\frac{\pi}{2}}$

(from (a))

$= [-x^2 \cos x + 2x \sin x + 2\cos x]_0^{\frac{\pi}{2}}$

$= (0 + \pi + 0) - (0 + 0 + 2) = \pi - 2$

6 (a) $h(7) = 48\sin\frac{7}{5} - 12\cos\frac{7}{5} + 12 - 49 = 8.261...$

$h(8) = 48\sin\frac{8}{5} - 12\cos\frac{8}{5} + 12 - 64 = -3.670...$

Change of sign, so result shown.

(b) $h'(t) = (48)\left(\frac{1}{5}\cos\frac{t}{5}\right) - (12)\frac{1}{5}\left(-\sin\frac{t}{5}\right) - 2t$

(c) $t_0 = 8$, so $t_1 = 8 - \dfrac{h(8)}{h'(8)} = 7.73561 = 7.736$ s (3 d.p.)

7 (a) $\dfrac{dy}{dx} = 12x^2 - 6x - 18$, $\dfrac{d^2y}{dx^2} = 24x - 6$

(b) $\dfrac{dy}{dx} = 0$, $12x^2 - 6x - 18 = 0$, $2x^2 - x - 3 = 0$

$(2x - 3)(x + 1) = 0$

Stationary points at

$x = -1$, $y = -4 - 3 + 18 + 10 = 21$

$x = \frac{3}{2}$, $y = 4\left(\frac{27}{8}\right) - 3\left(\frac{9}{4}\right) - 27 + 10 = -10.25$

When $x = -1$, $\dfrac{d^2y}{dx^2} < 0$, so $(-1, 21)$ is a maximum point.

When $x = \frac{3}{2}$, $\dfrac{d^2y}{dx^2} > 0$, so $\left(\frac{3}{2}, -10.25\right)$ is a minimum point.

(c) $\dfrac{d^2y}{dx^2} = 0$, $24x - 6 = 0$, $x = \frac{1}{4}$,

$y = 4\left(\frac{1}{64}\right) - 3\left(\frac{1}{16}\right) - 18\left(\frac{1}{4}\right) + 10 = 5.375$

When $x < \frac{1}{4}$ (e.g. $x = 0$), $\dfrac{d^2y}{dx^2} < 0$,

and when $x > \frac{1}{4}$ (e.g. $x = \frac{1}{2}$),

$\dfrac{d^2y}{dx^2} > 0$

Sign change in $\dfrac{d^2y}{dx^2}$ means C has one point of inflexion, at $(0.25, 5.375)$

STATISTICS

112. Sampling

1. (a) Systematic sampling
   (b) Adds a degree of system or process and is easy to operate; ensures the sample is evenly distributed across the population

2. Sampling fraction = $\frac{65}{450}$
   Number in sample playing football = $\frac{65}{450} \times 97 = 14$
   Number in sample playing:
   Tennis = 10; Rugby = 22; Squash = 19

3.

Age (years)	16–24	25–44	45–64	65+
Number of members	96	171 to 177*	201 to 207*	110
Number in sample	16	**29**	34	**18**

* Total of these two cells must be 376

113. Mean

1. (a) 93.4 g (1 d.p.)   (b) 94.2 g (1 d.p.)

2. (a) The midpoint of the 6–12 minutes group is 9 minutes.
   The midpoint of the 13–20 minutes group is 16.5 minutes.
   (b) $\bar{x} = \frac{\Sigma fx}{\Sigma f} = \frac{6 \times 3 + 11 \times 9 + 7 \times 16.5 + 8 \times 25.5}{32}$
   $= \frac{436.5}{32} = 13.6$ minutes (1 d.p.)

3. (a) $Q_2 = 1014.5$ kPa
   (b) IQR = $Q_3 - Q_1 = 1019 - 1011 = 8$ kPa

114. Median and quartiles

1. (a) 28
   (b) $n = 23, \frac{n}{2} = 11.5 \Rightarrow$ 12th value, so median $Q_2 = 23$
   $\frac{n}{4} = 5.75 \Rightarrow$ 6th value, so $Q_1 = 14$
   $\frac{3n}{4} = 17.25 \Rightarrow$ 18th value, so $Q_3 = 32$

2. Modal age = 25, median = 41, IQR = 52 − 29 = 23

3. (a) $Q_2 = 1014.5$ kPa
   (b) IQR = $Q_3 - Q_1 = 1019 - 1011 = 8$ kPa

115. Linear interpolation

1. $\frac{n}{2} = 135$, so the median is $(135 - 29) = 106$ values into the $10 \leq w < 15$ group.
   This group is 5 kg wide so each member is worth $\frac{5}{121}$ kg.
   $Q_2 = 10 + 106 \times \frac{5}{121}$ kg $= 14.380\,16... = 14.4$ kg (1 d.p.)

2. (a) $Q_1 = 26.6$ mph, $Q_2 = 37.1$ mph, $Q_3 = 47.9$ mph
   (b) 20% of vehicles exceed 51.66 mph. The claim is justified because more than 20% exceed 50 mph.

3. $Q_1 = 17$ mm, $Q_2 = 32$ mm, $Q_3 = 49.9$ mm (1 d.p.)

116. Standard deviation 1

1.

Mark	Frequency, f	Midpoint, x	$f \times x$
$0 < x \leq 10$	16	5	80
$10 < x \leq 30$	32	20	640
$30 < x \leq 50$	38	40	1520
$50 < x \leq 60$	24	55	1320
$60 < x \leq 80$	10	70	700

Mean = 35.5 marks, SD = 19.2 marks

2. Mean = 37.1 years, SD = 14.9 years

3. Mean = 23.1 letters, SD = 6.24 letters

4. (a) Mean = 147.0 hours, standard deviation = 70.7 hours
   (b) Although the mean in Hurn is higher, the SD is also greater, so the results are more spread out. Also, the sample size is small, so overall, these results do not support the conclusion.

117. Standard deviation 2

1. $\Sigma f = 160$
   $\Sigma fx = 12 \times 5 + 27 \times 12.5 + 85 \times 22.5 + 36 \times 40 = 3750$
   $\Sigma fx^2 = 12 \times 5^2 + 27 \times 12.5^2 + 85 \times 22.5^2 + 36 \times 40^2 = 105\,150$
   Variance $= \frac{105\,150}{160} - \left(\frac{3750}{160}\right)^2 = 107.871...$
   Standard deviation $= \sqrt{107.871...} = 10.386...$
   $= 10.4$ minutes (3 s.f.)

2. £0.873 million (3 s.f.)

3. (a) 38 mm and 70.5 mm   (b) 25.2 mm (3 s.f.)

118. Coding

1.

Yield, w (kg)	Frequency, f	Midpoint, w	$u = w - 80$	$f \times u$	u^2	$f \times u^2$
$65 \leq w < 75$	21	70	−10	−210	100	2100
$75 \leq w < 85$	18	80	0	0	0	0
$85 \leq w < 105$	11	95	15	165	225	2475
$105 \leq w < 125$	7	115	35	245	1225	8575
Total	**200**					**13 150**

Mean for $u = \frac{\Sigma fu}{n} = \frac{200}{57} = 3.508$, so mean for
$w = 3.508 + 80 = 83.5$ kg (3 s.f.)
Variance for $u = \frac{\Sigma fu^2}{n} - \left[\frac{\Sigma fu}{n}\right]^2 = \frac{13\,150}{57} - (3.5)^2 = 218.45$
Standard deviation for $u = \sqrt{218.45} = 14.78$, so standard deviation for $w = 14.8$ kg (3 s.f.)

2. Mean = 25.3, SD = 8.96

3. (a) Mean = 117.9, SD = 9.20
   (b) Mean = 120.6, SD = 9.66

119. Box plots and outliers

1. IQR = 40 − 28 = 12
   $1.25 \times$ IQR $= 1.25 \times 12 = 15$
   $Q_3 + 15 = 40 + 15 = 55$
   $Q_1 - 15 = 28 - 15 = 13$

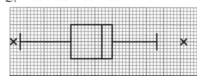

10 15 20 25 30 35 40 45 50 55 60 65

2. (a) (i) 28   (ii) Lower quartile
   (b) IQR = 36 − 28 = 8, 28 − 1.5 × 8 = 28 − 12 = 16;
   10 is less than this value so it is an outlier.

3.

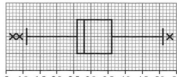

5 10 15 20 25 30 35 40 45 50 55

IQR = 10 $Q_3 + 15 = 36 + 15 = 51$ $Q_1 - 15 = 26 - 15 = 11$
Outliers at 7, 9 and 53

Answers

120. Cumulative frequency diagrams

G 1 (a)

Length, l (mm)	Number of insects	Cumulative frequency
$0 < l \leqslant 5$	65	65
$5 < l \leqslant 10$	50	115
$10 < l \leqslant 20$	60	175
$20 < l \leqslant 30$	25	200
$30 < l \leqslant 40$	15	215
$40 < l \leqslant 50$	10	225

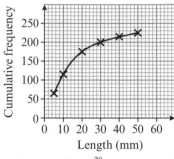

(b) 20th percentile $= \frac{20}{100} \times 225 = $ 45th value

80th percentile $= \frac{80}{100} \times 225 = $ 180th value

Interpercentile range $= 21 - 3 = 18$ mm

2 (a)

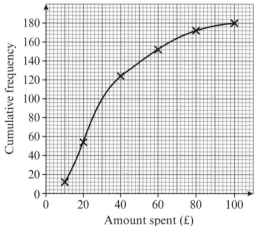

(b) Median $= £29$, IQR $= 46 - 18 = £28$

(c) 12 people   (d) $70 - 12 = £58$

121. Histograms

G 1 Frequency for $0 < t \leqslant 10$ class $= 2.8 \times 10 = 28$

Frequency for $10 < t \leqslant 30$ class $= 2 \times 20 = 40$

Time, t (minutes)	Number of cars
$0 < t \leqslant 10$	28
$10 < t \leqslant 30$	40
$30 < t \leqslant 60$	48
$60 < t \leqslant 80$	16

2 (a) Frequency density (height of bar) for $20 < v \leqslant 30$ is 11

The frequency for the $45 < v \leqslant 50$ group is 110

(b) 335 cars

3 Width $= 2$ cm, height $= 1.5$ cm

122. Comparing distributions

G 1 The median for the boys' marks (52) is less than the median for the girls' marks (60), so the boys did less well overall.

The IQR for the boys was 20 compared with 30 for the girls so the boys' marks were more closely grouped than the girls' marks.

Only 25% of the boys scored more than 58, whereas 50% of the girls scored more than 60.

2 (a) 1997: Mean $= 18.5 °C$, SD $= 2.99 °C$

2015: Mean $= 20.5 °C$, SD $= 2.36 °C$

(b) 1997: Median $= 17.7 °C$, IQR $= 4.5 °C$

2015: Median $= 20.8 °C$, IQR $= 2.8 °C$

In 2015, the mean is higher and the SD is lower, so the results are less spread.

or

In 2015, the median is higher and the IQR is smaller, so the results are less spread.

There is sufficient evidence to support the conclusion that average air temperatures have increased.

123. Correlation and cleaning data

G 1 (a) IQR $= 72.5 - 67.5 = 5$, $1.5 \times$ IQR $= 7.5$

$Q_1 - 7.5 = 60$, and since $55 < 60$, 55 is an outlier.

(b) To weigh 55 kg (approx 8.5 stone) and be 173 cm (approx 5′ 8″) tall isn't particularly unusual, so the data item could easily have been retained, but since 55 is an outlier there is some justification.

(c)

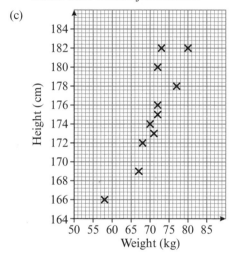

(d) The scatter diagram shows the 11 results to have good positive correlation which means that an increase in weight is usually accompanied by an increase in height.

2 (a) $Q_1 = 29$, $Q_2 = 33$ and $Q_3 = 39$

(b) $Q_2 + 1.5 \times$ IQR $= 39 + 1.5 \times 10 = 54$, so 70 is an outlier.

(c) A person of 70 is still likely to have a good short-term memory, so valid to retain this result.

124. Regression

G 1 (a) The gradient is 2.11, so every year the average CO_2 level increases by just over 2 parts per million.

(b) There is strong positive correlation so a linear model is suitable.

2 (a) For every 1 °C rise in temperature the energy consumption falls by 2.25 kWh.

(b) 25.7 kWh is the energy consumption when the temperature is 0 °C

(c) Strong negative correlation, so a linear model is suitable.

125. Using regression lines

1 (a) Reading off values of the dependent variable within the range of the given data. This is reliable.

(b) Estimating a value of the dependent variable outside the range of the given data. This is much less reliable.

2 (a) (i) 2005 is 14 years after 1991. The regression equation will give a reliable estimate of CO_2 since 14 is within the range 1 to 22 (interpolation).

(ii) 2016 is 25 years after 1991. This is not covered by the scale on the x-axis. The estimate will be unreliable (extrapolation).

(b) CO_2 (y) is the dependent variable. The regression equation cannot be used to predict the value of the date (x), the independent variable.

3 (a) (i) The answer is reliable because 14 °C is within the range of the given data (interpolation).

(ii) kWh (y) is the dependent variable. The regression equation cannot be used to predict the average temperature (x), the independent variable.

(b) When $x = 12$, the equation would give -1.3 kWh of energy, which is a negative quantity and clearly not possible. The household will always use some energy for heating, lighting and other electrical appliances. The regression equation only covers temperatures up to approximately 5 °C, so attempting to use it for $x = 12$ is unreliable (extrapolation) because this is outside the range of the given data.

126. Drawing Venn diagrams

G 1 (a) The 11 children who had a cat and a dog include the 2 children who had all three pets.

So $11 - 2 = 9$ children had a cat and a dog but not a rabbit. This is $C \cap D \cap R'$.

The 7 children who had a cat and a rabbit include the 2 children who had all three pets.

So $7 - 2 = 5$ children had a cat and a rabbit but not a dog. This is $C \cap R \cap D'$.

Similarly, $5 - 2 = 3$ is the number for the region $D \cap R \cap C'$.

The total number who had a cat is 31, but $9 + 5 + 2 = 16$ of these have already been counted, leaving $31 - 16 = 15$ as the number in the 'cat only' region.

Similarly 'dog only' $= 35 - (9 + 3 + 2) = 21$, and 'rabbit only' $= 18 - (5 + 3 + 2) = 8$.

The final calculation is to add up all the numbers found so far and subtract from 80 to find out how many children had none of these three pets.
$80 - (15 + 21 + 8 + 9 + 5 + 3 + 2) = 17$

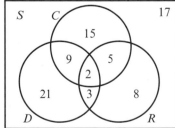

(b) Children who did not have a cat or a dog $= 25$

2 (a)

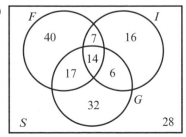

(b) The number who had been to exactly two of the three countries $= 17 + 7 + 6 = 30$

127. Using Venn diagrams

G 1 (a) The total number of students $=$
$21 + 4 + 12 + 6 + 15 + 22 = 80$

The number taking only one subject $=$
$21 + 12 + 15 = 48$

So the probability is $\frac{48}{80} = \frac{3 \times 16}{5 \times 16} = \frac{3}{5}$

(b) The number of students taking maths or English or both $= 21 + 4 + 12 + 6 = 43$

So probability $= \frac{43}{80}$

2 (a)

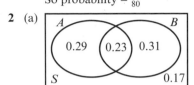

(b) $P(A) = 0.52$
$P(A' \cap B) = 0.31$

3 (a)

(b) $P(W \text{ or } J \text{ but not both}) = 0.37 + 0.15 = 0.52$

128. Independent events

1 (a) $q + r$ **(b)** $q + r - qr$

G 2 Total number of people $= 7 + 4 + 9 + 2 + 3 + 2 + 5 + 8 = 40$

$P(C) = \frac{7 + 4 + 2 + 3}{40} = \frac{16}{40} = \frac{2}{5}$

$P(G) = \frac{5 + 2 + 2 + 3}{40} = \frac{12}{40} = \frac{3}{10}$

$P(C \cap G) = \frac{2 + 3}{40} = \frac{5}{40} = \frac{1}{8}$

$P(C) \times P(G) = \frac{2}{5} \times \frac{3}{10} = \frac{6}{50} = \frac{3}{25}$

$\frac{1}{8} \neq \frac{3}{25}$ so the events are not independent

3 (a) $\frac{17}{25}$ **(b)** $\frac{51}{200}$

129. Tree diagrams

G 1 (a)

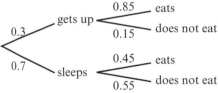

(b) $P(\text{does not eat}) = 0.3 \times 0.15 + 0.7 \times 0.55$
$= 0.045 + 0.385 = 0.43$

(c) $P(\text{gets up immediately} \mid \text{does not eat})$
$= \frac{P(\text{gets up immediately and does not eat})}{P(\text{does not eat})}$
$= \frac{0.045}{0.43} = 0.105$ (3 s.f.)

(d) $3 \times (0.43)^2 \times 0.57 = 0.316\,179$

2 (a)

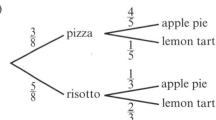

(b) P(Keisha eats either risotto or lemon tart, but not both) $= \frac{17}{60}$

(c) $\frac{36}{61}$

Answers

130. Random variables

1 (a) $P(X=1) = k \times 1^2 = k$ $\quad$ $P(X=2) = k \times 2^2 = 4k$

$P(X=3) = k \times 3^2 = 9k$ $\quad$ $P(X=4) = 3 \times k \times 4 = 12k$

$k + 4k + 9k + 12k = 1$, giving $k = \frac{1}{26}$

x	1	2	3	4
$P(X=x)$	$\frac{1}{26}$	$\frac{4}{26}$	$\frac{9}{26}$	$\frac{12}{26}$

(b) $P(X<3) = \frac{1}{26} + \frac{4}{26} = \frac{5}{26}$

2 (a)

y	1	2	3	4	5
$P(Y=y)$	$\frac{5}{35}$	$\frac{8}{35}$	$\frac{9}{35}$	$\frac{8}{35}$	$\frac{5}{35}$

(b) $P(Y \geqslant 3) = \frac{9}{35} + \frac{8}{35} + \frac{5}{35} = \frac{22}{35}$ (or $1 - (\frac{5}{35} + \frac{8}{35}) = \frac{22}{35}$)

3 (a) $a = 0.2$

w	-4	-1	0	1	3	6
$P(W=w)$	0.15	0.4	0.2	0.05	0.1	0.1

(b) $P(2W+5 \geqslant 4) = 0.45$

131. The binomial distribution

1 (a) Any two reasons from the following: fixed number of trials; two outcomes (allergic or not); fixed probabilities; independent trials.

(b) $P(X=2) = \binom{40}{2} \times (0.05)^2 \times (0.95)^{38} = 0.278$ (3 s.f.)

(c) 0.677 (3 s.f.)

2 (a) 0.068 (3 s.f.) $\qquad$ **(b)** 0.805 (3 s.f.)

3 The probability of picking a toffee is not fixed at 0.5.

4 (a) 0.237 (3 s.f.) $\qquad$ **(b)** 0.213 (3 s.f.)

(c) 0.764 (3 s.f.)

132. Hypothesis testing

1 $P(X \leqslant 7) = 0.886$, $P(X \geqslant 8) = 1 - 0.886 = 0.114$

Since $0.114 > 0.10$, there is not enough evidence to reject H_0

So the conclusion is that the dice is not biased towards 1

2 $H_0: \rho = 0.55$, $H_1: \rho > 0.55$; $X \sim B(18, 0.55)$

$P(X \geqslant 14) = 1 - P(X \leqslant 13) = 0.041$

$0.041 < 0.05$, so reject H_0 and accept H_1

The probability is higher than 0.55, so the striker has underestimated his chances of scoring.

3 $H_0: \rho = 0.519$, $H_1: \rho \neq 0.519$; $X \sim B(50, 0.519)$

$n\rho = 50 \times 0.519 \approx 26$ and since $19 < 26$ calculate $P(X \leqslant 19)$

Two-tailed test, so test $P(X \leqslant 19)$ at the 2.5% significance level.

$P(X \leqslant 19) = 0.034$

$0.034 > 0.025$ so there is not enough evidence to reject H_0.

There is no evidence to suggest that this result is different from the UK average.

133. Finding critical regions

1 Model this by $X \sim B(30, 0.2)$

$H_0: \rho = 0.2$, $H_1: \rho \neq 0.2$ (two-tailed test)

$P(X \leqslant 2) = 0.044 < 0.05$

$P(X \leqslant 3) = 0.123 > 0.05$

$P(X \geqslant 11) = 0.026 < 0.05$

$P(X \geqslant 10) = 0.061 > 0.05$

The critical region is $X \leqslant 2$ and $X \geqslant 11$

So catching fewer than 3 or more than 10 dark moths would indicate that pollution levels are changing.

2 (a) $H_0: \rho = 0.22$ $\qquad$ $H_1: \rho > 0.22$

$P(X \geqslant 14) = 0.041 < 0.05$, $P(X \geqslant 13) = 0.083 > 0.05$

Critical region is $X \geqslant 14$

(b) 0.041 or 4.1%

(c) 12 is not in the critical region so this is insufficient evidence to reject H_0 at the 5% significance level.

3 (a) $P(X \leqslant 20) = 0.018 < 0.025$, $P(X \leqslant 21) = 0.040 > 0.025$

$P(X \geqslant 31) = 0.050 > 0.025$, $P(X \geqslant 32) = 0.019 < 0.025$

Critical region is $X \leqslant 20$ and $X \geqslant 32$

(b) $0.018 + 0.019 = 0.037$ or 3.7%

(c) 19 is in the critical region so reject H_0 at the 5% significance level.

134. You are the examiner!

1 (a) Stratified sampling

(b) Total = 162, 15% of 162 rounds to 24 vehicles for the sample

Large-load vehicles = $0.15 \times 3 = 0.45 \rightarrow$ 1 vehicle

Light vans = $0.15 \times 135 = 20.25 \rightarrow$ 20 vehicles

Company cars = $0.15 \times 24 = 3.6 \rightarrow$ 3 vehicles

(to make a total of 24)

2 (a) x values are:

30 $\quad$ 37 $\quad$ 45 $\quad$ 46 $\quad$ 48 $\quad$ 50 $\quad$ 51 $\quad$ 51 $\quad$ 56 $\quad$ 60

Median = 49; IQR = $51 - 45 = 6$

(b) $Q1 - 1.5 \times IQR = 45 - 1.5 \times 6 = 36$, so 30 is an outlier

(c) It is not unusual for a team to score quite a lot of goals but not win many games (probably quite a few narrow defeats) and so only score a relatively low number of points so we retain the data for team F.

(d)

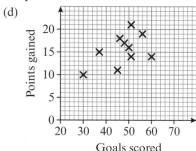

(e) Positive correlation which implies that the more goals you score, the more points you gain.

135. You are the examiner!

3 (a) Mean = $-88 \div 20 = -4.4$ cm

SD $= \sqrt{4292 \div 20 - (4.4)^2} = 13.97$ cm

(b) Mean = $100\,\text{m} - 4.4\,\text{cm} = 99.96\,\text{m}$ (2 d.p.)

SD = $0.1397\,\text{m} = 0.14\,\text{m}$ (2 d.p.)

(c) New mean = $-50 \div 19 = -2.63$ cm,

new $\Sigma x^2 = 4292 - 38^2 = 2848$

New SD $= \sqrt{2848 \div 19 - (2.63)^2} = 11.96$

New mean = $100\,\text{m} - 2.63\,\text{cm} = 99.97\,\text{m}$ (2 d.p.)

New SD = $0.1196\,\text{m} = 0.12\,\text{m}$ (2 d.p.)

4 (a)

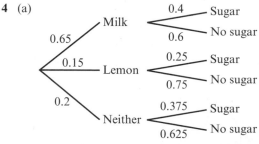

(b) P(does not take sugar) $= (0.65 \times 0.6) + (0.15 \times 0.75)$

$+ (0.2 \times 0.625)$

$= 0.39 + 0.1125 + 0.125$

$= 0.6275$

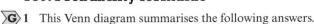

136. Measuring correlation

 1 (a) $r = 0.532$ (3 d.p.)

(b) $r = 0.532$ indicates a weak positive correlation between height and weight.

A linear model may not be the best; a different model might be a better fit.

2 (a) $r = -0.931$ (3 d.p.)

(b) $r = -0.931$ indicates a strong negative correlation which means that a linear regression model is suitable for these data. In general, as the hours of sunshine increase the amount of rainfall decreases.

3

log x	0.30	0.78	0.85	0.95	1.08	1.15	1.18	1.20
log y	0.18	0.30	0.40	0.48	0.60	0.65	0.81	0.90

(i) $r = 0.918$

(ii) $y = ax^n$, log y = log $a + n$ log x, $r = 0.904$

(iii) $y = kb^x$, log y = log $k + x$ log b, $r = 0.980$

All suggest a strong linear relationship, but an exponential relationship of the form $y = kb^x$ is the best fit for these data.

137. Hypothesis testing for 0 correlation

 1 (a) $r = 0.5686$

(b) $H_0: \rho = 0$, $H_1: \rho > 0$, sample size, $n = 9$, significance level = 0.05

From the critical values table, the critical value of r is 0.5822, so the critical region is $r > 0.5822$

$0.5686 < 0.5822$ The observed value of r does not lie in the critical region, so there is not enough evidence at the 5% level to reject H_0. The data does not support the coach's claim.

2 (a) $r = 0.7428$

(b) $H_0: \rho = 0$, $H_1: \rho > 0$, sample size, $n = 10$, significance level = 0.01

From the critical values table, the critical value of r is 0.7155, so the critical region is $r > 0.7155$

$0.7428 > 0.7155$ The observed value of r lies in the critical region, so there is enough evidence at the 1% level to reject H_0. The data suggests there is positive correlation between the verbal and spatial scores.

3 (a) $r = -0.8174$

(b) $H_0: \rho = 0$, $H_1: \rho < 0$

(c) For $n = 7$, 1% value is -0.8329, 2.5% value is -0.7545, so $-0.8329 < -0.8174 < -0.7545$, which means that the result is significant at the 2.5% level.

138. Conditional probability

 1 (a) The number choosing choc-chip = $10 + 8 + 3 + 4 = 25$

Of these 25, $3 + 4 = 7$ choose toffee, so the probability $= \frac{7}{25}$

(b) The number choosing vanilla or toffee = $5 + 2 + 8 + 3 + 4 + 9 = 31$

Of these 31, $8 + 3 + 4 = 15$ choose choc-chip, so the probability $= \frac{15}{31}$

2 (a) $\frac{11}{46}$

(b) $\frac{18}{39}$

(c) $\frac{9}{34}$

139. Probability formulae

 1 This Venn diagram summarises the following answers.

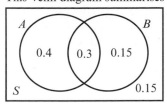

(a) $P(A' \cap B') = 1 - P(A \cup B) = 1 - 0.85 = 0.15$

(b) $P(A \cap B) = P(A) + P(B) - P(A \cup B)$
$= 0.7 + 0.45 - 0.85 = 0.3$

(c) $A \cap B'$ is the region within A but outside B.
$P(A \cap B') = 0.7 - 0.3 = 0.4$

(d) $A' \cup B$ is the region outside A but including all of B (the whole sample space, except the region in part (c)).
$P(A' \cup B) = 1 - P(A \cap B') = 1 - 0.4 = 0.6$

2.

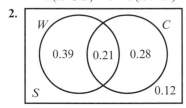

(a) $P(C \cap W) = 0.21$

(b) $P(W' \cap C') = 0.12$

(c) $P(C \mid W') = 0.7$

140. The normal distribution 1

1 (a) 0.0668 (b) 0.4648 (c) 0.1056

2 (a) $P(X > 45) = 0.7257$

(b) $P(X < 56) = 0.9452$

(c) $P(X < 40 \text{ or } X > 58) = 0.0775$

3 (a) $P(Y < 23) = 0.9255$

(b) $P(10 < Y < 15) = 0.1828$

(c) $P(10 < Y < 15 \text{ or } Y > 23) = 0.2572$

4 (a) $P(155 < H < 170) = 0.5695$

(b) $P(H > 175) = 0.0856$

(c) $(0.0856)^3 = 0.000\,627$ (3 d.p.)

141. The normal distribution 2

 1 (a) $X \sim N(80, 12^2)$, $P(X > 100) = 0.0478$

(b) Let S be the number of students who are awarded a distinction.
$S \sim B(30, 0.0478)$
$P(S > 3) = 1 - P(S \leq 3) = 1 - 0.9469 = 0.0531$

2 (a) $X \sim N(130, 40^2)$, $P(X > 174) = 0.1648$, so 16.48% are Class 1 oranges.
$P(92 < X < 174) = 0.6940$, so 69.4% are Class 2 oranges.
$P(X < 92) = 0.1412$, so 14.12% are Class 3 oranges.

(b) Let W be the number of oranges that are Class 1.
$W \sim B(20, 0.1648)$
$P(W \geq 5) = 1 - P(W \leq 4) = 1 - 0.7760 = 0.2240$

3 (a) $\rho = 0.025$ gives $z = 1.96$
$z = \dfrac{x - \mu}{\sigma}$, $1.96 = \dfrac{1957.8 - \mu}{55}$, so $1.96 \times 55 = 1957.8 - \mu$
$\mu = 1957.8 - 107.8 = 1850$

(b) $P(H > 1770) = 0.9271$ or $P(H < 1770) = 0.0729$

Let M be the number of light bulbs lasting more than 1770 hours.

$M \sim B(10, 0.9271)$

$P(M \geqslant 8) = 1 - P(M \leqslant 7) = 1 - 0.0315 = 0.9685$

or

Let K be the number of light bulbs lasting less than 1770 hours.

$K \sim B(10, 0.0729)$, $P(K \leqslant 2) = 0.9685$

142. The inverse normal function

1 (a) $P(X < a) = 0.305$, $a = 74.90$ (2 d.p.)

(b) $P(X > b) = 0.102$, $P(X < b) = 0.898$, $b = 92.70$ (2 d.p.)

(c) $P(X < c) = P(72 < X < c) + P(X < 72)$
$= 0.4 + 0.2119$
$= 0.6119$
$c = 82.84$ (2 d.p.)

2 (a) $Q_3 = 19\,072$ miles

(b) $Q_1 = 16\,928$ miles

3 (a) $P(W < w) = P(65 < W < w) + P(W < 65)$
$= 0.35 + 0.3621 = 0.7121$ so $w = 72.76\,kg$

(b) $P(\text{both weigh more than } 72.76\,kg) = (1 - 0.7121)^2$
$= 0.2879^2 = 0.083$ (3 d.p.)

4 (a) $P(D > d) = 107.54\,mm$

(b) $d_1 = $ 10th percentile, $P(D < d_1) = 0.1$, so $d_1 = 101.8609$
$d_2 = $ 80th percentile, $P(D < d_2) = 0.8$, so $d_2 = 107.0615$
10% to 80% interpercentile range $= 5.20\,mm$ (2 d.p.)

143. Finding μ and σ

1 $P(X > 440) = P\left(Z > \dfrac{440 - 452}{\sigma}\right) = 0.99$

$P(Z > -2.3263) = 0.99$ (using the percentage points table) since $P(Z > 2.3263) = 0.01$

$\dfrac{440 - 452}{\sigma} = -2.3263$ giving $\sigma = \dfrac{-12}{-2.3263} = 5.16$ (3 s.f.)

2 (a) $P(X > 20.6) = P\left(\dfrac{Z > 20.6 - \mu}{\sigma}\right) = 0.4$

$P(Z > 0.2533) = 0.4$ (using the percentage points table)

$\dfrac{20.6 - \mu}{\sigma} = 0.2533 \Rightarrow 20.6 - \mu = 0.2533\sigma$

$\mu = 20.6 - 0.2533\sigma$

(b) Similarly, $P(Z \geqslant 1.0364) = 0.15$ (using the percentage points table)

$P(Z < -1.0364) = 0.15$, hence $\dfrac{13.2 - \mu}{\sigma} = -1.0364$

$\mu = 13.2 + 1.0364\sigma$

Solving simultaneously gives

$\mu = 19.1$ (3 s.f.) and $\sigma = 5.74$ (3 s.f.)

144. Normal approximations

1 (a) $X \sim B(150, 0.45)$

(b) $\mu = np = 150 \times 0.45 = 67.5$
$\sigma = \sqrt{np(1 - p)} = \sqrt{150 \times 0.45 \times 0.55} = 6.0930$
$Y \sim N(67.5, 6.0930^2)$
$P(X < 55) \approx P(Y < 54.5) = 0.0164$

(c) $P(60 \leqslant X \leqslant 75) \approx P(59.5 < Y < 75.5) = 0.8108$

2 (a) $X \sim B(120, 0.6)$

(b) The number of seeds is large and the probability of germination, 0.6, is close to 0.5.
$\mu = np = 120 \times 0.6 = 72$
$\sigma = \sqrt{np(1 - p)} = \sqrt{120 \times 0.6 \times 0.4} = 5.3666$

(c) $Y \sim N(72, 5.3666^2)$
$P(X \geqslant 80) \approx P(Y > 79.5) = 0.0811$

3 (a) $X \sim B(800, 0.54)$

(b) The number of trials must be large and the probability of 'success' must be close to 0.5.

(c) $\mu = np = 800 \times 0.54 = 432$
$\sigma = \sqrt{np(1 - p)}$
$= \sqrt{800 \times 0.54 \times 0.46} = 14.097$
$P(420 \leqslant X \leqslant 450) \approx P(419.5 < Y < 450.5) = 0.7177$

145. Normal hypothesis testing

1 $H_0: \mu = 100$, $H_1: \mu < 100$

Let X represent the resistance and assume H_0 to be true, so that $X \sim N(100, 9^2)$

So for the sample mean, $\overline{X} \sim N\left(100, \dfrac{9^2}{15}\right)$

or $\overline{X} \sim N(100, 2.3238^2)$

$P(\overline{X} < 96.3) = 0.0557$

$0.0557 > 0.05$, so there is insufficient evidence to reject H_0

So the mean resistance is still 100 ohms.

2 $H_0: \mu = 177$, $H_1: \mu > 177$

Let X represent the height and assume H_0 to be true, so that $X \sim N(177, 7.5^2)$

So for the sample mean, $\overline{X} \sim N\left(100, \dfrac{7.5^2}{30}\right)$

or $\overline{X} \sim N(177, 1.3693^2)$

$P(\overline{X} > 179.8) = 0.0204$

$0.0204 < 0.05$, so there is sufficient evidence to reject H_0

So there is evidence that, in 2017, the mean height of male students was greater than $177\,cm$.

3 (a) Let X represent the diameters of the bicycle wheels.

Assume:

$H_0: \mu = 42$, $H_1: \mu \neq 42$, and that $X \sim N(42, 1.5^2)$

So for the sample mean, $\overline{X} \sim N\left(42, \dfrac{1.5^2}{22}\right)$

or $\overline{X} \sim N(42, 0.3198^2)$

$P(\overline{X} < a) = 0.025$ giving $a = 41.37$

$P(\overline{X} > b) = 0.025$, so $P(\overline{X} < b) = 0.975$ giving $b = 42.63$

So the critical region is $\overline{X} < 41.37$ or $\overline{X} > 42.63$

(b) The observed value of $41.6\,cm$ is not in the critical region, so there is insufficient evidence to reject H_0 at the 5% level of significance.

146. You are the examiner!

1 (a) Any two reasons from: fixed number of trials; independent outcomes; two possible outcomes; constant probability.

(b) $H_0: p = 0.28$, $H_1: p < 0.28$

Assume H_0 is true, then $X \sim B(40, 0.28)$

$P(X \leqslant 7) = 0.0924$

$0.0924 > 0.05$ so there is not sufficient evidence to reject H_0.

The claim that there will now be fewer faulty tail light bulbs is not justified at the 5% significance level.

2 Let $X \sim N(250, 42)$

(a) $P(X > 265) = 0.0103$

(b) $P(X < 240) = 0.0614$

(c) $P(245 < X < 260) = 0.7184$

(d) $\dfrac{6}{400} = 0.015$ so we want $P(X < a) = 0.015$; this gives $a = 235.936\ldots$ so reject all packets weighing less than $236\,g$.

147. You are the examiner!

3 (a) Using the percentage points table, $P(X > 9.65) = 0.05$
gives $z = 1.6449$

so $\dfrac{9.65 - 9.4}{\sigma} = 1.6449$, $1.6449\sigma = 0.25$

$\sigma = \dfrac{0.25}{1.6449} = 0.151984\ldots = 0.152$ (3 s.f.)

(b) $\mu = 9.4$, $\sigma = 0.152$, so $P(9.1 < X < 9.6) = 0.8817$

(c) $P(\text{a bolt cannot be used}) = 1 - 0.8817 = 0.1183$

$P(\text{neither can be used}) = (0.1183)^2 = 0.0134$

4 (a)

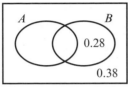

$P(A) = 1 - 0.28 - 0.38 = 0.34$

(b) $P(A \cup B) = 1 - 0.38 = 0.62$

(c)

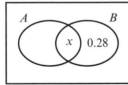

$P(A \mid B) = \dfrac{P(A \cap B)}{P(B)}$, so $\dfrac{1}{3} = \dfrac{x}{x + 0.28}$

$x + 0.28 = 3x$,

$0.28 = 2x$, $x = 0.14$

So $P(A \cap B) = 0.14$

(d) $P(B) = 0.28 + 0.14 = 0.42$

(e) $P(A) \times P(B) = 0.34 \times 0.42 = 0.1428$
and $P(A \cap B) = 0.14$ so the events are not independent.

(f) $P(B \cup C) = P(B) + P(C) - P(B \cap C)$
$0.64 = 0.42 + 0.32 - P(B \cap C)$, so $P(B \cap C) = 0.10$

(g)

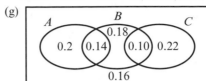

MECHANICS

148. Modelling in mechanics

1 (a) There is no friction.

(b) It has no weight.

(c) Acceleration is the same for both particles.

(d) Tension in the string is the same throughout its length.

(e) Each weight acts at a single point.

2 The string is light and inextensible, so the tension is the same throughout; the mass can be modelled as a particle, ignore any rotation of the mass; there is no air resistance and the motion will take place along the arc of a circle.

3 (a) 12.4 m   (b) 88.9 m   (c) 17.8 m

(d) The ball is modelled as a particle and there is no air resistance to the motion.

149. Motion graphs

 1 (a) v (m s^{-1})

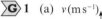

(b) Area = Area 1 + Area 2 + Area 3

$= (30 \times 40) + (20 \times 60) + (\frac{1}{2} \times 10 \times x) = 2500$

$1200 + 1200 + 5x = 2500$

$x = \frac{100}{5} = 20$

Deceleration $= \frac{10}{20} = 0.5 \text{ m s}^{-2}$

2 (a) v (m s^{-1})

(b) 80 m   (c) 35 s

150. Constant acceleration 1

1 (a) $s = ?$ $u = 5$ $v = 20$ $a = ?$ $t = 4$

$v = u + at$

$20 = 5 + a \times 4$ $4a = 15$ $a = 3.75 \text{ m s}^{-2}$

(b) $s = ?$ $u = 5$ $v = 20$ $a = 3.75$ $t = 4$

$s = \frac{1}{2}(5 + 20) \times 4 = 50 \text{ m}$

2 (a) 1.8 m s^{-2} (b) 4.375 m

3 (a) $a = -1.\dot{3}$ m s^{-2} (deceleration $= 1.\dot{3}$ m s^{-2})   (b) 600 m

151. Constant acceleration 2

1

PQ: $s = 45$ $u = u$ $v = ?$ $a = a$ $t = 2$

$45 = u \times 2 + \frac{1}{2}a \times 2^2$ ①

PR: $s = 165$ $u = u$ $v = ?$ $a = a$ $t = 6$

$165 = u \times 6 + \frac{1}{2}a \times 6^2$ ②

$45 = 2u + 2a$ ①

$165 = 6u + 18a$ ②

① $\times 3$: $135 = 6u + 6a$ ③

② $-$ ③: $30 = 12a$ $a = 2.5 \text{ m s}^{-2}$

Substitute in ①: $45 = 2u + 5$

$2u = 40$

$u = 20 \text{ m s}^{-1}$

2 (a) 37.75 m s^{-1}

(b) 102 m

(c) 6 s

152. Motion under gravity

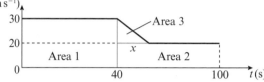 **1** (a) $s = ?$ $u = 21$ $v = 0$ $a = -9.8$ $t = ?$

$v^2 = u^2 + 2as$ so $0^2 = 21^2 - 2 \times 9.8 \times h$ $441 = 19.6h$

$h = 22.5 \text{ m}$

(b) $s = -1.5$ $u = 21$ $v = ?$ $a = -9.8$ $t = ?$

$v^2 = u^2 + 2as$, so $v^2 = 21^2 + 29.4 = 470.4$

so $v = 21.69 \text{ m s}^{-1}$

(c) $s = ?$ $u = 21$ $v = -22$ $a = -9.8$ $t = ?$

$v = u + at$

$-22 = 21 - 9.8t$

$t = 4.39 \text{ s}$

2 (a) $s = 50$ $u = 0$ $v = ?$ $a = a$ $t = 4$

$s = ut + \frac{1}{2}at^2$

$50 = 0 + \frac{1}{2}a \times 4^2$ $a = \frac{50}{8} = 6.25 \text{ m s}^{-2}$

(b) $v = u + at$

$v = 0 + 6.25 \times 4 = 25 \text{ m s}^{-1}$

(c) $s = ut + \frac{1}{2}at^2$

$s = 25 \times 3 - \frac{1}{2} \times 9.8 \times 9 = 30.9$

Total height $= 30.9 + 50 = 80.9 \text{ m}$

153. Forces

1 (a)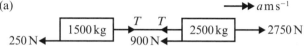

Van and car: $2750 - 900 - 250 = (2500 + 1500)a$

$1600 = 4000a$

$a = 0.4 \text{ m s}^{-2}$

(b)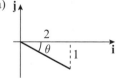

Car: $T - 250 = 1500a$

$T = 600 + 250$

$T = 850 \text{ N}$

2 (a) $T = 12\,608 \approx 13\,000 \text{ N}$ (2 s.f.)

(b) $R = 663 \approx 660 \text{ N}$ (2 s.f.)

154. Forces as vectors

1 (a)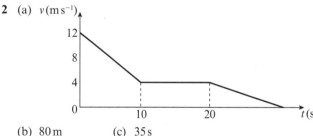

$\tan \theta = \frac{1}{2}$; $\theta = 26.6°$

angle $= 90 + 26.6 = 116.6° \approx 117°$ (3 s.f.)

(b) $\mathbf{R} = (3\mathbf{i} - 6\mathbf{j}) + (p\mathbf{i} + q\mathbf{j})$

$= (3 + p)\mathbf{i} + (-6 + q)\mathbf{j}$

$3 + p = -2(-6 + q)$

$3 + p = 12 - 2q$

$p + 2q = 9$

2 (a) 63°

(b) $p = -2$, $\mathbf{R} = -8\mathbf{j}$ N

3 (a) $p = -4$ and $q = 6$

(b) Magnitude $= 9.22$ N, angle $= 139.4°$

155. Motion in 2D

1 (a) $\frac{2\sqrt{13}}{5}\,\mathrm{m\,s^{-2}}$ or $1.44\,\mathrm{m\,s^{-2}}$ (3 s.f.)

(b) 146.3°

G 2 (a)
$$\mathbf{F} = m\mathbf{a}$$
$$4\mathbf{i} + 3\mathbf{j} = 0.5\mathbf{a}$$
$$\mathbf{a} = 8\mathbf{i} + 6\mathbf{j}$$
$$|\mathbf{a}| = \sqrt{8^2 + 6^2} = 10\,\mathrm{m\,s^{-2}}$$
$$s = ut + \tfrac{1}{2}at^2$$
$$= 0 + 0.5 \times 10 \times 5^2$$
$$= 125\,\mathrm{m}$$

(b) Resultant force = $4\mathbf{i} + 3\mathbf{j} + 1.3\mathbf{i} - 0.5\mathbf{j} = (5.3\mathbf{i} + 2.5\mathbf{j})$ N
$$a = 11.7\,\mathrm{m\,s^{-2}} \text{ to 3 s.f.}$$

3 $(2\mathbf{i} - 7\mathbf{j})$ N

156. Pulleys

G 1 (a) A: $4g - T = 4a$
$$4g - \frac{16g}{7} = T$$
$$T = \frac{12g}{7} \ (= 16.8 \approx 17\,\mathrm{N})$$
B: $T - mg = ma$
$$\frac{12g}{7} = m\left(g + \frac{4g}{7}\right)$$
$$\frac{12g}{7} = \frac{11mg}{7}$$
$$m = 1.1\,\mathrm{kg}$$

(b) $R(\uparrow)$: $v = u + at = 0 + \frac{4g}{7} \times 0.5 = \frac{2g}{7} = 2.8\,\mathrm{m\,s^{-1}}$

$R(\uparrow)$: $s = ut + \tfrac{1}{2}at^2 = 0 + \tfrac{1}{2} \times \frac{4g}{7} \times 0.5^2 = 0.7\,\mathrm{m}$

$R(\downarrow)$: $s = ut + \tfrac{1}{2}at^2 = 0.7 + 3 = 3.7\,\mathrm{m}$
$$3.7 = -2.8t + 4.9t^2$$
$$4.9t^2 - 2.8t - 3.7 = 0$$
$$t = \frac{2.8 \pm \sqrt{2.8^2 + 4 \times 4.9 \times 3.7}}{9.8}$$
$$= 1.2\,\mathrm{s}$$

2 $a = 3.92\,\mathrm{m\,s^{-2}}$, $T = 41.16\,\mathrm{N}$

157. Connected particles 1

G 1 (a) $F = ma$ for A: $T = 4.8a$
$F = ma$ for B: $1.2g - T = 1.2a$
Adding gives $1.2g = 6a$, so $a = 1.96\,\mathrm{m\,s^{-2}}$
Substituting gives $T = 4.8 \times 1.96 = 9.408\,\mathrm{N}$

(b) $s = 3 \quad u = 0 \quad v = ? \quad a = 1.96 \quad t = ?$
$v = 3.43\,\mathrm{m\,s^{-1}}$
$t = 1.75\,\mathrm{s}$

2 (a) $a = 1.4\,\mathrm{m\,s^{-2}}$, v after $2.5\,\mathrm{s} = 4.2\,\mathrm{m\,s^{-1}}$ (then u for motion under gravity)
Further time = $0.43\,\mathrm{s}$

(b) $s = 6.3\,\mathrm{m}$ for connected particles, than $s = 0.9\,\mathrm{m}$ for motion under gravity.
Total distance = $7.2\,\mathrm{m}$

158. Combining techniques

1 (a) $a = 1.6\,\mathrm{m\,s^{-2}}$
$m = 5.6875 \approx 5.7\,\mathrm{kg}$ (2 s.f.)

(b) (i) The measured mass $m = 5\,\mathrm{kg}$. This is smaller than the calculated mass $m = 5.7\,\mathrm{kg}$. This suggests that the resistance is greater than $15.5\,\mathrm{N}$.

(ii) Maybe the resistance should be modelled as a variable force.

159. Variable acceleration 1

G 1 (a) $s = t(t^2 - 11t + 24) = t(t - 3)(t - 8)$
$s = 0$ when $t = 3$ and when $t = 8$
Graph crosses t-axis at $t = 0$, $t = 3$, $t = 8$

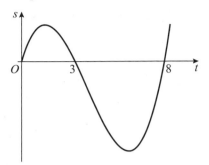

(b) Moves in positive direction from O then changes direction and passes O after $3\,\mathrm{s}$, continues in negative direction until changes direction again and returns to O after $8\,\mathrm{s}$.

(c) Differentiate to get $v = 3t^2 - 22t + 24$
Equate to zero to get $t = \frac{4}{3}$ and $t = 6$

(d) $t = \frac{4}{3}$ gives $s = 14.8$ and $t = 6$ gives $s = -36$
so $36\,\mathrm{m}$ from O in negative direction

2 (a) $t^3 - 24t^2 + 144t = t(t^2 - 24t + 144) = t(t - 12)^2$

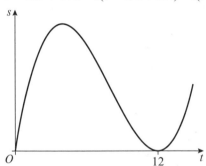

(b) $v = 16\,\mathrm{m\,s^{-1}}$ (c) $t = 4\,\mathrm{s}$ and $t = 12\,\mathrm{s}$

(d) This is when $t = 4$; $s = 28.44\,\mathrm{m}$

160. Variable acceleration 2

G 1 (a) P is instantaneously at rest when $v = 0$
$t^2 - 8t + 12 = 0$, $(t - 2)(t - 6) = 0$, so $t = 2$ and $t = 6$

(b) $t = 4$ gives $v = -4$
so maximum is $v = 12$ when $t = 0$

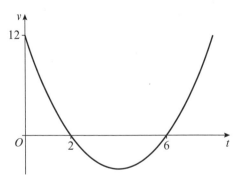

(c) $\int_0^2 v\,\mathrm{d}t + \int_2^5 v\,\mathrm{d}t$
Total distance = $19\frac{2}{3}\,\mathrm{m}$

2 (a) $8\,\mathrm{m\,s^{-1}}$

(b) $v = 8 - 2t^2 = 2(2 + t)(2 - t)$
Instantaneously at rest when $t = 2$

(c) At $t = 0$, $s = 0$; at $t = 2$, $s = 10\frac{2}{3}$; at $t = 4$, $s = -10\frac{2}{3}$
Total distance = $3 \times 10\frac{2}{3} = 32\,\mathrm{m}$

161. Deriving *suvat* formulae

 1 (a) Distance travelled = area under graph
so $s = A_1 + A_2$

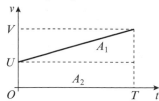

$A_1 = \frac{1}{2} \times$ base $\times$ height $= \frac{1}{2} \times T \times (V - U)$
and $A_2 = U \times T$
So $s = \frac{1}{2}T(V - U) + UT = \frac{1}{2}TV - \frac{1}{2}TU + UT$
$= \frac{1}{2}UT + \frac{1}{2}VT = \left(\frac{U + V}{2}\right)T$ as required

(b) (i) $s = \frac{1}{2}T(U + V)$
$= \frac{1}{2}T(U + U + aT)$
$= \frac{1}{2}T(2U + aT) = UT + \frac{1}{2}aT^2$

(ii) $s = \frac{1}{2}T(U + V) = \frac{(V - U)(V + U)}{2a}$, since $T = \frac{V - U}{a}$
$s = \frac{V^2 - U^2}{2a}$, so $2as = V^2 - U^2$ and $V^2 = U^2 + 2as$
as required

2 (a) $v = \int 0.8\,dt = 0.8t + c$
$v = 5$ when $t = 0$, so $c = 5$ and $v = 0.8t + 5$
$s = \int v\,dt = 0.4t^2 + 5t + k$
$s = 0$ when $t = 0$, so $k = 0$ and $s = 0.4t^2 + 5t$

(b) $16t - 0.3t^2 + 0.4t^2 + 5t = 720$
$0.1t^2 + 21t - 720 = 0$
$t^2 + 210t - 7200 = 0$
$(t - 30)(t + 240) = 0$
$t = 30\,s$

(c) When $t = 30$, $s = 16 \times 30 - 0.3 \times 900$
$= 480 - 270 = 210\,m$ from A

162. You are the examiner!

1 (a)

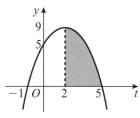

$A_1 + A_2 + A_3 = 23\,100$
$A_3 = 1575$

(b) $A_1 = \frac{1}{2} \times 210 \times 35 = 3675$
so $A_2 = 23\,100 - 3675 - 1575 = 17\,850$
$A_2 = (T_2 - 210) \times 35 = 17\,850$
so $(T_2 - 210) = 17\,850 \div 35 = 510$, so $T_2 = 720$
$A_3 = \frac{1}{2} \times (T_3 - 720) \times 35 = 1575$
so $(T_3 - 720) = 3150 \div 35 = 90$, so $T_3 = 810$
Time for the whole journey = 810 seconds
= 13.5 minutes

2 (a) $\mathbf{F}_1 + \mathbf{F}_2 + \mathbf{F}_3 = \mathbf{0}$ since the forces are in equilibrium
$(2p\mathbf{i} - \mathbf{j}) + (q\mathbf{i} - 5p\mathbf{j}) + 4\mathbf{i} - 7q\mathbf{j} = \mathbf{0}$
Sum of **i**-component coefficients = 0
Sum of **j**-component coefficients = 0
So $2p + q + 4 = 0$ and $-1 - 5p - 7q = 0$
(simultaneous equations)
Multiply $(2p + q = -4) \times 7$: $14p + 7q = -28$
Subtracting gives $9p = -27$ so $p = -3$
Substituting gives $q = 2$

(b) $\mathbf{F}_1 = (-6\mathbf{i} - \mathbf{j})\,N$ and $\mathbf{F}_2 = (2\mathbf{i} + 15\mathbf{j})\,N$
so $\mathbf{R} = \mathbf{F}_1 + \mathbf{F}_2 = (-4\mathbf{i} + 14\mathbf{j})\,N$

Magnitude of $\mathbf{R} = \sqrt{4^2 + 14^2} = \sqrt{212} = 14.56\,N$
Angle with **j**: $\tan\theta = \frac{4}{14}$ so $\theta = 15.9° \approx 16°$

163. You are the examiner!

3 (a) Apply $F = ma$ to both particles and
solve simultaneously:
$6g - T = 6a$ ①
$T - 4g = 4a$ ②
$2g = 10a$ ① + ②
$a = \frac{g}{5} = 1.96\,m\,s^{-2}$
$T = 4a + 4g = 4(a + g) = 4(1.96 + 9.8)$
$= 47.04\,N$

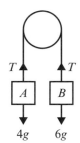

(b) Using $v = u + at$, $v = 0 + 1.96 \times 1.5 = 2.94\,m\,s^{-1}$

(c) A now moves under gravity with initial speed $2.94\,m\,s^{-1}$
Using $v = u + at$, $0 = 2.94 - 9.8t$, $t = 2.94 \div 9.8 = 0.3\,s$

(d) When connected, using $s = ut + \frac{1}{2}at^2$
$s = 0 + \frac{1}{2} \times 1.96 \times 1.5^2 = 2.205\,m$
When moving under gravity, using $v^2 = u^2 + 2as$
$0 = 2.94^2 - 2 \times 9.8 \times s$
$s = 2.94^2 \div 19.6 = 0.441\,m$
Total distance travelled by particle $A = 2.205 + 0.441$
$= 2.646\,m$

4 (a) $v = \int a\,dt = \int(4 - 2t)\,dt = 4t - t^2 + c$
When $t = 0$, $v = 5$, giving $c = 5$
$v = 5 + 4t - t^2$

(b) Greatest speed is when $a = 0$, $4 - 2t = 0$, $t = 2$
$v_{max} = 5 + 8 - 4 = 9\,m\,s^{-1}$

(c) A v–t sketch graph is useful here.

For instantaneous rest, $v = 0$
$5 + 4t - t^2 = 0$
$(5 - t)(1 + t) = 0$
$t = 5$ or $t = -1$ (inadmissible)
Distance (shaded area) $= \int_2^5 (5 + 4t - t^2)\,dt$
$= \left[5t + 2t^2 - \frac{t^3}{3}\right]_2^5$
$= (25 + 50 - \frac{125}{3}) - (10 + 8 - \frac{8}{3})$
$= 33\frac{1}{3} - 15\frac{1}{3}$
$= 18\,m$

164. Moments 1

 1 (a) $\circlearrowleft$ moment about $C = 2400 \times 0.4$
$\circlearrowright$ moment about $C = 150 \times 1.6 + F \times 3.6$
$960 = 3.6F + 240$
$F = 200\,N$

(b) $\circlearrowleft$ moment about $C = 2400 \times d$
$\circlearrowright$ moment about $C = 150 \times (2 - d) + 150 \times (4 - d)$
$2400d = 300 - 150d + 600 - 150d$
$2700d = 900$
$d = 33$ cm to nearest cm

2 (a) $R = 637 \approx 640$ N (2 s.f.)

(b) Distance $= 1.28 \approx 1.3$ m (2 s.f.)

165. Moments 2

1 (a) R($\uparrow$): $T + 4T = 70g$
$T = 14g = 137.2$ N
so $4T = 548.8 \approx 550$ N (2 s.f.)

(b) $\circlearrowleft$ moment about $C = T \times (4 - x) + 25g \times x$
$= 137.2(4 - x) + 245x$
$\circlearrowright$ moment about $C = 45g \times (2 - x) = 441(2 - x)$
$548.8 - 137.2x + 245x = 882 - 441x$
$548.8x = 333.2$
$x = 0.607$ m ≈ 61 cm (2 s.f.)

2 Tension $= 300$ N, weight $= 700$ N

166. Centres of mass

1 (a) $\circlearrowleft$ moment about $D = 1750 \times 6.5$
$\circlearrowright$ moment about $D = W \times 2.5$
$2.5W = 11\,375 \Rightarrow W = 4550$ N

(b) $\circlearrowleft$ moment about $D = 1750 \times 6.5$
$\circlearrowright$ moment about $D = W \times (5 - x)$
$\circlearrowleft$ moment about $C = W \times x$
$\circlearrowright$ moment about $C = 1500 \times 6.5$
$11\,375 = 5W - Wx$
$9750 = Wx$
$21\,125 = 5W$
$W = 4225$ N

2 (a) $\circlearrowleft$ moment about $D = 180 \times 3.5 = 240(6 - x) + W \times 6$
$630 = 1440 - 240x + 6W$
$240x - 6W = 810$
$40x - W = 135$

(b) $x = 4.7$ m, $W = 53$ N

167. Resolving forces

1. (a) $v^2 = u^2 + 2as$
$14^2 = 20^2 + 2 \times a \times 100$
$a = -1.02$
Deceleration $= 1.02$ m s^{-2}

(b) $T\cos\theta - 300 = 750 \times -1.02$
$0.9T = 300 - 765$
$T = -465 \div 0.9 = -516.66...$
Force $= 517$ N

(c) $-T\cos\theta - 500 - R = 1750 \times -1.02$
$517 \times 0.9 - 500 + 1785 = R$
$R = 1750$ N

2. (a) $a = 4.9$ m s^{-2}

(b) 42 N

168. Friction

1. (a) R($\rightarrow$): $160\cos 20° - F = 0$
$F = 150.35$ N
But $F = \mu R = 0.3R$, so $R = 501$ N

(b) R($\uparrow$): $R + 160\sin 20° - mg = 0$
$501.16 + 54.72 = m \times 9.8$
$555.88 = 9.8m$
$m = 56.7 \approx 57$ kg (2 s.f.)

2. $P = 871 \approx 870$ N (2 s.f.)

169. Sloping planes

1. (a) R($\searchdownnw$): $R - 4g\cos 30° = 0$
$R = 33.95 \approx 34$ N (2 s.f.)

(b) R($\nearrow$): $40 - 4g\sin 30° - F = 4a$
$F = \mu R = 0.5 \times 33.95 = 16.975$; $40 - 19.6 - 16.975 = 4a$
$a = 0.856 \approx 0.86$ m s^{-2} (2 s.f.)

2. (a) $a = 1.25$ m s^{-2}

(b) $\mu = 0.278 \approx 0.28$ (2 s.f.)

3. (a) $R = 32.36 \approx 32$ N (2 s.f.)

(b) $\mu = 0.644 \approx 0.64$ (2 s.f.)

170. Projectiles

1 (a)

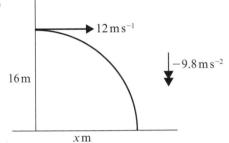

For the vertical motion: $s = -16$, $u = 0$, $a = -9.8$, $t = ?$
Using $s = ut + \frac{1}{2}at^2$,
$-16 = 0 - \frac{1}{2} \times 9.8 \times t^2$ giving $t = \sqrt{\dfrac{16}{4.9}} = 1.807...$
$= 1.8$ s (2 s.f.)
The ball lands after 1.8 seconds.

(b) For the horizontal motion: $s = x$, $u = 12$, $a = 0$, $t = 1.807...$
Distance = speed × time
$x = 12 \times 1.807... = 21.684... = 21.7$ m (3 s.f.)
The ball lands 21.7 m from the building.

(c) Using $v = u + at$ for the vertical motion,
$v_y = 0 - 9.8 \times 1.807... = -17.708...$
So, $v = \sqrt{12^2 + 17.708...^2}$ giving $v = 21.390...$
$= 21.4$ m s^{-1} (3 s.f.)
$\tan\alpha = \dfrac{17.708}{12}$ giving $\alpha = 55.87... = 55.9°$ (3 s.f.)
The ball lands with a speed of 21.4 m s^{-1} at an angle of 55.9° to the horizontal.

2 (a) Using $s = ut + \frac{1}{2}at^2$ for the vertical motion,
$-70 = 10.5t - 4.9t^2$, so $4.9t^2 - 10.5t - 70 = 0$ which simplifies to $7t^2 - 15t - 100 = 0$
$(7t + 20)(t - 5) = 0$ giving $t = 5$ s, so the cannonball hits sea level after 5 seconds.

(b) After 5 seconds the horizontal component of the speed
$= 21\cos 30° = 18.186...$ (constant)
The vertical component is given by using $v = u + at$,
$v_y = 21\sin 30° - 9.8 \times 5 = -38.5$ m s^{-1}
Speed $= \sqrt{18.186^2 + 38.5^2} = 42.6$ m s^{-1} (3 s.f.)

(c) Horizontal distance = speed × time
$= 18.186... \times 5 = 90.93...$
So the cannonball falls short of the pirate ship by just over 9 metres.

Answers

171. Projectile formulae

1 (a) $x = 14\cos\alpha\, t$ and, using $s = ut + \frac{1}{2}at^2$, $y = 14\sin\alpha\, t - 4.9t^2$

(b) $t = \dfrac{x}{14\cos\alpha} = \dfrac{10}{14\cos\alpha}$

Using $y = 14\sin\alpha\, t - 4.9t^2$,

$6 = 14\sin\alpha \times \dfrac{10}{14\cos\alpha} - 4.9\left(\dfrac{10}{14\cos\alpha}\right)^2$

$= 10\tan\alpha - \dfrac{4.9 \times 10^2}{14^2\cos^2\alpha}$

$= 10\tan\alpha - \dfrac{490\sec^2\alpha}{196}$

$= 10\tan\alpha - 2.5(1 + \tan^2\alpha)$

$2.5\tan^2\alpha - 10\tan\alpha + 8.5 = 0$

(c) $\tan\alpha = \dfrac{10 \pm \sqrt{100 - 4 \times 2.5 \times 8.5}}{5} = \dfrac{10 \pm \sqrt{15}}{5}$

$= 2.7745\ldots$ or $1.2254\ldots$

so $\alpha = 70.2°$ or $50.8°$ (3 s.f.)

2 (a)

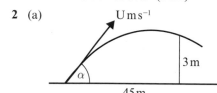

$x = U\cos\alpha\, t$ and, using $s = ut + \frac{1}{2}at^2$, $y = U\sin\alpha\, t - 4.9t^2$

$45 = U\cos\alpha\, t$ and $3 = U\sin\alpha\, t - 4.9t^2$

$3 = U\sin\alpha \times \dfrac{45}{U\cos\alpha} - 4.9\left(\dfrac{45}{U\cos\alpha}\right)^2$

$3 = 45\tan\alpha - \left(\dfrac{9922.5}{U^2\cos^2\alpha}\right)$

(b) $3 = 45\tan\alpha - \left(\dfrac{9922.5}{U^2\cos^2 32°}\right)$

$3 = 28.119\ldots - \dfrac{13796.85}{U^2}$, giving $U = \sqrt{\dfrac{13796.85}{25.119\ldots}}$

so $U = 23.436\ldots = 23.4\,\text{m s}^{-1}$

172. Static particles

1 (a) $R(\rightarrow)$: $T\cos\alpha = 5$ $\tan\alpha = \frac{3}{4}$ so $\cos\alpha = \frac{4}{5}$ $\sin\alpha = \frac{3}{5}$

$T \times \frac{4}{5} = 5 \Rightarrow T = \frac{25}{4}\,\text{N}$

(b) $R(\uparrow)$: $T + T\sin\alpha = W$

$\frac{25}{4} + \frac{25}{4} \times \frac{3}{5} = W \Rightarrow W = 10\,\text{N}$

2 (a) $T = 41.2\,\text{N}$ (b) $m = 4.475 \approx 4.5\,\text{kg}$ (2 s.f.)

3 $\alpha = 56°$, $T = 35.6 \approx 36\,\text{N}$ (2 s.f.)

173. Limiting equilibrium

1 (a) $R(\nwarrow)$: $P\sin 20° + 15\cos 20° = 20$

$P\sin 20° + 14.10 = 20$

$P = 17.3\,\text{N}$

(b) $R(\nearrow)$: $P\cos 20° = 15\sin 20° + F$

$17.3\cos 20° - 15\sin 20° = \mu \times 20$

$\mu = 0.56$

(c) $R = 15\cos 20° = 14.10\,\text{N}$

$F_{max} = 0.56 \times 14.10 = 7.90\,\text{N}$

Component of weight down plane $= 15\sin 20°$
$= 5.13\,\text{N}$

$5.13 < 7.90$ so parcel will not move

2 Parallel to plane: $T + F = 30g\sin 50°$

$T = 30g\sin 50° - 0.25 \times 30g\cos 50°$

$= 177.972\ldots = 180\text{N}$

174. Static rigid bodies

1 The ladder is on the point of slipping (limiting equilibrium), so $F = \mu R$

$R(\rightarrow)$: $F(= \mu R) = S$

$R(\uparrow)$: $R = 9W$ which gives $S = \mu 9W$

Taking moments about A:

$W \times a\cos\theta + 8W \times \dfrac{3a}{2}\cos\theta$

$= S \times 2a\sin\theta$

$W \times a \times \frac{3}{5} + 8W \times \frac{3a}{2} \times \frac{3}{5} = \mu 9W \times 2a \times \frac{4}{5}$

This simplifies to $3 + 36 = 72\mu$

So $\mu = \frac{39}{72} = \frac{13}{24}$

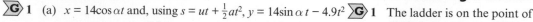

2 $R(\rightarrow)$: $F_1 = S$, but $F_1 = \mu R$ since friction is limiting, so $\mu R = S$

$R(\uparrow)$: $R + F_2 = W$, but $F_2 = 0.3S$ since friction is limiting,

so $R + 0.3S = W$,

hence $R + 0.3\mu R = W$ ①

Taking moments about B,

$W \times a\cos\theta + F_1 \times 2a\sin\theta$

$= R \times 2a\cos\theta$

$W \times a \times \dfrac{4}{\sqrt{65}} + \mu R \times 2a \times \dfrac{7}{\sqrt{65}} = R \times 2a \times \dfrac{4}{\sqrt{65}}$

(using $\tan\theta = \frac{7}{4}$ to obtain $\cos\theta$ and $\sin\theta$)

This simplifies to $4W + 14\mu R = 8R$ ②

① and ② give $4R + 1.2\mu R + 14\mu R = 8R$ hence $15.2\mu = 4$

giving $\mu = \dfrac{4}{15.2} = 0.263$ (3 s.f.)

175. Connected particles 2

1 (a) Q: $5g - T = 5a$ ①

P: $R = 4g\cos 40° = 30\,\text{N}$

$T - F - 4g\sin 40° = 4a$ ②

$T - 0.4 \times 30 - 25.2 = 4a$

$T - 37.2 = 4a$ ③

① + ②: $5g - 37.2 = 9a$

$11.8 = 9a$

$a = 1.31 \approx 1.3\,\text{m s}^{-2}$ (2 s.f.)

(b) From ③: $T - 37.2 = 4 \times 1.31$

$T = 42.44 \approx 42\,\text{N}$ (2 s.f.)

(c) $s = 0.6$ $u = 0$ $a = 1.31$

$v^2 = u^2 + 2as = 0 + 2 \times 1.31 \times 0.6$

$v = 1.25 \approx 1.3\,\text{m s}^{-1}$ (2 s.f.)

2 (a) $a = 0.4g$

(b) $T = 3.6mg$

176. Vectors in kinematics

1 (a) $\mathbf{r} = \mathbf{r_0} + \mathbf{v}\,t$

$7\mathbf{i} + 10\mathbf{j} = (2\mathbf{i} - 5\mathbf{j}) + \mathbf{v} \times 2.5$

$5\mathbf{i} + 15\mathbf{j} = 2.5\mathbf{v}$ $\mathbf{v} = 2\mathbf{i} + 6\mathbf{j}$

$v = \sqrt{4 + 36} = \sqrt{40} = 6.32\,\text{m s}^{-1}$

(b) $\mathbf{b} = 2\mathbf{i} - 5\mathbf{j} + (2\mathbf{i} + 6\mathbf{j})t$

2 Distance $= 13\,\text{m}$

3 (a) $\mathbf{v} = 4\mathbf{i} + 6\mathbf{j}$

(b) $\mathbf{p} = (12\mathbf{i} + 14\mathbf{j}) + (4\mathbf{i} + 6\mathbf{j})t$
$\mathbf{q} = (8\mathbf{i} - 4\mathbf{j}) + 10t\mathbf{j}$

(c) $\overrightarrow{PQ} = \mathbf{q} - \mathbf{p} = (-4\mathbf{i} - 18\mathbf{j}) + (-4\mathbf{i} + 4\mathbf{j})t$
$= (-4 - 4t)\mathbf{i} + (-18 + 4t)\mathbf{j}$
$d^2 = (-4 - 4t)^2 + (-18 + 4t)^2$
$= 32t^2 - 112t + 340$

177. Vectors and bearings

  1 (a)

$\tan\theta = \frac{2}{5} = 0.4 \qquad \theta = 21.8 \approx 22°$
Bearing $= 360° - 22° = 338°$

(b) Position vector of A at time $t = (4\mathbf{i} - 7\mathbf{j}) + (-2\mathbf{i} + 5\mathbf{j})t$
$\qquad\qquad = (4 - 2t)\mathbf{i} + (-7 + 5t)\mathbf{j}$
Position vector of B at time $t = (-20\mathbf{i} + 5\mathbf{j}) + (2\mathbf{i} + 3\mathbf{j})t$
$\qquad\qquad = (-20 + 2t)\mathbf{i} + (5 + 3t)\mathbf{j}$
$\mathbf{i}$ components equal: $4 - 2t = -20 + 2t$
$\qquad\qquad\qquad t = 6\,\text{s}$
$\mathbf{j}$ components at $t = 6$: $\quad A: -7 + 30 = 23$
$\qquad\qquad\qquad\qquad\qquad B: 5 + 18 = 23$
Position vector of P: $-8\mathbf{i} + 23\mathbf{j}$

2 (a) $108°$ $\qquad\qquad$ (b) $\mathbf{r} = 20\mathbf{i} - 20\mathbf{j}$
(c) $\mathbf{s} = (16 + 6t)\mathbf{i} - 8\mathbf{j}$ $\quad$ (d) 1440

178. Variable acceleration 3

1 (a) $v = \int a\,dt = \int 2\cos\pi t\,dt = \frac{2}{\pi}\sin\pi t + c$

When $t = 0$, $v = \frac{3}{\pi}$, so $\frac{3}{\pi} = \frac{2}{\pi}\sin 0 + c$, giving $c = \frac{3}{\pi}$

so $v = \frac{2}{\pi}\sin\pi t + \frac{3}{\pi}$

(b) Since the maximum value of $\sin\pi t$ is 1, maximum velocity $= \frac{2}{\pi} + \frac{3}{\pi} = \frac{5}{\pi}$

(c) $s = \int v\,dt = \int_0^4 \left(\frac{2}{\pi}\sin\pi t + \frac{3}{\pi}\right)dt = \left[\frac{-2}{\pi^2}\cos\pi t + \frac{3}{\pi}t\right]_0^4$

$= \left(\frac{-2}{\pi^2}\cos 4\pi + \frac{12}{\pi}\right) - \left(\frac{-2}{\pi^2}\cos 0 + 0\right)$

$= \frac{-2}{\pi^2} + \frac{12}{\pi} + \frac{2}{\pi^2}$

$= \frac{12}{\pi}\,\text{m or } 3.82\,\text{m (3 s.f.)}$

2 (a) v increases as t takes values from 0 to 4, so greatest speed is when $t = 4$, $v = 16\,\text{m s}^{-1}$

(b) $s = \int v\,dt = \int_0^4 (6t^{1.5} - 2t^2)\,dt = \left[\frac{12}{5}t^{2.5} - \frac{2}{3}t^3\right]_0^4$

$= 76.8 - 42.666\ldots = 34.133\ldots = 34.1\,\text{m (3 s.f.)}$

(c) $a = \frac{dv}{dt} = 0 + \frac{3}{2}(t - 2)^2$, so when $t = 5$, $a = 13.5\,\text{m s}^{-2}$

(d) From 4 to 6 seconds, $s = \int v\,dt = \int_4^6 \left(12 + \frac{(t-2)^3}{2}\right)dt$

$= \left[12t + \frac{(t-2)^4}{8}\right]_4^6$

$s = (72 + 32) - (48 + 2) = 54\,\text{m}$, so total distance in the first 6 seconds $= 34.1 + 54 = 88.1\,\text{m (3 s.f.)}$

179. Calculus with vectors

1 (a) $\mathbf{a} = \frac{d\mathbf{v}}{dt} = (6 - 3t^2)\mathbf{i} + 2t^{-0.5}\mathbf{j}$

(b) (i) Using $\mathbf{F} = m\mathbf{a}$ when $m = 3$,
$\mathbf{F} = 3\mathbf{a} = (18 - 9t^2)\mathbf{i} + 6t^{-0.5}\mathbf{j}$

(ii) When $t = 1$, $\mathbf{F} = 9\mathbf{i} + 6\mathbf{j}$, so magnitude of
$\mathbf{F} = \sqrt{9^2 + 6^2} = 10.8\,\text{N}$

(c) $18 - 9t^2 = 0$, $t^2 = 2$, $t = \sqrt{2} = 1.4\,\text{s (2 s.f.)}$

(d) $\mathbf{r} = \int \mathbf{v}\,dt = \int ((6t - t^3)\mathbf{i} + 4t^{0.5}\mathbf{j})\,dt = \left(3t^2 - \frac{t^4}{4}\right)\mathbf{i} + \frac{8}{3}t^{1.5}\mathbf{j} + \mathbf{c}$

When $t = 0$, $\mathbf{r} = \mathbf{i} - 2\mathbf{j}$, so $\mathbf{i} - 2\mathbf{j} = 0 + 0 + \mathbf{c}$, giving
$\mathbf{c} = \mathbf{i} - 2\mathbf{j}$

so $\mathbf{r} = \left(3t^2 - \frac{t^4}{4} + 1\right)\mathbf{i} + \left(\frac{8}{3}t^{1.5} - 2\right)\mathbf{j}$

and when $t = 4$, $\mathbf{r} = (48 - 64 + 1)\mathbf{i} + \left(\frac{64}{3} - 2\right)\mathbf{j}$
$= -15\mathbf{i} + 19.33\ldots\mathbf{j} = -15\mathbf{i} + 19.3\mathbf{j}$ (3 s.f.)

2 (a) Using $\mathbf{F} = m\mathbf{a}$, $12e^{-2t}\mathbf{i} - 8t^3\mathbf{j} = 4\mathbf{a}$, so $\mathbf{a} = 3e^{-2t}\mathbf{i} - 2t^3\mathbf{j}$

(b) $\mathbf{v} = \int \mathbf{a}\,dt = \int (3e^{-2t}\mathbf{i} - 2t^3\mathbf{j})\,dt = \frac{-3}{2}e^{-2t}\mathbf{i} - \frac{t^4}{2}\mathbf{j} + \mathbf{c}$

When $t = 0$, $\mathbf{v} = 6.5\mathbf{i} - 5\mathbf{j}$, so $6.5\mathbf{i} - 5\mathbf{j} = \frac{-3}{2}\mathbf{i} + \mathbf{c}$,

giving $\mathbf{c} = 8\mathbf{i} - 5\mathbf{j}$

So $\mathbf{v} = \left(\frac{-3}{2}e^{-2t} + 8\right)\mathbf{i} - \left(\frac{t^4}{2} + 5\right)\mathbf{j}$

(c) When $t = 2$, $\mathbf{v} = \left(\frac{-3}{2}e^{-4} + 8\right)\mathbf{i} - (8 + 5)\mathbf{j} = 7.9725\ldots\mathbf{i} - 13\mathbf{j}$

Speed at $t = 2$ is $\sqrt{7.9725\ldots^2 + 13^2} = 15.249\ldots$
$= 15.2\,\text{m s}^{-1}$ (3 s.f.)

180. You are the examiner!

1 (a) $\mathbf{a} = 2t\mathbf{i} + \frac{3}{\sqrt{t}}\mathbf{j}$, so $\mathbf{v} = \int \mathbf{a}\,dt = \int \left(2t\mathbf{i} + \frac{3}{\sqrt{t}}\mathbf{j}\right)dt = t^2\mathbf{i} + 6t^{0.5}\mathbf{j} + \mathbf{c}$

When $t = 4$, $\mathbf{v} = 17\mathbf{i} + 10\mathbf{j}$, so $17\mathbf{i} + 10\mathbf{j} = 16\mathbf{i} + 12\mathbf{j} + \mathbf{c}$,
giving $\mathbf{c} = \mathbf{i} - 2\mathbf{j}$
So $\mathbf{v} = (t^2 + 1)\mathbf{i} + (6t^{0.5} - 2)\mathbf{j}$

(b) $\mathbf{r} = \int \mathbf{v}\,dt = \int ((t^2 + 1)\mathbf{i} + (6t^{0.5} - 2)\mathbf{j})\,dt$

$= \left(\frac{t^3}{3} + t\right)\mathbf{i} + (4t^{1.5} - 2t)\mathbf{j} + \mathbf{w}$

When $t = 0$, $\mathbf{r} = 3\mathbf{i} - \mathbf{j}$, so $3\mathbf{i} - \mathbf{j} = 0 + 0 + \mathbf{w}$, giving
$\mathbf{w} = 3\mathbf{i} - \mathbf{j}$

So $\mathbf{r} = \left(\frac{t^3}{3} + t + 3\right)\mathbf{i} + (4t^{1.5} - 2t - 1)\mathbf{j}$

When $t = 1$, $\mathbf{r} = \frac{13}{3}\mathbf{i} + \mathbf{j}$

2 (a)

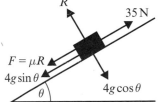

$\tan\theta = \frac{3}{4}$, so $\sin\theta = \frac{3}{5}$ and $\cos\theta = \frac{4}{5}$
Resolving perpendicular to the plane, $R = 4g\cos\theta = \frac{16}{5}g$

(b) Friction is limiting so $F = \mu R$, so $F = \mu\frac{16}{5}g$
Using force = mass × acceleration, parallel to the plane,
$35 - \mu\frac{16}{5}g - 4g\sin\theta = 4 \times 1.25$, so $35 - 31.36\mu - 23.52 = 5$

$31.36\mu = 6.48$, giving $\mu = \frac{6.48}{31.36} = 0.207$ (3 s.f.)

181. You are the examiner!

3 (a) Using $v^2 = u^2 + 2as$ for the vertical motion,
with $v = 0$, $u = 30 \sin 50°$, $a = -9.8$ and $s = h$
$0 = (30 \sin 50°)^2 - 19.6h$, giving
$h = \dfrac{(30 \sin 50°)^2}{19.6} = 26.9 \text{ m (3 s.f.)}$,
so greatest height $= 27.9 \text{ m}$

(b) Using $v = u + at$ for the vertical motion,
with $v = 0$, $u = 30 \sin 50°$, $a = -9.8$ and $t = T$ (time to greatest height),
$0 = 30 \sin 50° - 9.8T$, giving $T = 2.35 \text{ s (3 s.f.)}$

(c) Horizontal component of initial speed $= 30 \cos 50°$ (constant)
Time to travel 65 m horizontally $= \dfrac{\text{distance}}{\text{speed}}$
$= \dfrac{65}{30 \cos 50°} = 3.3707\ldots \text{ s}$

Using $s = ut + \frac{1}{2}at^2$ for the vertical motion, with
$u = 30 \sin 50°$, $a = -9.8$, $t = 3.3707\ldots$ and $s = h$
$h = 30 \sin 50° \times 3.3707\ldots - 4.9 \times (3.3707\ldots)^2$
$= 21.8 \text{ m (3 s.f.)}$, so height after $3.3037\ldots$ s is 22.8 m

So the cricket ball clears the roof of the cricket pavilion by approximately 2.8 m

4 (a) $\tan \theta = \frac{4}{3}$, so $\sin \theta = \frac{4}{5}$ and $\cos \theta = \frac{3}{5}$

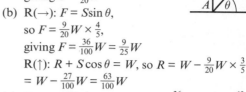

Taking moments about A,
$W \times 3a \cos \theta = S \times 4a$,
so $\frac{9}{5}W = 4S$,
giving $S = \frac{9}{20}W$

(b) $R(\rightarrow)$: $F = S \sin \theta$,
so $F = \frac{9}{20}W \times \frac{4}{5}$,
giving $F = \frac{36}{100}W = \frac{9}{25}W$
$R(\uparrow)$: $R + S \cos \theta = W$, so $R = W - \frac{9}{20}W \times \frac{3}{5}$
$= W - \frac{27}{100}W = \frac{63}{100}W$

(c) For equilibrium, $F \leqslant \mu R$, so $\frac{36}{100}W \leqslant \mu \times \frac{63}{100}W$,
giving $\mu \geqslant \frac{36}{63}$ or $\mu \geqslant \frac{4}{7}$

PRACTICE PAPERS

Paper 1 Pure Mathematics 1

1 (a) $y = 2x^3 - 5x^2 - 4x + 3$

$$\frac{dy}{dx} = 6x^2 - 10x - 4$$

(b) $\frac{d^2y}{dx^2} = 12x - 10$

(c) When $x = 2$, $\frac{dy}{dx} = 6(4) - 10(2) - 4 = 24 - 20 - 4 = 0$

So there is a stationary point at $x = 2$

(d) When $x = 2$, $\frac{d^2y}{dx^2} = 12(2) - 10 > 0$, so the stationary point is a minimum.

2 (a)

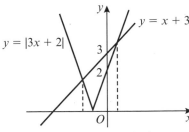

Two solutions where graphs intersect.

(b) $|3x + 2| = x + 3$

$3x + 2 = x + 3$ or $-3x - 2 = x + 3$

$x = \frac{1}{2}$ $\qquad\qquad$ $x = -\frac{5}{4}$

3 $(3k - 8)x^2 - kx + (3k - 5) = 0$

Equal roots when '$b^2 - 4ac$' = 0

$k^2 - 4(3k - 8)(3k - 5) = 0$

$-35k^2 + 156k - 160 = 0$

or $35k^2 - 156k + 160 = 0$

$(5k - 8)(7k - 20) = 0$

So $k = \frac{8}{5}$ or $\frac{20}{7}$

4 $\int 2x^2 \ln 3x \, dx$

$u = \ln 3x$, $\qquad \frac{du}{dx} = \frac{3}{3x} = \frac{1}{x}$

$\frac{dv}{dx} = 2x^2$, $\qquad v = \frac{2}{3}x^3$

So $\int 2x^2 \ln 3x \, dx = \frac{2}{3}x^3 \ln 3x - \int \left(\frac{2}{3}x^3\right)\left(\frac{1}{x}\right) dx$

$= \frac{2}{3}x^3 \ln 3x - \int \frac{2}{3}x^2 \, dx$

$= \frac{2}{3}x^3 \ln 3x - \frac{2}{9}x^3 + c$

5 $\cos^2(x - 70°) = 0.3$

$\cos(x - 70°) = \pm\sqrt{0.3} = \pm 0.54772...$

$(x - 70°)$ must lie in the range $-70°$ to $290°$

$x - 70° = -56.79°$ $\qquad\qquad$ $x = 13.21°$

$x - 70° = 56.79°$ $\qquad\qquad$ $x = 126.89°$

$x - 70° = 123.21°$ $\qquad\qquad$ $x = 193.21°$

$x - 70° = 236.79°$ $\qquad\qquad$ $x = 306.79°$

6 $f(x) = 2x^3 + 3x^2 - 12x + 4$ $\qquad f'(x) = 6x^2 + 6x - 12$

(a) $f(1) = 2 + 3 - 12 + 4 = -3$ $\Big\}$ so $f(x) = 0$ has a root

$f(2) = 16 + 12 - 24 + 4 = 8$ $\Big\}$ between $x = 1$ and $x = 2$

(b) $x_{n+1} = x_n - \frac{f(x_n)}{f'(x_n)}$ $\qquad x_1 = 2$

$x_2 = 2 - \frac{f(2)}{f'(2)} = 2 - \frac{8}{24} = 1.\dot{6}$

$x_3 = 1.\dot{6} - \frac{f(1.\dot{6})}{f'(1.\dot{6})} = 1.5580...$

(c) $f'(x) = 6(x^2 + x - 2) = 6(x + 2)(x - 1)$ which is zero when $x = 1$

So $x = 1$ corresponds to a stationary point.

The tangent at $x = 1$ has zero gradient, so Newton–Raphson cannot be used if $x_1 = 1$.

7 (a) $20, k, 8.45$ $\qquad$ Common ratio $= \frac{k}{20}$ and $\frac{8.45}{k}$

So $\frac{k}{20} = \frac{8.45}{k}$, $k^2 = 20 \times 8.45 = 169$, so $k = 13$

(b) $r = \frac{13}{20} = 0.65$ $\qquad S_{12} = \frac{20(1 - 0.65^{12})}{1 - 0.65} = 56.81...$

8 $|\overrightarrow{AC}| = |\overrightarrow{AB}| + |\overrightarrow{BC}| = -\mathbf{i} - \mathbf{j} - 4\mathbf{k}$

$|\overrightarrow{AB}| = \sqrt{1 + 4 + 25} = \sqrt{30}$, $|\overrightarrow{BC}| = \sqrt{4 + 9 + 1} = \sqrt{14}$

$|\overrightarrow{AC}| = \sqrt{1 + 1 + 16} = \sqrt{18}$

$\cos A = \frac{30 + 18 - 14}{2 \times \sqrt{30} \times \sqrt{18}} = \frac{17}{\sqrt{30}\sqrt{18}}$, $\angle BAC = 42.982...° = 43°$

9 $f(x) = 5x + 2x^3$

$f'(x) = \lim_{h \to 0} \frac{f(x + h) - f(x)}{h}$

$= \lim_{h \to 0} \frac{5(x + h) + 2(x + h)^3 - 5x - 2x^3}{h}$

$= \lim_{h \to 0} \frac{5\cancel{x} + 5h + 2\cancel{x^3} + 6x^2h + 6xh^2 + 2h^3 - 5\cancel{x} - 2\cancel{x^3}}{h}$

$= \lim_{h \to 0} (5 + 6x^2 + 6xh + 2h^2)$

As $h \to 0$, both $6xh$ and $2h^2 \to 0$

So $f'(x) = 5 + 6x^2$

10 (a) $\frac{2x + 5}{(2 - x)(1 + x)} \equiv \frac{A}{2 - x} + \frac{B}{1 + x}$

giving $A = 3$ and $B = 1$ (using 'cover up')

So $\frac{2x + 5}{(2 - x)(1 + x)} = \frac{3}{2 - x} + \frac{1}{1 + x}$

(b) $\frac{2x + 5}{(2 - x)(1 + x)} = 3(2 - x)^{-1} + 1(1 + x)^{-1}$

$= 3 \times 2^{-1}\left(1 - \frac{x}{2}\right)^{-1} + 1(1 + x)^{-1}$

$\approx \frac{3}{2}\left(1 + (-1)\left(-\frac{x}{2}\right) + \frac{(-1)(-2)}{1 \times 2}\left(-\frac{x}{2}\right)^2\right)$

$+ 1\left(1 + (-1)(x) + \frac{(-1)(-2)(x)^2}{1 \times 2}\right)$

$= \frac{3}{2}\left(1 + \frac{x}{2} + \frac{x^2}{4}\right) + 1(1 - x + x^2)$

$= \frac{5}{2} - \frac{1}{4}x + \frac{11}{8}x^2, |x| < 1$

11 (a) $y = 2x^3 - 4x^2 + 1$

$\frac{dy}{dx} = 6x^2 - 8x$ which is zero when $x = 0$ and $x = \frac{4}{3}$

When $x = 0$, $y = 1$; when $x = \frac{4}{3}$, $y = 2\left(\frac{64}{27}\right) - 4\left(\frac{16}{9}\right) + 1 = -\frac{37}{27}$

$\frac{d^2y}{dx^2} = 12x - 8$ which is < 0 when $x = 0$ and > 0 when $x = \frac{4}{3}$

So $(0, 1)$ is a maximum point and $\left(\frac{4}{3}, -\frac{37}{27}\right)$ is a minimum point.

(b) When $x = -\frac{2}{3}$, $\frac{dy}{dx} = 6\left(-\frac{2}{3}\right)^2 - 8\left(-\frac{2}{3}\right) = \frac{8}{3} + \frac{16}{3} = \frac{24}{3} = 8$

So the tangent at $x = -\frac{2}{3}$ has gradient 8.

(c) $\dfrac{dy}{dx} = 6x^2 - 8x$; solve $6x^2 - 8x = 8$,

i.e. $3x^2 - 4x - 4 = 0$

$(3x + 2)(x - 2) = 0$,

$x = -\frac{2}{3}$ and $x = 2$

So P has an x-coordinate of 2,

and y-coordinate $= 2(8) - 4(4) + 1 = 1$

(d) Gradient of normal at $P = -\frac{1}{8}$

Equation of normal at P is $y - 1 = -\frac{1}{8}(x - 2)$

i.e. $8y - 8 = -x + 2$, i.e. $x + 8y = 10$

12 (a) $P = a \times 10^{bt}$

$\log_{10} P = \log_{10}(a \times 10^{bt})$

$= \log_{10} a + \log_{10}(10^{bt})$

$= \log_{10} a + bt \log_{10} 10$

$= \log_{10} a + bt$

which is of the form $Y = C + MX$ where $Y = \log_{10} P$,

$C = \log_{10} a$, $M = b$ (gradient) and $X = t$

(b) The intercept on the vertical axis is $\log_{10} a$

(c) $\log_{10} a = 3.84$ so $a = 10^{3.84} = 6918.3$ (1 d.p.)

Gradient, $b = \dfrac{4.13 - 3.84}{5} = 0.058$

So $P = 6918.3 \times 10^{0.058t}$

(d) In 2018, $t = 8$, so estimated $P = 6918.3 \times 10^{(0.058 \times 8)}$

$= 20\,137.214\ldots$

Accept answers rounding to 20136 or 20137

13 (a) Volume = area of cross-section × length

$120 = \frac{1}{2} \times 3x \times 4x \times l$, giving $l = \dfrac{20}{x^2}$

Total length, $L = 2(3x + 4x + 5x) + 3l$ (hypotenuse = $5x$)

so $L = 24x + \dfrac{60}{x^2}$

(b) $\dfrac{dL}{dx} = 24 - \dfrac{120}{x^3}$ which is zero when $x = \sqrt[3]{5} = 1.71$ cm (2 d.p.)

So minimum $L = 24(1.71) + \dfrac{60}{(1.71)^2} = 61.56$ cm (2 d.p.)

(c) $\dfrac{d^2y}{dx^2} = \dfrac{360}{x^4}$ which is > 0 when $x = 1.71$

So 61.56 cm is the minimum value of L.

14 (a) Area of R

$= \dfrac{0.5}{2}[1.4142 + 9.4868 + 2(2.7042 + 4.4721 + 6.7315)]$

$= 9.67915 = 9.680$ (3 d.p.)

(b) Dividing the area into more strips would give a better estimate.

(c) Area of $R = \displaystyle\int_1^3 x\sqrt{1 + x^2}\,dx = \left[\frac{1}{3}(x^2 + 1)^{\frac{3}{2}}\right]_1^3$

$= \frac{1}{3}\left(10^{\frac{3}{2}} - 2^{\frac{3}{2}}\right) = 9.5981\ldots = 9.598$ (3 d.p.)

Using integration by substitution:

Let $u = \sqrt{1 + x^2}$ then $u^2 = 1 + x^2$ $x = 1 \Rightarrow u = \sqrt{2}$

$x = 3 \Rightarrow u = \sqrt{10}$

and $2u\,du = 2x\,dx$ so $u\,du = x\,dx$

and the integral becomes $\displaystyle\int_{\sqrt{2}}^{\sqrt{10}} u \times u\,du = \int_{\sqrt{2}}^{\sqrt{10}} u^2\,du = \left[\dfrac{u^3}{3}\right]_{\sqrt{2}}^{\sqrt{10}}$

leading to area = 9.598, as above

Paper 2 Pure Mathematics 2

1 $y = 3x(5x - 2)^3$

$\dfrac{dy}{dx} = 3x[3(5x - 2)^2(5)] + (5x - 2)^3(3)$

$= 45x(5x - 2)^2 + 3(5x - 2)^3$

$= (5x - 2)^2(45x + 15x - 6)$ or $3(5x - 2)^2(15x + 5x - 2)$

$= (60x - 6)(5x - 2)^2$ or $3(5x - 2)^2(20x - 2)$

$= 6(10x - 1)(5x - 2)^2$

$n = 2$, $A = 10$, $B = -1$

2 (a) $2\left(1 - \dfrac{\theta^2}{2}\right) - 3\theta + 5\left(1 - \dfrac{\theta^2}{2}\right)^2 = 2 - \theta^2 - 3\theta + 5\left(1 - \theta^2 + \dfrac{\theta^4}{4}\right)$

$= 2 - \theta^2 - 3\theta + 5 - 5\theta^2$

$= 7 - 3\theta - 6\theta^2$

(b) Sean should use radians:

$5° = 5 \times \dfrac{\pi}{180} = \dfrac{\pi}{36}$ radians

$7 - 3\theta - 6\theta^2 = 7 - 3\left(\dfrac{\pi}{36}\right) - 6\left(\dfrac{\pi}{36}\right)^2$

$= 6.692\,507\ldots$

$= 6.693$ (3 d.p.)

3 (a) Using $s = r\theta$, where $\theta =$ angle CBD, $1.12 = 3.2\theta$

So $\theta = \dfrac{1.12}{3.2} = 0.35$ radians

(b) Angle $ABD = \dfrac{\pi}{3} - 0.35 = 1.0471\ldots - 0.35$

$= 0.697$ radians (3 d.p.)

(c) Area of sector $= \frac{1}{2}r^2\theta = \frac{1}{2} \times (3.2)^2 \times 0.35 = 1.792$

Area of $\triangle ABD = \frac{1}{2} \times 2.6 \times 3.2 \times \sin(0.697) = 2.6703\ldots$

So area of cross-section $= 4.46\,\text{m}^2$ (2 d.p.)

4 (a) $2y^2 - y = 6x - 3x^2$

$4y\dfrac{dy}{dx} - \dfrac{dy}{dx} = 6 - 6x$ (differentiating implicitly)

So $\dfrac{dy}{dx} = \dfrac{6 - 6x}{4y - 1}$

(b) $\dfrac{dy}{dx} = 0$ when $x = 1$, so $2y^2 - y = 6 - 3$

Solving $2y^2 - y - 3 = 0$ gives $(2y - 3)(y + 1) = 0$

$y = \dfrac{3}{2}$, $y = -1$

So $\dfrac{dy}{dx} = 0$ at $\left(1, \frac{3}{2}\right)$ and $(1, -1)$

5 Proof by contradiction:

Assume $x^2 - y^2 = 18$, and x, y are integers.

$(x + y)(x - y) = 18$ and 18 has factor pairings of 1×18, 2×9, 3×6

So $\left.\begin{array}{l} x + y = 18 \\ x - y = 1 \end{array}\right\} \begin{array}{l} x = 9.5 \\ y = 8.5 \end{array}$

or $\left.\begin{array}{l} x + y = 9 \\ x - y = 2 \end{array}\right\} \begin{array}{l} x = 5.5 \\ y = 3.5 \end{array}$

or $\left.\begin{array}{l} x + y = 6 \\ x - y = 3 \end{array}\right\} \begin{array}{l} x = 4.5 \\ y = 1.5 \end{array}$

none of which give integer values of x and y so there is a contradiction.

Hence there are no integer solutions to $x^2 - y^2 = 18$.

6 $3\cos 2\theta = 2 - \sin \theta$

$\cos 2\theta = 1 - 2\sin^2\theta$, so the equation becomes

$3(1 - 2\sin^2\theta) = 2 - \sin \theta$

i.e. $6\sin^2\theta - \sin \theta - 1 = 0$

$(3\sin \theta + 1)(2\sin \theta - 1) = 0$

$\sin \theta = -\frac{1}{3}$, $\theta = -19.47°$ or $-160.53°$

$\sin \theta = \frac{1}{2}$, $\theta = 30°$ or $150°$

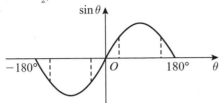

7 $a = 14$ $d = 4$

Sum of first $2n$ terms = sum of next n terms

This is equivalent to saying

Sum of first $3n$ terms = $2 \times$ sum of first $2n$ terms

i.e. $\frac{3n}{2}[28 + (3n - 1)4] = 2 \times \frac{2n}{2}[28 + (2n - 1)4]$

$3n(24 + 12n) = 4n(24 + 8n)$

$72n + 36n^2 = 96n + 32n^2$

$4n^2 - 24n = 0$

$4n(n - 6) = 0$

Since $n = 0$ is a trivial solution, $n = 6$

8 (a) $\sqrt[3]{8 - x} = \sqrt[3]{8\left(1 - \frac{x}{8}\right)} = 2\sqrt[3]{1 - \frac{x}{8}} = 2\left(1 - \frac{x}{8}\right)^{\frac{1}{3}}$

$= 2\left[1 + \frac{1}{3}\left(-\frac{x}{8}\right) + \frac{\left(\frac{1}{3}\right)\left(-\frac{2}{3}\right)}{1 \times 2}\left(-\frac{x}{8}\right)^2 + \dots\right]$

$= 2\left(1 - \frac{x}{24} - \frac{1}{576}x^2 - \dots\right)$

$= 2 - \frac{x}{12} - \frac{1}{288}x^2 - \dots$ So $k = -\frac{1}{288}$

(b) The expansion is valid for $\left|\frac{x}{8}\right| < 1$, i.e. $|x| < 8$

So substituting $x = 2$ to work out $\sqrt[3]{6}$ is valid.

(c) Using $x = 2$, $\sqrt[3]{8 - 2} = \sqrt[3]{6} = 2 - \frac{1}{6} - \frac{1}{72} = 1.81944\dots$

Exact value = $1.81712\dots$, so these are both 1.82 (3 s.f.)

9 (a) $T = 22 + me^{-kt}$

$T = 90$ when $t = 0$, so $90 = 22 + m$, so $m = 68$

$T = 75$ when $t = 2$, so $75 = 22 + 68e^{-2k}$

$e^{-2k} = \frac{53}{68}$, so $e^{2k} = \frac{68}{53}$, $2k = \ln\left(\frac{68}{53}\right)$, $k = 0.124\,607\dots$

(b) When $t = 10$, $T = 22\,68e^{-10k} = 22 + 68e^{-1.246\dots}$

$= 41.6\,°C$ (1 d.p.)

(c) As t increases, $e^{-kt} \to 0$, so $T \to 22\,°C$, meaning $20\,°C$ is impossible.

10 $ar^2 - ar = 40$ a = 1st term, r = common ratio

$ar^4 - ar^2 = 30$

$ar(r - 1) = 40$ ①

and $ar^2(r^2 - 1) = 30$, i.e. $ar^2(r + 1)(r - 1) = 30$ ②

Dividing ② by ①, $r(r + 1) = \frac{3}{4}$, i.e. $4r^2 + 4r - 3 = 0$

i.e. $(2r + 3)(2r - 1) = 0$, so $r = -\frac{3}{2}$ or $r = \frac{1}{2}$

When $r = -\frac{3}{2}$, $a\left(-\frac{3}{2}\right)\left(-\frac{5}{2}\right) = 40$, so $a = \frac{160}{15} = \frac{32}{3}$

When $r = \frac{1}{2}$, $a\left(\frac{1}{2}\right)\left(-\frac{1}{2}\right) = 40$, so $a = -160$

11 (a) $f(x) = 2e^x - \frac{1}{2}\ln 2x - 4$

$f'(x) = 2e^x - \frac{1}{2}\left(\frac{2}{2x}\right) = 2e^x - \frac{1}{2x}$

(b) At P, $x = \alpha$ and $f'(x) = 0$

So $2e^\alpha - \frac{1}{2\alpha} = 0$, giving $2e^\alpha = \frac{1}{2\alpha}$ or $\alpha = \frac{1}{4}e^{-\alpha}$

(c) Using $x_{n+1} = \frac{1}{4}e^{-x_n}$ with $x_1 = 0.5$

$x_2 = 0.151632\dots = 0.1516$ (4 d.p.)

$x_3 = 0.214825\dots = 0.2148$ (4 d.p.)

$x_4 = 0.201670\dots = 0.2017$ (4 d.p.)

$x_5 = 0.20434\dots = 0.2043$ (4 d.p.)

(d) Use $x = 0.20385$ to give $f(x) = -0.00055\dots$

Use $x = 0.20395$ to give $f(x) = 0.00089\dots$

There is a change of sign, so $\alpha = 0.2039$ (4 d.p.)

12 $x = 11t$ $y = -5t^2 + 8t + 2$ $0 \leqslant t \leqslant k$

(a) $t = 0$ gives $y = 2$, so the shot is thrown from a height of 2 m.

(b) $t = k$ is when the shot hits the ground.

So solve $y = -5t^2 + 8t + 2 = 0$, i.e. $5t^2 - 8t - 2 = 0$

$t = \frac{8 \pm \sqrt{64 + 40}}{10} = 1.8198\dots$ (positive solution only)

So the shot will land after 1.82 seconds (2 d.p.)

(c) Horizontal distance = $11 \times 1.8198\dots = 20$ metres

(d) Using calculus, $\frac{dy}{dt} = -10t + 8$, zero when $t = \frac{4}{5} = 0.8$

So, maximum height = $-5(0.8)^2 + 8(0.8) + 2 = 5.2$ m

Or completing the square:

$-5t^2 + 8t + 2 = -5\left(t^2 - \frac{8}{5}t\right) + 2$

$= -5\left(t - \frac{4}{5}\right)^2 + \frac{16}{5} + 2$

$= -5\left(t - \frac{4}{5}\right)^2 + \frac{26}{5}$

which has a maximum value of $\frac{26}{5} = 5.2$ m

13 (a) $f(x) = e^{2x} + 1$, since $e^{2x} > 0$ for all values of x the range of f is $f(x) > 1$

(b) $f(x + 2) = 10$, $e^{2(x+2)} + 1 = 10$

i.e. $e^{2(x+2)} = 9$, so $2(x + 2) = \ln 9$

so $x + 2 = \frac{1}{2}\ln 9 = \ln 9^{\frac{1}{2}} = \ln 3$

So $x = \ln 3 - 2$ is an exact solution of this equation.

(c) Let $y = f^{-1}(x)$, then $f(y) = x$

i.e. $e^{2y} + 1 = x$, $e^{2y} = x - 1$, $2y = \ln(x - 1)$

So $y = f^{-1}(x) = \frac{1}{2}\ln(x - 1)$ or $\ln(x - 1)^{\frac{1}{2}}$ or $\ln\sqrt{x - 1}$

Domain for f^{-1} is $x > 1$

(d)

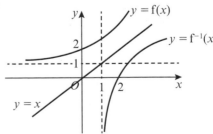

14 $y = 8x - 4x^{\frac{3}{2}} - 3$

$\dfrac{dy}{dx} = 8 - 6x^{\frac{1}{2}}$

At $x = 4$, $\dfrac{dy}{dx} = 8 - 12 = -4$

Tangent at P has equation

$y + 3 = -4(x - 4)$

$y = -4x + 13$

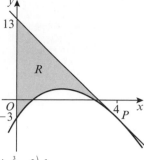

Area $R = \displaystyle\int_0^4 (-4x + 13) - (8x - 4x^{\frac{3}{2}} - 3)\,dx$

$= \displaystyle\int_0^4 (16 - 12x + 4x^{\frac{3}{2}})\,dx$

$= \left[16x - 6x^2 + \frac{8}{5}x^{\frac{5}{2}}\right]_0^4$

$= \left(64 - 96 + \frac{256}{5}\right) - (0)$

$= 19.2$

Paper 3 Statistics and Mechanics

Section A: Statistics

1 (a) Area for $15 < x \leqslant 20$ group $= 2 \times 8 = 16$

Frequency of 12 equivalent to area of 16

So $A = \frac{4}{3} \times f$ or $f = \frac{3}{4}A$

Width of $20 < x \leqslant 30$ group $= 4\,cm$. $f = 15$, so $A = 20$

So height of $20 < x \leqslant 30$ group $= 5\,cm$

(b) Mean $= 14.6$ hours, standard deviation $= 9.09$ hour

(c) Median $= 10 + \frac{12}{18} \times 5$ (12th item in $10 < x \leqslant 15$ group)

$= 13.3$ hours

2 (a) $Y \sim B(30, 0.4)$ Test for $2\frac{1}{2}\%$ in a two-tailed test.

$P(Y \leqslant 6) = 0.0172$ $P(Y \geqslant 17) = 0.0481$

$P(Y \leqslant 7) = 0.0435$ $P(Y \geqslant 18) = 0.0212$

Critical region is $Y \leqslant 6$ and $Y \geqslant 18$

(b) Actual significance level is $0.0172 + 0.0212 = 0.0384$ or 3.84%

(c) $Y = 17$ is not in the critical region.

There is not enough evidence to reject H_0 at the 5% significance level.

3 (a) $P(X > 24\,000) = 0.7625$

(b) $P(X > k) = 0.95$ gives $k = 20\,743$

(c) $H_0 : \mu = 26\,500$, $H_1 : \mu > 26\,500$

(d) Test statistics are:

$\mu = 26\,500$

Standard deviation for sample $= \dfrac{3300}{\sqrt{12}} = 952.6$

$P(Y > 28\,200) = 0.0372$

Since $0.0372 < 0.05$, the result is significant.

Reject H_0: there is evidence to suggest that these tyres have a longer mean lifetime.

4 (a) $r = 0.6178$

(b) $H_0 : \rho = 0$ $H_1 : \rho > 0$

We are testing whether or not there is a linear relationship.

For $n = 7$, the 5% value (1-tail test) is 0.6694

So the critical region is $r > 0.6694$

Since $0.6178 < 0.6694$, there is not sufficient evidence at the 5% level to reject H_0. So the claim that there is a linear relationship between the daily mean temperature and the daily total rainfall is not supported.

(c) **F** is Beijing, **G** is Jacksonville.

(d) We could consider a larger sample size. These are data for only one month and could be subject to abnormal weather conditions. Results will vary according to the time of year the survey took place.

5 (a) $P(A \mid B) = \dfrac{P(A \cap B)}{P(B)}$, so $0.4 = \dfrac{P(A \cap B)}{0.6}$

$P(A \cap B) = 0.24$

(b) $P(A' \cap B') = P((A \cup B)')$

$P(A \cup B) = P(A) + P(B) - P(A \cap B)$

$= 0.5 + 0.6 - 0.24$

$= 0.86$

So $P(A' \cap B') = 1 - 0.86 = 0.14$

(c) $P(A) \times P(B) = 0.5 \times 0.6 = 0.3 \neq 0.24$

so $P(A) \times P(B) \neq P(A \cap B)$

So A and B are not independent events.

(d)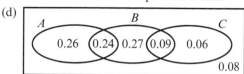

6 (a) $X \sim B(10, 0.42)$

(b) 'More pink' means at least 6 pink.

$P(X \geqslant 6) = 0.2016$

(c) Use a normal approximation, $n = 80$, $p = 0.42$

$\mu = 80 \times 0.42 = 33.6$, $\sigma^2 = 80 \times 0.42 \times 0.58 = 19.488$

so $\sigma = \sqrt{19.488} = 4.41452\ldots$

$Y \sim N(33.6, 4.41452\ldots^2)$; use a continuity correction.

$P(X \geqslant 30) \approx P(Y > 29.5) = 0.8235$

Section B: Mechanics

7 (a) $v = \displaystyle\int a\,dt = \int (2t^3 - 7t)\,dt = \dfrac{t^4}{2} - \dfrac{7t^2}{2} + c$

When $t = 0$, $v = 5$ so $c = 5$

So $v = \dfrac{t^4}{2} - \dfrac{7t^2}{2} + 5$

(b) Instantaneously at rest when $v = 0$

$\dfrac{t^4}{2} - \dfrac{7t^2}{2} + 5 = 0$

i.e. $t^4 - 7t^2 + 10 = 0$

$(t^2 - 2)(t^2 - 5) = 0$

$t = \sqrt{2}$ and $t = \sqrt{5}$

So the particle is instantaneously at rest after $\sqrt{2}\,$s and $\sqrt{5}\,$s.

8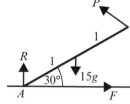

Force P acts at an unknown angle, so take moments about B to set up an equation in $15g$, R and F.

$R \times 2 \cos 30° = 15g \times 1 \cos 30° + F \times 2 \sin 30°$

Friction is limiting, so $F = \mu R = \frac{2}{5}R$

So $R \times 2 \times \dfrac{\sqrt{3}}{2} = 15g \times \dfrac{\sqrt{3}}{2} + \frac{2}{5}R \times 2 \times \dfrac{1}{2}$

$R(2\sqrt{3} + 0.8) = 15g \times \sqrt{3}$

giving $R = 95.6\,$N (3 s.f.)

9 (a) $\mathbf{r}_P = \int \mathbf{v}\,dt = \int ((6t-5)\mathbf{i} + 4\mathbf{j})\,dt = (3t^2 - 5t)\mathbf{i} + 4t\mathbf{j} + \mathbf{c}$

When $t = 0$, $\mathbf{r}_P = 2\mathbf{i} + \mathbf{j}$, so $\mathbf{c} = 2\mathbf{i} + \mathbf{j}$

So $\mathbf{r}_P = (3t^2 - 5t + 2)\mathbf{i} + (4t + 1)\mathbf{j}$

(b) For Q, after t seconds, $\mathbf{r}_Q = (5\mathbf{i} + 7\mathbf{j}) + t(3\mathbf{i} + w\mathbf{j})$
$$= (5 + 3t)\mathbf{i} + (7 + wt)\mathbf{j}$$

When $t = T$, $\mathbf{r}_P = \mathbf{r}_Q$

Equating the **i** components, $3T^2 - 5T + 2 = 5 + 3T$

i.e. $3T^2 - 8T - 3 = 0$, i.e. $(3T + 1)(T - 3) = 0$

So the cars meet when $T = 3$, i.e. after 3 seconds.

(c) Equating the **j** components, $4T + 1 = 7 + wT$

i.e. $13 = 7 + 3w$, giving $w = 2$

10 (a) Component of acceleration due to gravity down the slope of the inclined plane is $g\sin\alpha$

$\tan\alpha = \frac{3}{4}$, so $\sin\alpha = \frac{3}{5}$ and $\cos\alpha = \frac{4}{5}$

From A to B, using $v^2 = u^2 + 2as$,

$36 = u^2 - 2 \times g\sin\alpha \times 2.5$

$36 = u^2 - 3g$, giving $u = 8.1\,\text{m s}^{-1}$ (2 s.f.)

So speed of projection from A is $8.1\,\text{m s}^{-1}$

(b) From B to C, using $v^2 = u^2 + 2as$,

$0 = 36 + 2 \times a \times 2$, so $a = 9\,\text{m s}^{-2}$

Resolving perpendicular to plane, $R = 3g\cos\alpha = \frac{12}{5}g$

So frictional force acting down plane $= \frac{12}{5}g\mu$

Using Newton's 3rd law, $-\frac{12}{5}g\mu - 3g\sin\alpha = 3 \times (-9)$

i.e. $\frac{12}{5}g\mu = 27 - \frac{9}{5}g$, giving $\mu = 0.397... = 0.40$

(c) At C, weight component down slope $= 3g\sin\alpha = \frac{9}{5}g$

Friction (acting up slope) $= \mu R = 0.4 \times \frac{12}{5}g = \frac{4.8}{5}g$

So the particle will slide back down the plane.

11 (a) Horizontal component of initial velocity $= 40\cos 25°$
$$= 36.3\,\text{m s}^{-1}\ (3\ \text{s.f.})$$

Vertical component $= 40\sin 25° = 16.9\,\text{m s}^{-1}$ (3 s.f.)

Using $s = ut + \frac{1}{2}at^2$ for the vertical motion,

$-11 = 16.9t - 5t^2$, i.e. $5t^2 - 16.9t - 11 = 0$

$$t = \frac{-16.9 \pm \sqrt{16.9^2 - 4 \times 5 \times (-11)}}{10}$$

giving $t = 3.9385... = 3.94\,\text{s}$ (3 d.p.)

(b) Using $v = u + at$ for the vertical motion,

$v = 16.9 - 10 \times 3.94$
$$= -22.5$$

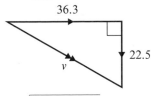

$v = \sqrt{36.3^2 + 22.5^2}$
$$= 42.7\,\text{m s}^{-1}\ (3\ \text{s.f.})$$

(c) $\tan\theta = \dfrac{22.5}{36.3}$, giving $\theta = 31.8°$ (3 s.f.)

(d) Any two of:

- take air resistance/wind into account
- use a more accurate value of g (e.g. $9.8\,\text{m s}^{-2}$)
- consider the dimensions of the ball
- golfers put 'spin' on the ball to bring it down at a steeper angle, so take this into account.

Notes

Notes

Notes

Notes

Notes

....
....
....
....
....
....
....
....
....
....
....
....
....
....
....
....
....
....
....
....
....
....
....
....
....
....
....
....
....
....
....

Notes

Published by Pearson Education Limited, 80 Strand, London, WC2R 0RL.

www.pearsonschoolsandfecolleges.co.uk

Copies of official specifications for all Pearson qualifications may be found on the website: qualifications.pearson.com

Text © Pearson Education Ltd 2018
Typeset and illustrated by Techset
Produced by ProjectOne
Cover illustration by Miriam Sturdee

The right of Glyn Payne to be identified as author of this work has been asserted by him in accordance with the Copyright, Designs and Patents Act 1988.

First published 2018

21 20 19 18
10 9 8 7 6 5 4 3 2

British Library Cataloguing in Publication Data
A catalogue record for this book is available from the British Library

ISBN 978 1 292 19060 0

Printed in Slovakia by Neografia

Notes from the publisher

1. While the publishers have made every attempt to ensure that advice on the qualification and its assessment is accurate, the official specification and associated assessment guidance materials are the only authoritative source of information and should always be referred to for definitive guidance.

Pearson examiners have not contributed to any sections in this resource relevant to examination papers for which they have responsibility.

2. Pearson has robust editorial processes, including answer and fact checks, to ensure the accuracy of the content in this publication, and every effort is made to ensure this publication is free of errors. We are, however, only human, and occasionally errors do occur. Pearson is not liable for any misunderstandings that arise as a result of errors in this publication, but it is our priority to ensure that the content is accurate. If you spot an error, please do contact us at resourcescorrections@pearson.com so we can make sure it is corrected.